Homework Helpers

Eureka Math
Grade 7

Special thanks go to the Gordan A. Cain Center and to the Department of Mathematics at Louisiana State University for their support in the development of *Eureka Math*.

Homework Helpers

Grade 7
Module 1

G7-M1-Lesson 1: An Experience in Relationships as Measuring Rate

Rate and Unit Rates

Find each rate and unit rate.

1. $8.96 for 8 pounds of grapefruit

    $$\frac{8.96}{8} = 1.12$$

    > I determine the cost of one pound of grapefruit in order to find the rate. To do this, I divide the cost by the number of pounds.

    Rate: 1.12 *dollars per pound*

    Unit Rate: 1.12

2. 300 miles in 4 hours

    $$\frac{300}{4} = 75$$

    > The label explains the numerical value of the rate.

    Rate: 75 *miles per hour*

    Unit Rate: 75

Ratios and Rates

3. Dan bought 8 shirts and 3 pants. Devonte bought 12 shirts and 5 pants. For each person, write a ratio to represent the number of shirts to the number of pants they bought. Are the ratios equivalent? Explain.

    The ratio of the number of shirts Dan bought to the number of pants he bought is 8: 3.

    The ratio of the number of shirts Devonte bought to the number of pants he bought is 12: 5.

    > The order of the ratios is important. In this case, it is stated that the ratio is shirts to pants, which means the first number in the ratio represents shirts and the second number represents pants.

    The ratios are not equivalent because Dan's unit rate is $\frac{8}{3}$ *or* $2\frac{2}{3}$, *and Devonte's unit rate is* $\frac{12}{5}$ *or* $2\frac{2}{5}$.

    > I know these are not equivalent ratios because they do not have the same unit rate.

4. Veronica got hired by two different families to babysit over the summer. The Johnson family said they would pay her $180 for every 20 hours she worked. The Lopez family said they would pay Veronica $165 for every 15 hours she worked. If Veronica spends the same amount of time babysitting each family, which family would pay her more money? How do you know?

> Calculating the unit rate helps compare different rates and ratios.

Veronica will earn $9 per hour when she babysits for the Johnson family and will earn $11 per hour when she babysits for the Lopez family. Therefore, she will earn more money from the Lopez family if she spends the same amount of time babysitting for each family.

© 2015 Great Minds eureka-math.org
G7-M1-HWH-1.3.0-09.2015

G7-M1-Lesson 2: Proportional Relationships

Proportional Quantities

1. A vegetable omelet requires a ratio of eggs to chopped vegetables of 2 to 7.

> This means that I use 2 eggs and 7 chopped vegetables to make an omelet.

a. Complete the table to show different amounts that are proportional.

Number of Eggs	2	4	6
Number of Vegetables	7	14	21

> Answers may vary, but I need to create ratios that are equivalent to the ratio $2:7$.

b. Why are these quantities proportional?

The number of eggs is proportional to the number of chopped vegetables since there exists a constant number, $\frac{7}{2}$, that when multiplied by any given number of eggs always produces the corresponding amount of chopped vegetables.

2. The gas tank in Enrique's car has 15 gallons of gas. Enrique was able to determine that he can travel 35 miles and only use 2 gallons of gas. At this constant rate, he predicts that he can drive 240 more miles before he runs out of gas. Is he correct? Explain.

> Once I calculate the unit rate, I use this to determine how many miles Enrique can travel with the gas remaining in his tank by multiplying both values by 15.

Gallons of Gas Used	1	2	15
Miles Traveled	17.5	35	262.5

Enrique can travel 227.5 more miles because has he can only travel 262.5 miles with 15 gallons of gas, but he has already traveled 35 miles. $262.5 - 35 = 227.5$. Therefore, Enrique's prediction is not correct because he will run out of gas before traveling 240 more miles.

© 2015 Great Minds eureka-math.org
G7-M1-HWH-1.3.0-09.2015

G7-M1-Lesson 3: Identifying Proportional and Non-Proportional Relationships in Tables

Recognizing Proportional Relationships in Tables

In each table, determine if y is proportional to x. Explain why or why not.

> To determine if y is proportional to x, I determine if the unit rates, or value of each ratio, are equivalent.

1.

x	y
3	6
4	8
5	10
6	11

$\frac{6}{3} = 2 \qquad \frac{8}{4} = 2 \qquad \frac{10}{5} = 2 \qquad \frac{11}{6} = 1\frac{5}{6}$

No, y is not proportional to x because the values of all the ratios $y{:}\,x$ are not equivalent. There is not a constant where every measure of x multiplied by the constant gives the corresponding measure in y.

2.

x	y
6	2
9	3
12	4
15	5

$\frac{2}{6} = \frac{1}{3} \qquad \frac{3}{9} = \frac{1}{3} \qquad \frac{4}{12} = \frac{1}{3} \qquad \frac{5}{15} = \frac{1}{3}$

Yes, y is proportional to x because the values of the ratios $y{:}\,x$ are equivalent. Each measure of x multiplied by this constant of $\frac{1}{3}$ gives the corresponding measure in y.

> If I multiply each x-value by $\frac{1}{3}$, the outcome will be the corresponding y-value.

© 2015 Great Minds eureka-math.org
G7-M1-HWH-1.3.0-09.2015

EUREKA MATH

3. Ms. Lynch is planning a field trip for her class. She knows that the field trip will cost $12 per person.

   a. Create a table showing the relationships between the number of people going on the field trip and the total cost of the trip.

Number of People	1	2	3	4
Total Cost ($)	12	24	36	48

> I choose any value for the number of people, and then multiply this value by 12 to determine the total cost.

   b. Explain why the cost of the field trip is proportional to the number of people attending the field trip.

   The total cost is proportional to the number of people who attend the field trip because a constant value of 12 exists where each measure of the number of people multiplied by this constant gives the corresponding measure of the total cost.

   c. If 23 people attend the field trip, how much will the field trip cost?

   > I know the relationship is proportional, so I can use the constant of 12 to determine the total cost of the field trip if 23 people attend.

   $23(12) = 276$

   If 23 people attend the field trip, then the total cost of the trip is $276.

G7-M1-Lesson 4: Identifying Proportional and Non-Proportional Relationships in Tables

Recognizing Proportional Relationships

1. For his birthday, Julian received 15 toy cars. He plans to start collecting more cars and is going to buy 3 more every month.

   a.   Complete the table below to show the number of toy cars Julian has after each month.

   > Julian has 15 toy cars when he decided to start collecting more. Therefore, at month 0 he already has 15 toy cars.

Time (in months)	0	1	2	3
Number of Cars	15	18	21	24

   > Julian has 18 toy cars after one month because he had 15 cars and then bought 3 more during the first month.

   b.   Is the number of toy cars Julian has proportional to the number of months? Explain your reasoning.

   The number of toy cars Julian has is not proportional to the number of months because the ratios are not equivalent. 15: 0 is not equivalent to 18: 1.

   > If an additional explanation is needed, please refer to Lesson 3.

© 2015 Great Minds eureka-math.org
G7-M1-HWH-1.3.0-09.2015

EUREKA MATH

2. Hazel and Marcus are both training for a race. The tables below show the distances each person ran over the past few days.

Hazel:

Days	2	5	9
Miles	6	15	27

Marcus:

Days	3	6	8
Miles	6	11	20

a. Which of the tables, if any, represent a proportional relationship?

Hazel:

$$\frac{6}{2} = 3 \qquad \frac{15}{5} = 3 \qquad \frac{27}{9} = 3$$

The number of miles Hazel ran is proportional to the number of days because the constant of 3 is multiplied by each measure of days to get the corresponding measure of miles. There is not a constant value for Marcus's table, so this table does not show a proportional relationship.

Marcus:

$$\frac{6}{3} = 2 \qquad \frac{11}{6} = 1\frac{5}{6} \qquad \frac{20}{8} = 2\frac{1}{2}$$

These ratios do not have the same value, so the number of miles is not proportional to the number of days.

b. Did Hazel and Marcus both run a constant number of miles each day? Explain.

Hazel ran the same number of miles, 3, each day, but Marcus did not run a constant number of miles each day because the relationship between the number of miles he ran and the number of days is not proportional.

G7-M1-Lesson 5: Identifying Proportional and Non-Proportional Relationships in Graphs

Recognizing Proportional Graphs

Determine whether or not the following graphs represent two quantities that are proportional to each other. Explain your reasoning.

1.

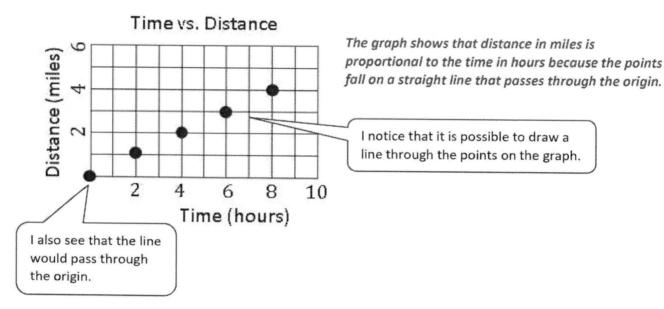

The graph shows that distance in miles is proportional to the time in hours because the points fall on a straight line that passes through the origin.

I notice that it is possible to draw a line through the points on the graph.

I also see that the line would pass through the origin.

2.

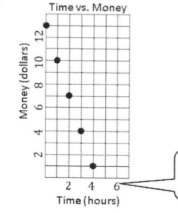

The graph shows that money in dollars is not proportional to the time in hours because the line that contains the points does not pass through the origin.

I notice the points fall on a line, but the line does not pass through the origin.

Create a table and a graph for the ratios $3 : 8$, 2 to 5, and $4 : 13$. Does the graph show that the two quantities are proportional to each other? Explain why or why not.

3.

x	y
3	8
2	5
4	13

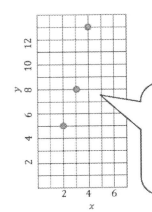

The first number in each ratio represents the x-value, and the second number in each ratio represents the y-value.

The x-value tells me how far to move right on the graph, and the y-value tells me how far to move up on the graph.

The graph shows that y is not proportional to x because the points do not fall on a straight line.

I do not have to determine if the line would pass through the origin because it is already clear that the points do not fall on a line.

EUREKA
MATH™

G7-M1-Lesson 6: Identifying Proportional and Non-Proportional Relationships in Graphs

Recognizing Proportional Relationships in Graphs

Create a table and a graph, and explain whether or not Kirk's height and age are proportional to each other. Use your table and graph to support your reasoning.

Kirk's parents kept track of his growth during the first few years of his life.

- Kirk weighed 7 pounds 6 ounces and was 20 inches tall when he was born.
- When Kirk was three years old, he was 31 inches tall.
- Kirk was 48 inches tall when he was seven years old.
- On his tenth birthday, Kirk was 4 feet 7 inches tall.

> I need to convert Kirk's height to inches to be consistent with the other values.

Problem:

Kirk's mom keeps track of his height for the first ten years of his life. The ratios in the table represent Kirk's age in years to his height in inches. Create a table and a graph, and explain whether or not the quantities are proportional to each other.

Age (years)	Height (inches)
0	20
3	31
7	48
10	55

> The ratios in the table are not equivalent, so right away I know that the relationship is not proportional.

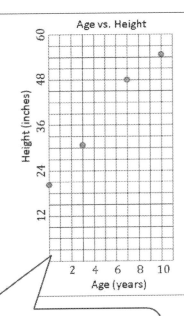

Explanation:

Kirk's height is not proportional to his age because the ratios in the table are not equivalent. The graph also shows that this relationship is not proportional because the points do not fall on a straight line that passes through the origin.

The graph is not proportional for two reasons: the points do not fall on a line, and they also do not pass through the origin.

G7-M1-Lesson 7: Unit Rate as the Constant of Proportionality

Calculating the Constant of Proportionality

For each of the following problems, calculate the constant of proportionality to answer the follow-up question.

1.   Red apples are on sale for $0.99/pound.

> The unit rate is provided for me, so I do not have to complete any calculations to find the constant of proportionality.

a.   What is the constant of proportionality, or k?

The constant of proportionality, k, is 0.99.

> The constant of proportionality is the cost for one pound of apples, so I use this value to determine the cost of any number of pounds of apples.

b.   How much will 8 pounds of apples cost?

$$(8\text{lb.})\left(\frac{\$0.99}{\text{lb.}}\right) = \$7.92$$

Eight pounds of apples will cost 7.92.

2.   Shirts are on sale: 4 shirts for $34.

a.   What is the constant of proportionality, or k?

$$\frac{34}{4} = 8.50$$

> The constant of proportionality means that one shirt costs $8.50.

The constant of proportionality, k, is 8.50.

b.   How much will 9 shirts cost?

$$(9\text{ shirts})\left(\frac{\$8.50}{\text{shirt}}\right) = \$76.50.$$

Nine shirts will cost 76.50.

EUREKA
MATH™

3. Holly babysits for one family regularly. In the month of October, she worked 120 hours and earned $1,320. In November, Holly worked 110 hours and earned $1,210. Due to the family taking a vacation in December, Holly only earned $770 for the 70 hours she worked that month.

   a. Is the amount of money Holly earned each month proportional to the number of hours she worked? Explain why or why not.

> I do not have to make a table, but it helps me organize the data.

Time (hours)	70	110	120
Amount Earned ($)	770	1,210	1,320

$$\frac{770}{70} = 11 \qquad \frac{1,210}{110} = 11 \qquad \frac{1,320}{120} = 11$$

> This division not only shows the relationship is proportional, but it also reveals the unit rate and constant of proportionality.

The amount of money Holly earns is proportional to the amount of time she works because the ratios are equivalent. The constant of 11 can be multiplied by the time she works, in hours, and the result will be the corresponding amount earned.

> I can only answer this question if the relationship is proportional. The constant of proportionality does not exist if the relationship is not proportional.

   b. Identify the constant of proportionality, and explain what it means in the context of the situation.

The constant of proportionality, k, is 11. The constant of proportionality tells us how much money Holly earns each hour.

   c. How much money will Holly earn if she babysits for 150 hours next month?

> Similar to the previous problems, I can use the constant of proportionality to determine how much Holly will earn for any specified number of hours.

$$(150 \text{ hours})\left(\frac{\$11}{\text{hour}}\right) = \$1,650$$

Holly will earn $1,650 if she works 150 hours next month.

G7-M1-Lesson 8: Representing Proportional Relationships with Equations

Writing Equations

Write an equation that will model the proportional relationship given in each real-world situation.

1. Kaedon completed a 75 mile bike race in 3.75 hours. Consider the number of miles he can ride per hour.

   a. Find the constant of proportionality in this situation.

$$\frac{75}{3.75} = 20$$

   The constant of proportionality is 20.

   > To find the constant of proportionality, I need to divide the distance by time.

   b. Write an equation to represent the relationship.

   Let m represent the number of miles Kaedon rides his bike.

   Let h represent the number of hours Kaedon rides his bike.

$$m = 20h$$

   > The equation shows that I can multiply the constant of proportionality by the number of hours to determine the number of miles.

   > Although I can choose any variables for my equation, it is important to define the variables that are in the equation.

EUREKA MATH

2. Clark is starting a new company and needs to order business cards. He plans on ordering 50 business cards a month. Business Cards Galore has offered to print all the business cards Clark needs for a flat rate of $37.50 a month. The different prices for Print Options are shown on the graph below. Which is the better buy?

a. Find the constant of proportionality for the situation.

Business Cards	5	15	20
Cost (dollars)	3.50	10.50	14.00

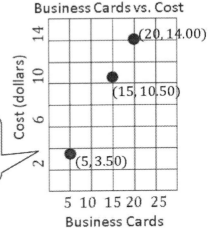

Business Cards vs. Cost

> If I choose, I can translate the graph to a table to organize the data needed to calculate the constant of proportionality.

$$\frac{3.50}{5} = 0.7 \qquad \frac{10.50}{15} = 0.7 \qquad \frac{14.00}{20} = 0.7$$

The constant of proportionality is 0.7.

b. Write an equation to represent the relationship.

Let c represent the cost in dollars.

Let b represent the number of business cards.

$$c = 0.7b$$

> I can substitute values from the given ratios to make sure that my equation is correct.
>
> $$3.50 = 0.7(5)$$
> $$3.50 = 3.50$$

c. Use your equation to find the answer to Clark's question above. Justify your answer with mathematical evidence and a written explanation.

Before I compare the cost of the two companies, it is necessary to determine the cost of 50 business cards if Clark chooses to order from Print Options. Using the equation, b can be substituted with 50 since b represents the number of business cards. This work is shown below.

$$c = 0.7(50)$$
$$c = 35$$

The calculation shows the cost for 50 business cards from Print Options is $35.00. If Clark orders 50 business cards from Business Cards Galore, it will cost him $37.50, which is more than the price at Print Options. Therefore, the better buy is to order business cards from Print Options.

G7-M1-Lesson 9: Representing Proportional Relationships with Equations

Applications of Proportional Relationships

Use the table to answer the following questions.

Time (hours)	Payment (dollars)
0	0
5	75
12	180
18	270

a. Which variable is the dependent variable and why?

The dependent variable is the payment because the amount someone gets paid depends on the number of hours he works.

b. Is the payment proportionally related to the time? If so, what is the equation that relates the payment to the number of hours?

> I notice that the ratios are equivalent, which means the relationship is proportional.

$$\frac{75}{5} = 15 \qquad \frac{180}{12} = 15 \qquad \frac{270}{18} = 15$$

Yes, the payment is proportionally related to time because every number of hours can be multiplied by 15 to get the corresponding measure of dollars.

Let h represent the time in hours, and let d represent the payment in dollars.

$$d = 15h$$

c. What is the constant of proportionality?

The constant of proportionality is 15.

> The unit rate, or constant of proportionality, is multiplied by the independent variable, and the result is the dependent variable.

EUREKA MATH

© 2015 Great Minds eureka-math.org
G7-M1-HWH-1.3.0-09.2015

d. If the time is known, can you find the payment? Explain how this value would be calculated.

The payment can be determined if I know the number of hours. To calculate the payment, I multiply the number of hours by 15.

> If I am given the value of one variable, I am able to use the equation to calculate the value of the other variable.

e. If the payment is known, can you find the time? Explain how this value would be calculated.

The time can be determined if I know the payment. To calculate the number of hours, I divide the payment by 15.

f. What would the payment be if a person worked 22 hours?

$$d = 15h$$
$$d = 15(22)$$
$$d = 330$$

> I am given the value of h, so I substitute 22 into the equation to represent h.

If a person worked 22 hours, he would receive a payment of $330.

g. How long would a person have to work if he wanted to receive a payment of $540?

$$d = 15h$$
$$540 = 15h$$
$$540 \div 15 = 15h \div 15$$
$$36 = h$$

> This time, I am given the value of d, so I substitute 540 into the equation to represent d.

A person would have to work 36 *hours to receive a payment of* $540.

> I use my knowledge of properties of equality from sixth grade to solve these equations. Therefore, I divide both sides of the equation by 15 to determine the value of h.

h. How long would a person have to work if he wanted to receive a payment of $127.50?

$$d = 15h$$
$$127.50 = 15h$$
$$127.50 \div 15 = 15h \div 15$$
$$8.5 = h$$

A person would have to work 8.5 *hours to receive a payment of* $127.50.

G7-M1-Lesson 10: Interpreting Graphs of Proportional Relationships

Interpreting Proportional Relationships

1. The graph to the right shows the relationship of the gallons of gas to the distance (in miles) traveled by a small car.

> The first number in the ordered pair represents the x-value, which is the number of gallons of gas. The second number in the ordered pair represents the y-value, which is the distance, in miles, traveled.

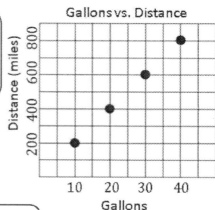

Gallons vs. Distance

a. What does the point $(20, 400)$ represent in the context of the situation?

   With 20 gallons of gas, the car can travel 400 miles.

> I remember from Lessons 5 and 6 what a proportional graph should look like.

b. Is the distance traveled by the car proportional to the gallons of gas? Explain why or why not.

   The distance traveled is proportional to the gallons of gas because the points fall on a line and pass through the origin, $(0, 0)$.

c. Write an equation to represent the distance traveled by the car. Explain or model your reasoning.

   $$\frac{400}{20} = 20$$

> I need to determine the constant of proportionality before writing the equation. Therefore, I must find the quotient of $\frac{y}{x}$.

   The constant of proportionality, or unit rate of $\frac{y}{x}$, is 20 and can be substituted into the equation $y = kx$ in place of k.

   Let d represent the distance, in miles, and let g represent the number of gallons of gas.

   $d = 20g$

> I know that the product of the independent variable and the constant of proportionality is the dependent variable.

EUREKA MATH™

d. How far can a car travel with one gallon of gas? Explain or model your reasoning.

A car can travel 20 miles with one gallon of gas because the constant of proportionality represents the distance that can be traveled per one gallon of gas.

> If I didn't recognize this value to be the constant of proportionality, I could use my equation to answer this equation.
>
> $$d = 20(1)$$

2. Ms. Stabler is creating playdough for her classroom. The recipe requires a few different ingredients, but the relationship between flour and salt for the playdough is shown in the table below.

Cups of Flour	4	6	7	10
Cups of Salt	2	3	3.5	5

> Before writing an equation, I must first determine the constant of proportionality.
>
> $$\frac{2}{4} = \frac{1}{2} \quad \frac{3}{6} = \frac{1}{2} \qquad \frac{3.5}{7} = \frac{1}{2} \quad \frac{5}{10} = \frac{1}{2}$$

a. Write an equation to represent this relationship.

Let f represent the cups of flour and s represent the cups of salt needed for the playdough recipe.

$$s = \frac{1}{2}f$$

b. Using this equation, how many cups of salt are required if Ms. Stabler uses 13 cups of flour?

$$s = \frac{1}{2}f$$

$$s = \frac{1}{2}(13)$$

$$s = 6.5$$

> I am given the amount of flour that is used for a batch of playdough. I can substitute this value for f in my equation.

Ms. Stabler will need 6.5 cups of salt.

c. How many cups of flour are needed if Ms. Stabler uses 4 cups of salt?

> This time, I am given the amount of salt that is used for a batch of playdough. I can substitute this value for s in my equation.

$$s = \frac{1}{2}f$$

$$4 = \frac{1}{2}f$$

$$\left(\frac{2}{1}\right)(4) = \left(\frac{2}{1}\right)\left(\frac{1}{2}f\right)$$

$$8 = f$$

> To solve for f, I need to multiply both sides of the equation by the multiplicative inverse of $\frac{1}{2}$, or I could divide both sides by the coefficient, which is $\frac{1}{2}$ in this equation.

Ms. Stabler will need 8 cups of flour.

d.   Graph the relationship.

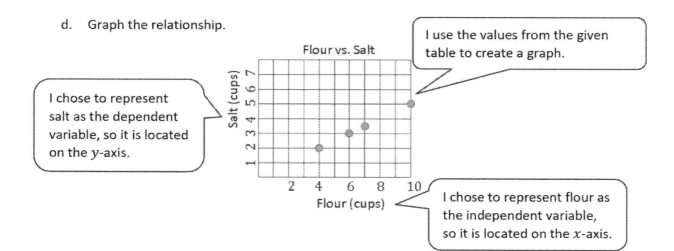

I use the values from the given table to create a graph.

I chose to represent salt as the dependent variable, so it is located on the *y*-axis.

I chose to represent flour as the independent variable, so it is located on the *x*-axis.

Lesson 10:   Interpreting Graphs of Proportional Relationships

EUREKA
MATH

G7-M1-Lesson 11: Ratios of Fractions and Their Unit Rates

Complex Ratios

1. Determine the quotient: $3\frac{3}{5} \div 4\frac{2}{3}$.

Before I do any calculations, I need to change each mixed number to a fraction greater than one.

$$3\frac{3}{5} \div 4\frac{2}{3}$$

$$\frac{18}{5} \div \frac{14}{3}$$

In sixth grade, I learned to invert and multiply when dividing fractions.

$$\frac{18}{5} \times \frac{3}{14}$$

To multiply fractions, I multiply the two numerators and then multiply the two denominators.

$$\frac{54}{70}$$

The numerator and denominator have a common factor of 2, so I divide both by 2.

$$\frac{27}{35}$$

The quotient is $\frac{27}{35}$.

2. Michael is building a new fence that is 15 feet long. In order for the fence to be stable, he needs to use a post every $1\frac{1}{4}$ feet. How many posts does Michael need?

To answer this question, I need to divide the fence length by the distance between each post.

$$15 \div 1\frac{1}{4}$$

To convert a whole number to a fraction greater than 1, I can make the denominator 1 because $\frac{15}{1} = 15$.

$$\frac{15}{1} \div \frac{5}{4}$$

$$\frac{15}{1} \times \frac{4}{5}$$

$$\frac{60}{5}$$

$$12$$

Michael will need 12 posts for his fence.

3. A smoothie recipe calls for 1.2 cups of strawberries for one batch. Ms. Neal uses 4.8 cups of strawberries today.

   a. How many batches did Ms. Neal make today?

   > I do not have to convert the decimals to fractions, but I choose to use fractions because that is what I practiced in previous problems.

   $$4.8 \div 1.2$$
   $$4\frac{4}{5} \div 1\frac{1}{5}$$
   $$\frac{24}{5} \div \frac{6}{5}$$
   $$\frac{24}{5} \times \frac{5}{6}$$
   $$4$$

   > To determine the number of batches, I need to calculate the quotient of the amount of strawberries used and the amount of strawberries required for one batch.

   Ms. Neal made 4 batches of the smoothie recipe.

   b. If Ms. Neal can make 5 smoothies in each batch, how many smoothies did she make today?

   $$5(4) = 12$$

   Ms. Neal made 20 smoothies today.

   > I already determined that Ms. Neal made 4 batches today, so I can multiply this by the number of smoothies in each batch.

4. Garrek plans to drink 3 quarts of water every 4 days. How many <u>gallons</u> does he drink every day? (Recall: 4 quarts = 1 gallon.)

   Garrek drinks $\frac{3}{4}$ gallons every 4 days.

   > I can determine the number of gallons of water Garrek drinks daily by dividing the number of gallons he drinks by the number of days it took him to drink that amount of water.

   $$\frac{3}{4} \div \frac{4}{1}$$
   $$\frac{3}{4} \times \frac{1}{4}$$
   $$\frac{3}{16}$$

   > I divide the number of quarts Garrek drinks by the number of quarts in a gallon, 4, to determine the number of gallons Garrek drinks every 4 days.

   Garrek drinks $\frac{3}{16}$ gallons of water every day.

EUREKA MATH

G7-M1-Lesson 12: Ratio of Fractions and Their Unit Rates

1. The area of a poster is $51\frac{1}{3}$ ft^2. The same image from the poster can also be found on a postcard with an area of $1\frac{5}{6}$ ft^2.

> Just like in previous lessons, I must divide the two values to determine the unit rate.

   a. Find the unit rate, and explain, in words, what the unit rate means in the context of this problem.

> I realize I am dividing mixed numbers just like I did in Lesson 11.

$$\frac{51\frac{1}{3}}{1\frac{5}{6}} = \frac{\frac{154}{3}}{\frac{11}{6}} = \frac{154}{3} \times \frac{6}{11} = 28$$

   The unit rate is 28, which means the poster's area is 28 times the area of the postcard.

> I know the unit rate from the poster to the postcard. The second unit rate would be the opposite; from the postcard to the poster.

   b. Is there more than one unit rate that can be calculated? How do you know?

   Yes, there is another unit rate, which would be $\frac{1}{28}$. I know there can be another unit rate because it would explain that the postcard's area is $\frac{1}{28}$ the area of the poster.

2. The length of a bedroom on a blueprint is $4\frac{1}{2}$ in. The length of the actual room is $12\frac{1}{4}$ ft. What is the value of the ratio of the length of the bedroom on the blueprint to the length of the actual room? What does this ratio mean in this situation?

> To calculate the value of the ratio, I must divide the length of the blueprint by the length of the actual bedroom.

$$\frac{4\frac{1}{2}}{12\frac{1}{4}} = \frac{9}{2} \div \frac{49}{4} = \frac{9}{2} \times \frac{4}{49} = \frac{18}{49}$$

The value of the ratio is $\frac{18}{49}$. This means that for every 18 in. on the blueprint, there are 49 ft. in the actual bedroom.

> Unlike the unit rate, there is only one correct way to calculate the value of a ratio.

> There are 12 cookies in one dozen.

3. To make a dozen cookies, $\frac{1}{4}$ cup sugar is needed.

a. How much sugar is needed to make one cookie?

$$\frac{1}{4} \div 12$$

$$\frac{1}{4} \times \frac{1}{12}$$

$$\frac{1}{48}$$

> To determine the amount of sugar needed for one cookie, I need to find the unit rate.

I will need $\frac{1}{48}$ cup of sugar to make one cookie.

b. How many cups of sugar are needed to make 4 dozen cookies?

$$\frac{1}{48}(48) = 1$$

I will need 1 cup of sugar to make 4 dozen cookies.

> There are 12 cookies in each dozen, so there are 48 cookies in four dozen.

c. How many cookies can you make with $3\frac{1}{4}$ cups of sugar?

$$3\frac{1}{4} \div \frac{1}{48}$$

$$\frac{13}{4} \div \frac{1}{48}$$

$$\frac{13}{4} \times \frac{48}{1}$$

$$156$$

> I need to divide the amount of sugar I have by the amount of sugar that is required to make one cookie.

I can make 156 cookies with $3\frac{1}{4}$ cups of sugar.

Lesson 12:   Ratio of Fractions and Their Unit Rates

© 2015 Great Minds eureka-math.org
G7-M1-HWH-1.3.0-09.2015

EUREKA MATH

G7-M1-Lesson 13: Finding Equivalent Ratios Given the Total Quantity

Chip is painting a few rooms the same color pink. Therefore, Chip needs to mix the same ratio of red paint to white paint for every room.

    a.   Complete the following table, which represents the number of gallons of paint needed to complete the paint job.

Room	Red Paint	White Paint	Total Paint
Office	2	3	5
Kitchen	4	6	10

> After I find the total paint in the kitchen, I notice that the total paint needed for the office is half of 10. Therefore, Chip will need half as much of red and white paint for the office.

> I see that the unit rate of white paint to red paint is $\frac{2}{3}$. I can multiply the amount of white paint needed by the unit rate to calculate the amount of red paint needed for the bedroom.

$$\frac{2}{3}(8) = \frac{16}{3} = 5\frac{1}{3}$$

Bedroom	$5\frac{1}{3}$	8	$13\frac{1}{3}$

$$\frac{3}{2}\left(6\frac{1}{3}\right) = \frac{3}{2}\left(\frac{19}{3}\right) = \frac{19}{2} = 9\frac{1}{2}$$

> To calculate the amount of white paint Chip needs for the living room, I need to use the unit rate of red paint to white paint, which is $\frac{3}{2}$.

> I need to find a common denominator in order to add the red paint and white paint together.

$$6\frac{1}{3} + 9\frac{1}{2} = 6\frac{2}{6} + 9\frac{3}{6} = 15\frac{5}{6}$$

Living Room	$6\frac{1}{3}$	$9\frac{1}{2}$	$15\frac{5}{6}$

b.   Write an equation to represent the relationship between the amount of red paint and white paint.

Let r represent the amount of red paint and w represent the amount of white paint.

$w = \frac{3}{2}r \text{ or } r = \frac{2}{3}w$

> The equation will look different, depending which unit rate I decide to use.

c.   What is the relationship between the amount of red paint and the amount of white paint needed?

The amount of red paint is $\frac{2}{3}$ the amount of white paint used for the pink paint mixture.

> If I multiply the amount of white paint used by $\frac{2}{3}$, I will know how much red paint is used.

EUREKA
MATH

© 2015 Great Minds eureka-math.org
G7-M1-HWH-1.3.0-09.2015

G7-M1-Lesson 14: Multi-Step Ratio Problems

1. An insurance agent earns a commission equal to $\frac{1}{20}$ of his total sales. What is the commission earned if he sells \$2,800 of insurance?

$\left(\frac{1}{20}\right)(2,800) = 140$

He will earn \$140 *in commissions.*

> I want to find the part of the total sales that represents the commission by multiplying the part by the total sales.

2.

   a. What is the cost of a \$960 refrigerator after a discount of $\frac{1}{6}$ the original price?

$\frac{1}{6}(960) = 160$

$960 - 160 = 800$

After the discount, the cost of the refrigerator is \$800.

> I know I save \$160, so I subtract that from the total to find the cost after the discount.

   b. What is the fractional part of the original price that the customer will pay?

$1 - \frac{1}{6} = \frac{5}{6}$

> 1 represents the original price, so I subtract the discount to determine the fractional part I pay.

3. Tom bought a new computer on sale for $\frac{1}{5}$ off the original price of \$750. He also wanted to use his frequent shopper discount of $\frac{1}{10}$ off the sales price. How much did Tom pay for the computer?

> If the discount is $\frac{1}{5}$, then Tom will pay $\frac{4}{5}$ of the original price.

$\left(\frac{4}{5}\right)(750) = 600$

$\left(\frac{9}{10}\right)(600) = 540$

> The frequent shopper discount is $\frac{1}{10}$, so Tom pays $\frac{9}{10}$ of the sale price.

Tom will pay \$540 *for the computer.*

4. Stores often markup original prices to make a profit. A store paid a certain price for a television and marked it up by $\frac{5}{3}$ of the price paid. The store then sold the television for $800. What was the original price?

Let x represent the original price.

$$x + \frac{5}{3}x = 800$$
$$\frac{8}{3}x = 800$$
$$\left(\frac{3}{8}\right)\left(\frac{8}{3}x\right) = \left(\frac{3}{8}\right)(800)$$
$$x = 300$$

I first add the coefficients $\left(1 + \frac{5}{3} = \frac{8}{3}\right)$, and then I multiply both sides of the equation by the multiplicative inverse of $\frac{8}{3}$.

The $800 is the price when the original price is added to the markup rate ($\frac{5}{3}$ of the original price).

The original price of the television is $300.

EUREKA
MATH

G7-M1-Lesson 15: Equations of Graphs of Proportional Relationships Involving Fractions

Proportional Relationships

1. Jose is on the track team and keeps track of the number of calories he burns. The data is shown in the table below.

Minutes	Calories
3	$7\frac{1}{2}$
7	$17\frac{1}{2}$
$12\frac{1}{2}$	$31\frac{1}{4}$

The given information in the first row of the table is enough to calculate the unit rate.

$7\frac{1}{2} \div 3 = 2\frac{1}{2}$

Therefore, the unit rate is $2\frac{1}{2}$.

a. Use the given ratio to complete the table.

$7\left(2\frac{1}{2}\right) = 7\left(\frac{5}{2}\right) = \frac{35}{2} = 17\frac{1}{2}$

$31\frac{1}{4} \div 2\frac{1}{2} = \frac{125}{4} \div \frac{5}{2} = \frac{125}{4} \times \frac{2}{5} = 12\frac{1}{2}$

I use the unit rate to calculate the missing values on the table.

b. What is the constant of proportionality of calories to minutes?

The constant of proportionality is $2\frac{1}{2}$ because I would find the quotient of calories and minutes, just like I did for the unit rate.

c. Write an equation that models the relationship between the number of minutes Jose ran and the calories he burned.

Let m represent the minutes he ran and c represent the calories she burned.

$c = 2\frac{1}{2}m$

I remember writing equations in earlier lessons.

d.   If Jose wants to burn 50 calories, how long would he have to run?

I can substitute 50 in for c in the equation and then use the multiplicative inverse to solve for m.

$$c = 2\frac{1}{2}m$$

$$50 = 2\frac{1}{2}m$$

$$\left(\frac{2}{5}\right)(50) = \left(\frac{2}{5}\right)\left(\frac{5}{2}m\right)$$

$$20 = m$$

Jose will have to run for 20 minutes to burn 50 calories.

2.   Jenna loves to cook lasagna and often cooks large portions. The graph below shows the relationship between the pounds of meat and the cups of cheese needed for each batch of lasagna.

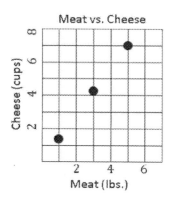

Meat vs. Cheese

This is the same as calculating the constant of proportionality.

a.   Using the graph, determine how many cups of cheese Jenna will use with one pound of meat.

The point (5,7) is on the graph, so I can use these values to determine the constant of proportionality or $\frac{y}{x}$. Even though I can choose any point on the graph, this is only point that does not require estimating the location.

$$\frac{7}{5} = 1\frac{2}{5}$$

Jenna will use $1\frac{2}{5}$ cups of cheese with one pound of meat.

b.   Use the graph to determine the equation that models the relationship between meat and cheese.

Let m represent the amount of meat, in pounds, used in lasagna, and let c represent the amount of cheese, in cups.

$$c = 1\frac{2}{5}m$$

Lesson 15:   Equations of Graphs of Proportional Relationships Involving Fractions

EUREKA MATH

c. If Jenna uses $2\frac{1}{2}$ cups of meat for a batch of lasagna, how much cheese will she use?

$$c = 1\frac{2}{5}\left(2\frac{1}{2}\right)$$

$$c = \left(\frac{7}{5}\right)\left(\frac{5}{2}\right)$$

$$c = \frac{35}{10}$$

$$c = 3\frac{1}{2}$$

Jenna will use $3\frac{1}{2}$ cups of cheese.

EUREKA
MATH™

© 2015 Great Minds eureka-math.org
G7-M1-HWH-1.3.0-09.2015

G7-M1-Lesson 16: Relating Scale Drawings to Ratios and Rates

Enlargements and Reductions

1. For parts (a) and (b), identify if the scale drawing is a reduction or an enlargement of the actual picture.

a.   Actual Picture   Scale Drawing

I need to determine if the scale drawing is smaller or larger than the actual picture. If the scale drawing is larger than the actual picture, the actual picture was enlarged to create the new image.

This is an example of an enlargement.

b.   Actual Picture   Scale Drawing

If the scale drawing is smaller than the actual picture, the new image is called a reduction.

This is an example of a reduction.

EUREKA MATH

2. Name the coordinates of Triangle 1. Plot the points to form Triangle 2. Then decide if the triangles are scale drawings of each other.

Triangle 1

Coordinates: $A\,(2,0)$ B $(2,12)$ C $(10,0)$

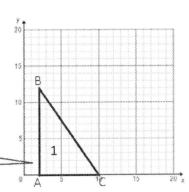

I can write a point as (x, y). I start at the origin $(0,0)$ and travel right (x) and then up (y). So point A would be right 2 and up 0 making it $(2,0)$.

Triangle 2

Coordinates: $E(10,10)$, $F(10,13)$, $G(12,10)$

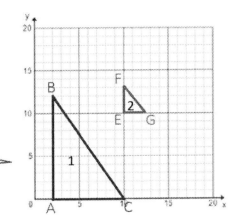

I can plot points the same way. If the point is $(10,13)$, I would start at the origin $(0,0)$ and then move 10 units to the right and 13 units up and plot the point.

Value of the Ratio for the Heights: $\frac{3}{12}$ *or* $\frac{1}{4}$

Value of the Ratio for the Lengths of the Bases: $\frac{2}{8}$ *or* $\frac{1}{4}$

The triangles are scale drawings of each other. The lengths of all the sides in Triangle 2 are $\frac{1}{4}$ *as long as the corresponding sides lengths in Triangle 1.*

If these two triangles are scale drawings of one another, the corresponding side lengths must be proportional. I can check the ratios of the corresponding side lengths and see if all the ratios are the same.

G7-M1-Lesson 17: The Unit Rate at the Scale Factor

Working with Scale Factors

1. Layton traveled from New York City to his mother's house 91 km away. On the map, the distance between the two locations was 7 cm. What is the scale factor?

$$91 \text{ km} = 9,100,000 \text{ cm}$$

$$\frac{7}{9,100,000}$$

$$\frac{1}{1,300,000}$$

The scale factor is $\frac{1}{1,300,000}$.

> I convert one of these measurements, so they both have the same units. I know that there are 1,000 m in 1 km. And there are 100 cm in 1 m. That means that there are 100,000 cm in 1 km.

> I can determine the constant of proportionality, which is the scale factor. I notice that both have a common factor of 7, so I divide the numerator and denominator by 7.

2. Frank advertises for his business by placing an ad on a highway billboard. A billboard on the highway measures 14 ft. by 48 ft. Frank liked the look of the billboard so much that he had it turned into posters that could be placed around town. The posters measured 28 in. by 96 in. Determine the scale factor used to create the posters.

> I need to compare the dimensions, but I need common units. I know that there are 12 inches per foot.

$$14 \text{ ft.} \times 12 \frac{\text{in.}}{\text{ft.}} = 168 \text{ in.}$$

$$\frac{28}{168}$$

$$\frac{1}{6}$$

The scale factor of the reduction from the highway billboard to the poster is $\frac{1}{6}$.

EUREKA MATH

3. Use the scale drawings and measurements to complete the following.

Actual   **Scale Drawing**

16 ft.

22 ft.

> I can see that the scale drawing is an enlargement, so I know the scale factor will be greater than 1.

a. Determine the scale factor.

> I can compare the length of the scale drawing with the corresponding side of the actual drawing.

$$\frac{22}{16}$$

$$\frac{11}{8}$$

The scale factor is $\frac{11}{8}$.

b. Determine the length of the arrow using a scale factor of $\frac{3}{8}$.

> I can calculate the length of the new arrow by multiplying the length of the original by the scale factor.

$$16 \times \frac{3}{8}$$

$$\frac{16}{1} \times \frac{3}{8}$$

$$\frac{48}{8}$$

$$6$$

> I can write 16 as $\frac{16}{1}$ and then multiply the numerators and multiply the denominators.

The length of the arrow will be 6 ft.

6 ft.

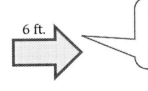

> Now I can draw an arrow with a corresponding side measuring 6 ft.

G7-M1-Lesson 18: Computing Actual Lengths from a Scale Drawing

Actual Lengths

1. A snack food company has bought a larger space on a page in a magazine to place an ad. The original ad needs to be enlarged so that $\frac{1}{4}$ in. will now be shown as $\frac{7}{8}$ in. Find the length of the snack food package in the new ad if the package in the original ad was $1\frac{3}{8}$ in.

$$\frac{\frac{7}{8}}{\frac{1}{4}}$$

> I divide the new measurement by the old corresponding measurement to find the scale factor.

$$\frac{7}{8} \div \frac{1}{4}$$

$$\frac{7}{8} \times \frac{4}{1}$$

> When I divide fractions, I rewrite the problem as multiplying by the reciprocal. Then I just multiply the numerators and multiply the denominators.

$$\frac{28}{8}$$

$$\frac{7}{2}$$

The scale factor used to enlarge the ad is $\frac{7}{2}$.

> Now I can multiply the original length by the scale factor to determine the length in the new ad.

$$1\frac{3}{8} \text{ in.} \times \frac{7}{2}$$

$$\frac{11}{8} \text{ in.} \times \frac{7}{2}$$

$$\frac{77}{16} \text{ in.}$$

$$4\frac{13}{16} \text{ in.}$$

> I divide 16 into 77 in order to rewrite the fraction greater than 1 as a mixed number. The remainder will be the numerator in the mixed number.

The length of the package in the new ad will be $4\frac{13}{16}$ inches.

EUREKA MATH™

2. Hector is building a scale model of the Statue of Liberty. For the model, 1 inch represents 8 feet on the actual Statue of Liberty.

   a. If the actual Statue of Liberty is 305 feet tall, what is the height of Hector's scale model?

   1 inch of the scale drawing corresponds to 8 feet of the actual statue.

   I know the actual height, so I must divide to determine the height of the model of the statue.

   $$k = 8$$
   $$y = kx$$
   $$305 = 8x$$
   $$305 \div 8 = 8x \div 8$$
   $$38\frac{1}{8} = x$$

   In the equation $y = kx$, x is the height of the model in inches, and y is the height of the actual statue in feet.

   The height of the model will be $38\frac{1}{8}$ inches.

   b. The length of the statue's right arm in Hector's model is $5\frac{1}{4}$ inches. How long is the arm on the actual statue?

   I can use the same formula as in part (a), but this time I want to calculate the actual height, so I will multiply.

   $$k = 8$$
   $$y = kx$$
   $$y = 8\left(5\frac{1}{4}\right)$$
   $$y = \frac{8}{1}\left(\frac{21}{4}\right)$$
   $$y = \frac{168}{4}$$
   $$y = 42$$

   The length of the right arm of the actual Statue of Liberty is 42 feet.

3. A model of the second floor of a house is shown below where $\frac{1}{4}$ inch represents 3 feet in the actual house. Use a ruler to measure the drawing, and find the actual length and width of Bedroom 1.

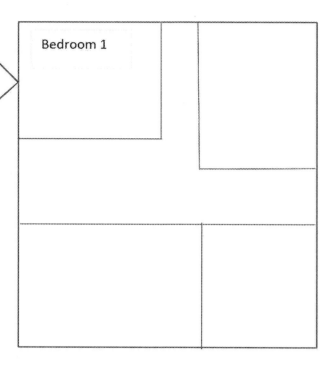

I can use my ruler to measure the length and width of Bedroom 1 in inches. I need to make sure I am as accurate as possible.

Bedroom 1

Length of Bedroom 1: $1\frac{1}{2}$ *inches*

Width of Bedroom 1: $1\frac{1}{4}$ *inches*

I can divide the actual length by the length on the scale drawing to determine the scale factor.

$$\frac{3}{\frac{1}{4}}$$

$$\frac{3}{1} \div \frac{1}{4}$$

$$3 \times 4$$

When I invert and multiply, I get $\frac{3}{1} \times \frac{4}{1}$. This is the same as 3×4.

$$12$$

The scale factor is 12.

© 2015 Great Minds eureka-math.org
G7-M1-HWH-1.3.0-09.2015

EUREKA
MATH

For the length of Bedroom 1: $1\frac{1}{2} \times 12$

To determine the actual length
and width of Bedroom 1,
I multiply the measurements
from the scale drawing by the
scale.

$\frac{3}{2} \times \frac{12}{1}$

$\frac{36}{2}$

18

For the width of Bedroom 1: $1\frac{1}{4} \times 12$

$\frac{5}{4} \times \frac{12}{1}$

$\frac{60}{4}$

15

The actual bedroom is 18 feet long and 15 feet wide.

G7-M1-Lesson 19: Computing Actual Area from a Scale Drawing

Areas

1. The rectangle depicted by the drawing has an actual area of 128 square units. What is the scale factor from the actual rectangle to the scale drawing shown below? (Note: Each square on the grid has a length of 1 unit.)

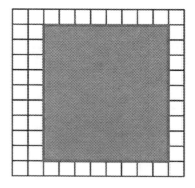

> I can count to determine the length and width of the rectangle.

$$A = \text{length} \times \text{width}$$
$$A = 8 \text{ units} \times 9 \text{ units}$$
$$A = 72 \text{ square units}$$

> I need to determine the area of the scale drawing.

The ratio of the area of the scale drawing to the area of the actual rectangle is the scale factor squared or (r^2).

$$r^2 = \frac{72}{128}$$
$$r^2 = \frac{9}{16}$$
$$r = \frac{3}{4}$$

> I know that the scale factor of the drawing must be $\frac{3}{4}$ because $\frac{3}{4} \times \frac{3}{4} = \frac{9}{16}$.

The scale factor is $\frac{3}{4}$.

EUREKA MATH

2. A quilter designing a new pattern for an extremely large quilt to exhibit in a museum drew a sample quilt on paper using a scale of 1 in. to $2\frac{2}{3}$ ft. Determine the total area of the square quilt from the drawing.

Drawing of Square Block

 $8\frac{1}{4}$ in.

> The block is a square, which means that all the sides will be the same length.

The value of the ratio of areas:

$$r^2 = \left(\frac{2\frac{2}{3}}{1}\right)^2$$

$$r^2 = \left(2\frac{2}{3}\right)^2$$

> I can start by determining the value of the ratio of areas. Because there are two dimensions, I will need to square the ratio of the lengths.

$$r^2 = \left(\frac{8}{3}\right)^2$$

$$r^2 = \frac{64}{9}$$

Area of scale drawing:

$$A = \left(8\frac{1}{4}\right)\left(8\frac{1}{4}\right)$$

> I also need the area of the scale drawing.

$$A = \left(\frac{33}{4}\right)\left(\frac{33}{4}\right)$$

$$A = \frac{1089}{16}$$

Let x represent the scale drawing area and y represent the actual area.

$$y = kx$$

$$y = \left(\frac{64}{9}\right)\left(\frac{1089}{16}\right)$$

$$y = 484$$

> I can multiply the area of the drawing by the value of the ratios of the areas to determine the area of the actual quilt.

The area of the actual quilt is 484 square feet.

3. Below is a floorplan for part of an apartment building where $\frac{1}{2}$ inch corresponds to 16 feet of the actual apartment building. The tenants in Apartment #3 claim that Apartment #2 is bigger. Are they right? Explain.

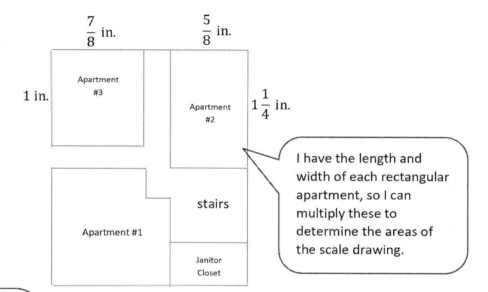

I have the length and width of each rectangular apartment, so I can multiply these to determine the areas of the scale drawing.

I have a whole number in the numerator and a fraction in the denominator, so to simplify this, I will divide. To divide fractions, I invert and multiply by the reciprocal of the second fraction.

The value of the ratio of the areas:

$$r^2 = \left(\frac{16}{\frac{1}{2}}\right)^2$$

$$r^2 = \left(\frac{16}{1} \div \frac{1}{2}\right)^2$$

$$r^2 = (16 \times 2)^2$$

$$r^2 = 32^2$$

$$r^2 = 1024$$

I can rewrite a whole number as a fraction by writing 16 as $\frac{16}{1}$. And in the same way, I can rewrite $\frac{2}{1}$ as 2.

© 2015 Great Minds eureka-math.org
G7-M1-HWH-1.3.0-09.2015

EUREKA MATH

The areas of the scale drawing:

Apartment #2

$$A = \left(\frac{5}{8} \text{ in.}\right)\left(1\frac{1}{4}\text{ in.}\right)$$

$$A = \left(\frac{5}{8}\text{ in.}\right)\left(\frac{5}{4}\text{ in.}\right)$$

$$A = \frac{25}{32}\text{ in.}^2$$

> To calculate the actual area of each apartment, I will multiply the value of the ratio of the areas by the area of the apartment on the scale drawing.

Actual Area of Apartment #2:

$$A = (1024 \text{ ft.})\left(\frac{25}{32}\text{ ft.}\right)$$

$$A = 800 \text{ ft}^2$$

> I can follow the same process for Apartment #3.

Apartment #3

$$A = (1 \text{ in.})\left(\frac{7}{8}\text{ in.}\right)$$

$$A = \frac{7}{8}\text{ in.}^2$$

Actual Area of Apartment #3:

$$A = (1024 \text{ ft.})\left(\frac{7}{8}\text{ ft.}\right)$$

$$A = 896 \text{ ft}^2$$

Apartment #3 is bigger than Apartment #2 by 96 square feet. The tenants were incorrect.

> Now that I have an area for both apartments, I can see that Apartment #3 is bigger. The tenants were incorrect. I can subtract to see just how much bigger Apartment #3 is than Apartment #2.

© 2015 Great Minds eureka-math.org
G7-M1-HWH-1.3.0-09.2015

G7-M1-Lesson 20: An Exercise in Creating a Scale Drawing

Designing a Tree House

Your parents have designated you as the official tree house designer. Your job is to create a top view scale drawing of the tree house of your dreams. Show any special areas or furniture that you would have in the tree house. Use a scale factor of $\frac{1}{12}$.

Sample Answers are Shown Below:

The tree house will be rectangular with a length of 12 feet and a width of 15 feet. The area of the tree house is 180 square feet, and the perimeter is 54 feet.

A scale factor of $\frac{1}{12}$ means that 1 inch on my scale drawing corresponds to 12 inches, or 1 foot, on the real tree house.

(Note: Assume that each square on the grid has a length of 1 inch.)

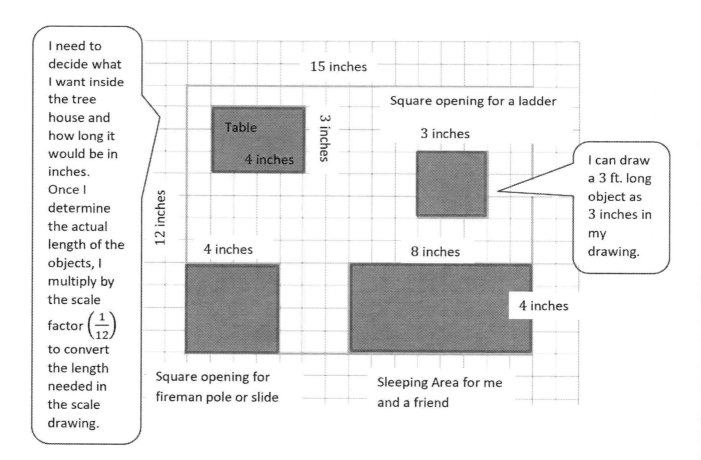

I need to decide what I want inside the tree house and how long it would be in inches. Once I determine the actual length of the objects, I multiply by the scale factor $\left(\frac{1}{12}\right)$ to convert the length needed in the scale drawing.

15 inches

Square opening for a ladder

3 inches

Table
4 inches

3 inches

I can draw a 3 ft. long object as 3 inches in my drawing.

12 inches

4 inches

8 inches

4 inches

Square opening for fireman pole or slide

Sleeping Area for me and a friend

EUREKA MATH

G7-M1-Lesson 21: An Exercise in Changing Scales

Scale Drawing with Different Scales

1. The original scale factor for a scale drawing of a square patio is $\frac{1}{60}$, and the length of the original drawing measures to be 15 inches.

> I noticed that the problem gives the length of the square in the scale drawing but not the length of the actual patio.

   a. What is the length on the new scale drawing if the scale factor of the new scale drawing length to actual length is $\frac{1}{72}$?

> I will use the first scale factor to determine the actual length of the patio.

$$15 \text{ in.} \div \frac{1}{60} = 900 \text{ in.}$$

$$900 \text{ in.} \times \frac{1}{72} = 12.5 \text{ in.}$$

> I use the actual length of the patio and the second scale factor to determine the length in the new scale drawing.

The length of the square in the new scale drawing is 12.5 inches.

   b. What is the scale factor of the new scale drawing to the original scale drawing (Scale Drawing 2 to Scale Drawing 1)?

> I can calculate the scale factor of the new scale drawing by dividing the new scale factor by the original scale factor.

$$\frac{\frac{1}{72}}{\frac{1}{60}}$$

$$\frac{1}{72} \div \frac{1}{60}$$

$$\frac{1}{72} \times \frac{60}{1}$$

$$\frac{60}{72}$$

$$\frac{5}{6}$$

> 60 and 72 have a common factor of 12. I divide them both by 12 to write the scale factor another way.

The scale factor of the new scale drawing to the original scale drawing is $\frac{5}{6}$.

c. If the length of the patio on the new scale drawing is 24 cm, what is the actual length, in meters, of the patio?

I divide the length in the new scale drawing by the scale factor to get back to the original length of the patio.

$$24 \text{ cm} \div \frac{1}{72}$$
$$24 \text{ cm} \times 72$$
$$1728 \text{ cm}$$
$$17.28 \text{ m}$$

There are 100 cm for every 1 m. So, I divide the number of centimeters by 100 to convert to meters.

The patio is 17.28 meters long.

d. What is the surface area of the actual patio? Round your answer to the nearest tenth.

The patio is a square, where all sides are equal, so I will multiply the side lengths to determine the area.

$$A = 17.28 \text{ m} \times 17.28 \text{ m}$$
$$A = 298.5984 \text{ m}^2$$

The area of the patio is about 298.6 m².

The 5 is in the tenths place. I can see that this number is closer to 6 tenths than 5 tenths because of the 9 in the hundredths place.

e. If the actual patio is 0.1 m thick, what is the volume of the patio? Round your answer to the nearest tenth.

I can calculate the volume of a prism by multiplying the length, width, and height. The thickness would be the height.

$$V = 17.28 \text{ m} \times 17.28 \text{ m} \times 0.1 \text{ m}$$
$$V = 29.85984 \text{ m}^3$$

The volume of the patio is about 29.9 m³.

When I multiply meters times meters times meters, I get meters cubed.

f. If the patio is made entirely of concrete, and 1 cubic meter of concrete weighs about 2.65 tons, what is the weight of the entire patio? Round your answer to the nearest unit.

Each cubic meter of concrete weighs 2.65 tons, and I have 29.9 cubic meters.

$$29.9 \text{ m}^3 \times \frac{2.65 \text{ tons}}{1 \text{ m}^3} = 79.235 \text{ tons}$$

The patio weighs about 79 tons.

I know that rounding to the nearest unit is the same as rounding to the nearest ones place. And 79 and 2 tenths is closer to 79 than to 80.

EUREKA MATH™

G7-M1-Lesson 22: An Exercise in Changing Scales

Changing Scales

1. The actual lengths are labeled on the scale drawing. Measure the lengths, in centimeters, of the scale drawing with a ruler, and draw a new scale drawing with a scale (Scale Drawing 2 to Scale Drawing 1) of $\frac{2}{3}$.

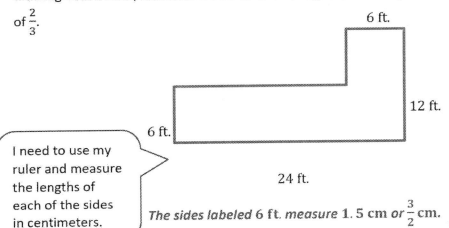

6 ft.

6 ft.

12 ft.

24 ft.

> I need to use my ruler and measure the lengths of each of the sides in centimeters.

The sides labeled 6 ft. measure 1.5 cm or $\frac{3}{2}$ cm.

The side labeled 12 ft. measures 3 cm.

The side labeled 24 ft. measures 6 cm.

> The scale is given as a fraction, so it might be easier to write the lengths as fractions instead of decimals.

New scale drawing lengths:

$$\frac{3}{2}\ cm \times \frac{2}{3} = 1\ cm$$

$$3\ cm \times \frac{2}{3} = 2\ cm$$

$$6\ cm \times \frac{2}{3} = 4\ cm$$

> I can take the measurements and multiply by the scale to determine the lengths of the new image.

> I use my ruler to draw the new image with the measurements I calculated.

1 cm

2 cm

1 cm

4 cm

2. Compute the scale factor of the new scale drawing (SD2) to the first scale drawing (SD1) using the information from the given scale drawings.

SD1: Original Scale Factor: $\frac{3}{4}$ SD2: New Scale Factor: $\frac{9}{8}$

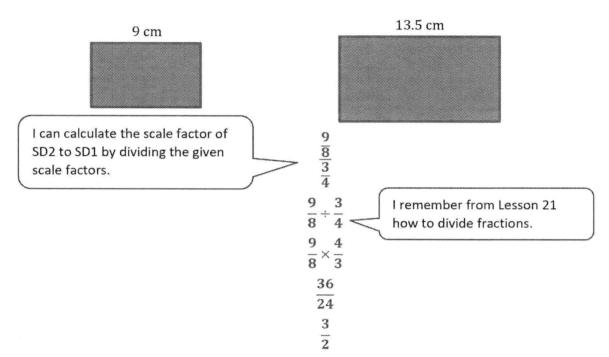

The scale factor of SD2 to SD1 is $\frac{3}{2}$.

EUREKA
MATH

Homework Helpers

Grade 7
Module 2

G7-M2-Lesson 1: Opposite Quantities Combine to Make Zero

Positions on the Number Line

1. Refer to the integer game when answering the following questions.

   a. When playing the Integer Game, what two cards could have a score of -14?

      There are many possible answers. Some of the pairs that make -14 include -10 and -4, -12 and -2, or -15 and 1.

      > I need to start at zero and find two moves so that the second move ends on -14. I can begin my moves with many different numbers.

   b. If the two cards played in a round are the same distance from zero but are on opposite sides of zero, what is the score for the round?

      The two given cards would be opposites, and the score for the round would be zero.

      > Positive cards move to the right of zero, and negative cards move to the left. So if I start at zero and move 5 to the right and then 5 to the left, I will end up back at zero.

2. Hector was given $20 as a gift. He spent $12 at the store and then planned to spend $14 more on a second item. How much more would he need in order to buy the second item? Be sure to show your work using addition of integers.

   Hector would need $6 more.

   $$20 + (-12) + (-14) + 6 = 0$$

   > Hector doesn't have enough money. To have enough money, he needs to end on 0 on the number line. If Hector adds $20 + (-12) + (-14)$, he ends on -6.

   > The money he is given can be positive, and the amount he spends will be negative.

3. Use the 8 card and its additive inverse to write a real-world story problem about their sum.

> An additive inverse is the same distance from zero, but on the opposite side of zero on the number line.

The temperature in the morning was −8°F.

If the temperatures rises 8 degrees, what is the new temperature?

Answer: $(−8) + 8 = 0; 0°F$

> Real-world problems with integers could include money, temperatures, elevations, or even sports.

4. Write an addition number sentence that corresponds to the arrows below.

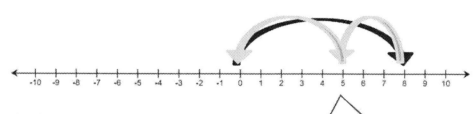

$8 + (−3) + (−5) = 0$

> I start from 0 and can see arrows moving to the right and then to the left. An arrow moving to the right shows a positive addend, and an arrow moving to the left shows a negative addend.

EUREKA MATH

G7-M2-Lesson 2: Using the Number Line to Model the Addition of Integers

Adding Integers on a Number Line

1. When playing the Integer Game, Sally drew three cards, 3, −12, and 8. Then Sally's partner gave Sally a 5 from his hand.

    > I use arrows to represent each number. Negative numbers will face left, and positive numbers will face right.

    a. What is Sally's total? Model the answer on the number line and using an equation.

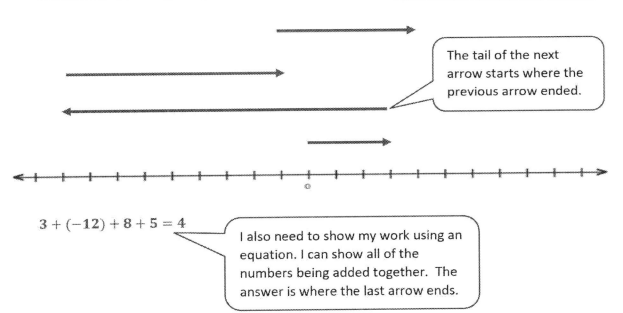

    > The tail of the next arrow starts where the previous arrow ended.

$$3 + (-12) + 8 + 5 = 4$$

    > I also need to show my work using an equation. I can show all of the numbers being added together. The answer is where the last arrow ends.

    b. What card(s) would you need to get your score back to zero? Explain.

    A −4 card would bring the score back to 0. The number −4 is the additive inverse of 4. It is the same distance from 0 on the number line but in the opposite direction. So when I add 4 and −4, the answer would be 0.

    > I could also choose more than one card, but the sum must be −4.

2. Write a story problem and an equation that would model the sum of the numbers represented by the arrows in the number diagram below.

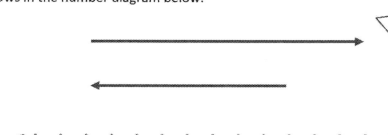

> The bottom arrow is 8 units and faces left. So it shows -8. The second arrow is 11 units and faces to the right. So that arrow represents 11.

In the morning, I lost $8. Later in the day, I got paid $11. How much money do I have at the end of the day?

$$-8 + 11 = 3$$

I had $3 at the end of the day.

> An equation requires that I also state the answer when the sum is calculated.

3. Mark an integer between -2 and 4 on a number line, and label it point K. Then, locate and label each of the following points by finding the sums.

> My answer will depend on what I pick for K. For this example, I pick -1 for K.

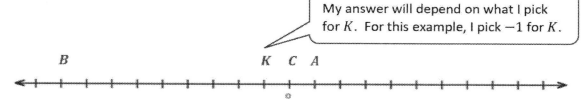

a. Point A: $K + 2$

    Point A: $-1 + 2 = 1$

> I can use K to help me when adding the other numbers. I will always start at K to determine where each point should be located on the number line.

b. Point B: $K + (-8)$

    Point B: $-1 + (-8) = -9$

c. Point C: $(-4) + 5 + K$

    Point C: $(-4) + 5 + (-1) = 0$

G7-M2-Lesson 3: Understanding Addition of Integers

1. Refer to the diagram to the right.

   a. What integers do the arrows represent?

      6 and −14

   b. Write an equation for the diagram to the right.

      $6 + (−14) = −8$

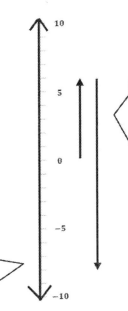

> The second arrow is pointing to the sum. So I can write an equation showing the sum of the two integers being equal to the sum.

> The length and direction of the arrows will tell me what integers they represent. If the arrow points up, it is positive, and if it points down, it is negative.

   c. Describe the sum in terms of the distance from the first addend. Explain.

      The sum is 14 units below 6 because $|−14| = 14$. I counted down from 6 fourteen units and stopped at −8.

   d. Describe the arrows you would use on a vertical number line in order to solve $−3 + −9$.

      The first arrow would start at 0 and be three units long, pointing downward because the addend is negative. The second arrow would start at −3 and be nine units long, also pointing downward. The second arrow would end at −12.

> The absolute value of the numbers will give me the length of the arrow, and the sign will tell me what direction the arrow should face.

© 2015 Great Minds eureka-math.org
G7-M2-HWH-1.3.0-09.2015

2. Given the expression $84 + (-29)$, can you determine, without finding the sum, the distance between 84 and the sum? Is the sum to the right or left of 84 on the number line?

   The distance would be 29 units from 84. The sum is to the left of 84 on the number line.

   > If I draw a sketch of the sum, I start at 0 and move 84 units to the right. I would then have to move 29 units to the left, which means the sum will be 29 units to the left of 84.

3. Refer back to the Integer Game to answer this question. Juno selected two cards. The sum of her cards is 16.

   > If needed, I can draw a number line to see what would happen if both of Juno's cards are negative.

   a. Can both cards be negative? Explain why or why not.

      No. In order for the sum to be 16, at least one of the addends would have to be positive. If both cards are negative, then Juno would count twice going to the left/down, which would result in a negative sum.

   b. Can one of the cards be positive and the other be negative? Explain why or why not.

      Yes. She could have -4 and 20 or -2 and 18. The card with the greatest absolute value would have to be positive.

      > I can create a number line to determine if this is possible. This visual will also help me see that the longer arrow (larger absolute value) must be positive to get a positive sum.

4. Determine the afternoon temperatures for each day. Write an equation that represents each situation.

   a. The morning temperature was 8°F and then fell 11 degrees in the afternoon.

      $$8 + (-11) = -3$$
      The afternoon temperature will be -3°F.

      > I can show the temperature falling as adding a negative because it would show a move down on a vertical number line.

   b. The morning temperature was -5°F and then rose 9 degrees in the afternoon.

      $$-5 + 9 = 4$$
      The afternoon temperature will be 4°F.

      > I can show the temperature rising as adding a positive because it would show a move up on a vertical number line.

EUREKA MATH

G7-M2-Lesson 4: Efficiently Adding Integers and Other Rational Numbers

1. Use the diagram below to complete each part.

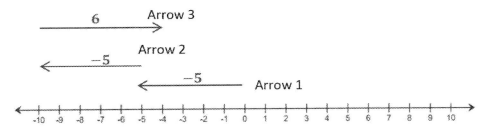

a.   How long is each arrow? What direction does each arrow point?

Arrow	Length	Direction
1	5	*left*
2	5	*left*
3	6	*right*

b.   Label each arrow with the number the arrow represents.

> I can use the length and direction of each arrow to help me determine what number it represents. If it is facing left, it represents a negative number. If it is facing right, it represents a positive number.

c.   Write an equation that represents the sum of the numbers. Find the sum.

$$(-5) + (-5) + 6 = -4$$

> These three arrows represent a sum. The third arrow ends on the answer, or the sum, of all three numbers being represented by the three arrows.

2. Which of these story problems describes the sum $24 + (-17)$? Check all that apply.

_____X_____ Morgan planted 24 tomato plants at the beginning of spring. She sold 17 of the plants at the

farmer's market. How many plants does she have now?

> Selling some of the plants would be represented as negative numbers when trying to figure out how many plants Morgan has left.

_____X_____ Morgan started with 24 tomato plants. Then her mother took 8 of the plants, and her aunt

took 9 of the plants. How many plants does Morgan have now?

> If I combine the amounts taken by each family member, I get $(-8) + (-9) = -17$. So this would also show -17 plants being added to the total.

_____ Morgan owes her mother 24 tomato plants but only has 17 to give her. How many tomato

plants short of the total needed is Morgan?

> The amount of plants Morgan owes her mom would be represented by a negative value, while the 17 plants she has would be represented by a positive number. Therefore, the signs of the two addends are opposites of the addends in the given expression.

3. Ezekiel is playing the Integer Game. He has the cards -7 and 4.

a. What card would Ezekiel need to draw next to win with a score of zero?

> I need to calculate the sum of his two cards.

$$-7 + 4 = -3$$
$$-3 + 3 = 0$$

> If I add a number and its opposite, I will get zero. So I know that the next card drawn has to be the opposite of -3.

Ezekiel would need to draw a 3.

EUREKA MATH

b. Ezekiel drew two more cards, and his new score is the opposite of his original score. What two cards might he have drawn?

His cards must have a sum of 3.

The cards could be 1 and 5.

$$-7 + 4 + 1 + 5 = -7 + 10 = 3$$

> I know that the new sum is the opposite of -3. That means that all four cards together must have a sum of 3. On a number line, I see that -3 and 3 are 6 units apart. So the two new cards must have a sum of 6.

4. $\frac{1}{5} + \left(-3\frac{7}{10}\right)$

> To add fractions, I need common denominators. I will use the least common multiple of 5 and 10.

$$\frac{2}{10} + \left(-3\frac{7}{10}\right)$$

$$\frac{2}{10} + \left(-\frac{37}{10}\right)$$

$$-\frac{35}{10}$$

$$-3\frac{5}{10}$$

$$-3\frac{1}{2}$$

> I can write a mixed number as a fraction greater than 1 to help me add the numerators correctly.

G7-M2-Lesson 5: Understanding Subtraction of Integers and Other Rational Numbers

Adding the Opposite

1. Choose an integer between 3 and -3 on the number line, and label it point M. Locate and label the following points on the number line. Show your work.

> I can choose any number I want between 3 and -3. For this example, I choose -2.

a. Point A: $M - 6$

   Point A: $-2 - 6$

   $-2 + (-6)$

   -8

> To subtract, I add the opposite. Therefore, I move to the left, just like I would if I subtract a positive.

b. Point B: $(M - 5) + 5$

   Point B: $(-2 - 5) + 5$

   $(-2 + (-5)) + 5$

   -2 *(same value as M)*

> If I subtract a number and then add the same number, the original value will remain the same. I can see this on the number line, moving left and then moving right the same number of units.

c. Point C: $-M - (-3)$

   Point C: $-(-2) - (-3)$

   $2 + 3$

   5

> When I see a negative in front of a number, I can read that as "the opposite of." So $-(-2)$ would mean the opposite of -2, which would be 2.

EUREKA
MATH™

© 2015 Great Minds eureka-math.org
G7-M2-HWH-1.3.0-09.2015

2. You and your partner were playing the Integer Game in class. Here are the cards in both hands.

Your hand   *Your partner's hand*

   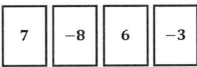

a. Find the value of each hand. Who would win based on the current scores? (The score closest to 0 wins.)

My hand: $-6 + 5 + 3 + (-4) = -2$

Partner's hand: $7 + (-8) + 6 + (-3) = 2$

> I find that both numbers are 2 units from 0, one is to the right, and the other is to the left. Neither player is closer to 0.

My partner and I would tie because -2 and 2 are both 2 units from 0.

b. Find the value of each hand if you discarded the -4 and selected a 4 and your partner discarded the -3 and selected a 3. Show your work to support your answer. Then decide who would now win the game.

My hand: Discard the -4,

$$-2 - (-4)$$
$$-2 + 4$$
$$2$$

> Discarded means that it was thrown out or taken away. So I need to subtract those values from the scores I found in part (a).

Select a 4,

$$2 + 4$$
$$6$$

Partner's hand: Discard the -3,

$$2 - (-3)$$
$$2 + 3$$
$$5$$

Select a 3,

$$5 + 3$$
$$8$$

My hand would win because 6 is the value that is closer to 0.

3. Explain what is meant by the following, and illustrate with an example:

    "For any real number, g, $4 - g = 4 + (-g)$."

> For this question, I need to explain why $4 - g$ is equivalent to $4 + (-g)$, and I have to give an example where I pick the value of g and show this is true.

Subtracting a number is the same as adding its additive inverse. Here is an example.

$g = 10$, $4 - (10)$ *is the same as* $4 + (-10)$ *because* -10 *is the opposite of* 10.

$4 - 10 = -6$

$4 + (-10) = -6$

So, $4 - 10 = 4 + (-10)$ *because they both equal* -6.

> I can substitute 10 for g in both expressions. Both expressions will give me the same answer (-6), showing the statement is true.

4. Write two equivalent expressions that represent the situation. What is the difference in their elevations?

    A mountain climber hikes to an altitude of 8,400 feet. A diver reaches a depth of 180 feet below sea level.

$$8,400 - (-180)$$
$$8,400 + 180$$
$$8,580$$

> A distance above sea level would be represented as a positive integer, and the distance below sea level would be a negative integer.

> I can also show this as addition. I need to add the distance above sea level with the distance below sea level to determine the total difference in their elevations.

The difference in their elevations is $8,580$ *ft.*

Lesson 5:   Understanding Subtraction of Integers and Other Rational Numbers

EUREKA MATH

© 2015 Great Minds eureka-math.org
G7-M2-HWH-1.3.0-09.2015

G7-M2-Lesson 6: The Distance Between Two Rational Numbers

1. Find the distance between the two rational numbers.

   a. $|-6 - 15|$

$$|-6 - 15|$$
$$|-6 + (-15)|$$
$$|-21|$$
$$21$$

> The bars on either side indicate absolute value. After I calculate the difference, I determine the absolute value. I can determine this by finding the distance the answer is from 0. Distances are always positive.

   b. $|6 - (-15)|$

$$|6 - (-15)|$$
$$|6 + 15|$$
$$|21|$$
$$21$$

   c. $|-7 - 5.4|$

$$|-7 - 5.4|$$
$$|-7 + (-5.4)|$$
$$|-12.4|$$
$$12.4$$

> I can work with signed decimals the same as I work with integers. I will still subtract by adding the opposite.

   d. $|7 - (-5.4)|$

$$|7 - (-5.4)|$$
$$|7 + 5.4|$$
$$|12.4|$$
$$12.4$$

© 2015 Great Minds eureka-math.org
G7-M2-HWH-1.3.0-09.2015

2. Do you notice any special relationships between parts (a) and (b) or between parts (c) and (d)? Explain.

> The distance between two sets of opposites is the same.

The answers in parts (a) and (b) were the same because I was working with opposites. I found the distance between −6 to 15 and then found the distance between 6 and −15. The same relationship occurred in parts (c) and (d).

EUREKA MATH

G7-M2-Lesson 7: Addition and Subtraction of Rational Numbers

Represent each of the following problems using both a number line diagram and an equation.

1. Mannah went diving to check out different sea creatures. The total dive was 5.8 meters below sea level, and Mannah stops at 1.2 meters from the deepest part of the dive to look at a fish. How far from sea level will he be when he stops?

$$-5.8 - (-1.2)$$

$$-5.8 + 1.2$$

$$-4.6$$

> Because Mannah is below sea level, the depth of the dive will be negative. Then I will take away -1.2 meters because he already made this part of the journey back up to sea level (0 meters) before he stops to see the fish.

Mannah will be 4.6 meters below sea level when he stops to look at the fish.

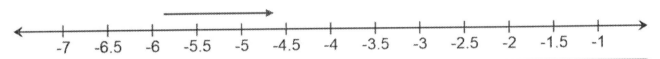

> I can check my work using the number line. I know that Mannah is heading towards sea level, or 0, so an arrow that is 1.2 units long facing right matches my equation and shows my work is correct.

2. A sturgeon was swimming $1\frac{1}{2}$ feet below sea level when it jumped up 4 feet before returning back to the water. How far above sea level was the fish at its highest point?

$$-1\frac{1}{2} + 4 = 2\frac{1}{2}$$

The sturgeon reached $2\frac{1}{2}$ feet above sea level.

> The initial location of the sturgeon is negative because it is below sea level. The sturgeon is jumping up, adding to its elevation.

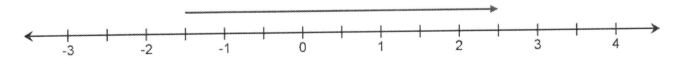

3. Marissa earned $16.75 babysitting and placed the money on a debit card. While shopping, she wanted to spend $22.40 on a new skirt. What would her new balance be on the debit card if she makes the purchase?

$$16.75 + (-22.40) = -5.65$$

The account balance would be $-\$5.65$.

The skirt Marissa wants to buy costs more than she earned. So she would have a negative balance on her debit card.

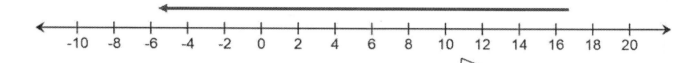

This time my arrow will start at a positive number and go left to show that she is adding a negative when spending the money she earned.

EUREKA MATH

G7-M2-Lesson 8: Applying the Properties of Operations to Add and Subtract Rational Numbers

1. Jerod dropped his wallet at the grocery store. The wallet contained $40. When he got home, his grandfather felt sorry for him and gave him $28.35. Represent this situation with an expression involving rational numbers. What is the overall change in the amount of money Jerod has?

$$-40 + 28.35 = -11.65$$

The overall change in the amount of money Jerod has is *−11.65 dollars.*

> The sum of losing the money and then gaining money should be closer to zero but still negative because Jerod was given less money than he lost.

> Losing the wallet would be a negative because now he doesn't have the money anymore. But then we need to add a positive on to the total when the grandfather gives him money.

2. Zoe is completing some math problems. What are the answers? Show your work.

   a. $-9 + -\frac{2}{3}$

   > In the lesson, I practiced writing a mixed number as the sum of two signed numbers. I can do the reverse of that here and write the sum of two signed numbers as a mixed number.

   $-9\frac{2}{3}$

   b. $16 - 19\frac{4}{5}$

   $$16 + \left(-19\frac{4}{5}\right)$$

   > I write the mixed number as the sum of two signed numbers, and then I can combine the integers together. Finally, the two signed numbers will combine to form a mixed number.

   $$16 + \left(-19 + \left(-\frac{4}{5}\right)\right)$$

   $$16 + (-19) + \left(-\frac{4}{5}\right)$$

   $$-3 + \left(-\frac{4}{5}\right)$$

   $$-3\frac{4}{5}$$

c. $\left(\frac{1}{8} + \frac{3}{4}\right) + \left(\left(-\frac{1}{8}\right) + \left(-\frac{3}{4}\right)\right)$

> I rewrite the fractions with common denominators before adding.

$\left(\frac{1}{8} + \frac{6}{8}\right) + \left(\left(-\frac{1}{8}\right) + \left(-\frac{6}{8}\right)\right)$

$\left(\frac{7}{8}\right) + \left(-\frac{7}{8}\right)$

> I am adding a sum and its opposite. I know this because the second sum in parentheses has the opposite sign but the same absolute value.

0

Lesson 8:   Applying the Properties of Operations to Add and Subtract Rational Numbers

© 2015 Great Minds eureka-math.org
G7-M2-HWH-1.3.0-09.2015

EUREKA MATH

G7-M2-Lesson 9: Applying the Properties of Operations to Add and Subtract Rational Numbers

1. Show all steps needed to rewrite each of the following expressions as a single rational number.

   a. $14 - \left(-8\frac{4}{9}\right)$

$$14 + 8\frac{4}{9}$$

$$14 + 8 + \frac{4}{9}$$

> I can separate the mixed number so that I can work with the whole number and the fraction separately.

$$22 + \frac{4}{9}$$

$$22\frac{4}{9}$$

   b. $-2\frac{2}{5} + 4.1 - 8\frac{1}{5}$

$$-2\frac{2}{5} - 8\frac{1}{5} + 4.1$$

> I apply the commutative property because the two mixed numbers have common denominators already.

$$-2\frac{2}{5} + \left(-8\frac{1}{5}\right) + 4.1$$

$$-2 + \left(-\frac{2}{5}\right) + (-8) + \left(-\frac{1}{5}\right) + 4.1$$

$$-2 + (-8) + \left(-\frac{2}{5}\right) + \left(-\frac{1}{5}\right) + 4.1$$

$$-10 + -\frac{3}{5} + 4.1$$

> I can rewrite the decimal as a fraction, $4\frac{1}{10}$. And I can write $\frac{3}{5}$ as $\frac{6}{10}$ so that I have common denominators to add.

$$-10\frac{3}{5} + 4.1$$

$$-10\frac{3}{5} + 4\frac{1}{10}$$

$$-10\frac{6}{10} + 4\frac{1}{10}$$

$$-6\frac{5}{10}$$

2. Explain, step by step, how to arrive at a single rational number to represent the following expression. Show both a written explanation and the related math work for each step.

$$4 - \left(-3\frac{2}{9}\right) + 2\frac{1}{3}$$

Rewrite the subtraction as adding the inverse. $4 + 3\frac{2}{9} + 2\frac{1}{3}$

Get common denominators. $4 + 3\frac{2}{9} + 2\frac{3}{9}$

Separate each mixed number into the sum of its parts. $4 + 3 + \frac{2}{9} + 2 + \frac{3}{9}$

Reorder the addends so that I can add the whole number addends and add the fractional addends. $4 + 3 + 2 + \frac{2}{9} + \frac{3}{9}$

Add the whole number addends and then the fractional addends. $9 + \frac{5}{9}$

Add the whole number addend and fractional addend together. $9\frac{5}{9}$

EUREKA
MATH

G7-M2-Lesson 10: Understanding Multiplication of Integers

Integer Game

Describe sets of two or more matching integer cards that satisfy the criteria in each problem below.

1. Cards increase the score by six points.

    Picking up: six 1's, three 2's, or two 3's

    OR

    Removing: six (−1)'s, three (−2)'s, or two (−3)'s

    > I can increase my score two ways: picking up positive value cards (pos. × pos.) or removing negative value cards from my hand (neg. × neg.)

2. Cards decrease the score by 4 points.

    Picking up: four (−1)'s or two (−2)'s

    OR

    Removing: four 1's or two 2's

    > I can decrease my score two ways: picking up negative value cards (pos. × neg.) or removing positive value cards from my hand (neg. × pos.).

3. Removing cards that increase the score by 8 points.

    Eight (−1)'s, four (−2)'s, or two (−4)'s

    > If I want to remove cards to increase my score, I must remove negative value cards.

4. Bruce is playing the Integer Game and is given the opportunity to discard a set of matching cards. Bruce determines that if he discards one set of cards, his score will increase by 8. If he discards another set, then his score will decrease by 15. If his matching cards make up all seven cards in his hand, what cards are in Bruce's hand?

    There are two possibilities:

    −4, −4, 3, 3, 3, 3, 3 or −2, −2, −2, −2, 5, 5, 5

    > Removing negative cards increases Bruce's score and removing positive cards decreases Bruce's score.

G7-M2-Lesson 11: Develop Rules for Multiplying Signed Numbers

Multiplying Integers

1. Explain why $(-3) \times (-2) = 6$. Use patterns, an example from the Integer Game, or the properties of operations to support your reasoning.

> Instead of using the Integer Game to explain why the product is positive, I could have also used the patterns I saw in the four quadrants during class today.

> *If I think about the Integer Game, removing negative cards from my hand, increases my score. Therefore, the problem presented indicates that I removed three cards (-3) each with a value of -2. This change would increase my score by 6 points.*

2. Emilia receives allergy shots in order to decrease her allergy symptoms. Emilia must pay $20 each time she receives a shot, which is twice a week. Write an integer that represents the change in Emilia's money from receiving shots for 8 weeks. Explain your reasoning.

$$2(8) = 16$$

Emilia receives 16 shots in 8 weeks.

> Each time Emilia pays for a shot, her money decreases by $20, which is indicated with -20 in my equation.

$$-20(16) = -320$$

The change in Emilia's money after 8 weeks of receiving shots twice a week is $-\$320$.

> I could have picked a different real-world example, but it would still require that -2 is repeated three times.

3. Write a real-world problem that can be modeled by $3 \times (-2)$.

    The temperature has decreased two degrees each hour for the last three hours. What is the change in temperature after the three hours?

> A decrease of 2 degrees describes the -2 in the original expression.

EUREKA
MATH™

© 2015 Great Minds eureka-math.org
G7-M2-HWH-1.3.0-09.2015

G7-M2-Lesson 12: Division of Integers

1. Find the missing value in each column.

Column A

$-16 \div 8 = -2$

$16 \div -8 = -2$

$-16 \div -8 = 2$

$16 \div 8 = 2$

Column B

$-32 \div 8 = -4$

$32 \div -8 = -4$

$-32 \div -8 = 4$

$32 \div 8 = 4$

> I know that when the dividend and divisor have the same sign, the quotient will be positive. I also know that when the dividend and divisor have opposite signs, the quotient will be negative.

2. Describe the pattern you see in each column's answers in Problem 1, relating it to the divisors and dividends. Why is this so?

The first two quotients in each column are negative because the dividend and divisor have opposite signs but the same absolute values, which means the answers will have a negative value. The last two quotients in each column are positive because the dividend and divisor have the same signs and absolute values, which means the answer will be a positive value.

3. Describe the pattern you see between the answers in Column A and Column B in Problem 1. Why is this so?

The quotients in Column B are each double the corresponding quotients in Column A. This is true because the divisors in each column are the same, but the dividends in Column B are double the corresponding dividends in Column A. Since 32 is double 16 and the divisors remain the same, the quotients will also be double.

> If the divisor's value doubled and the dividend remained constant, the value of the new quotient would be half of the value of the original quotient.

G7-M2-Lesson 13: Converting Between Fractions and Decimals Using Equivalent Fractions

Converting Terminating Decimals to Fractions

Convert each terminating decimal to a fraction in its simplest form.

1. 0.8

> The decimal place farthest to the right is the tenths place. Therefore, my denominator will be 10, and my numerator will be 8.

$$0.8 = \frac{8}{10} = \frac{4}{5}$$

> The numerator and denominator have a greatest common factor of 2. I can divide this common factor out to write the fraction in simplest form.

2. 0.375

> The decimal place farthest to the right is the thousandths place. Therefore, my denominator will be 1,000, and my numerator will be 375.

$$0.375 = \frac{375}{1,000} = \frac{75}{200} = \frac{15}{40} = \frac{3}{8}$$

> Instead of finding the greatest common factor, I kept dividing by a smaller common factor until the only common factor between the numerator and denominator was 1.

3. 0.05

> The extra 0 does not change anything, I still look at the decimal place farthest to the right to determine the denominator.

$$0.05 = \frac{5}{100} = \frac{1}{20}$$

EUREKA MATH

Converting Fractions to Decimals

I need to write each fraction with a denominator that is a power of 10.

Convert each fraction or mixed number to a decimal using an equivalent fraction.

In order to make my denominator a power of 10, I need to multiply both the numerator and denominator by 2.

4. $\frac{2}{5}$

$$\frac{2}{5} = \frac{2 \times 2}{5 \times 2} = \frac{4}{10} = 0.4$$

In order to make my denominator a power of 10, I need the same number of 2's and 5's in the denominator. Therefore, I need another factor of 5.

5. $\frac{7}{20}$

$$\frac{7}{20} = \frac{7}{2^2 \times 5} = \frac{7 \times 5}{2^2 \times 5^2} = \frac{35}{100} = 0.35$$

If the denominator is 100, then the decimal farthest to the right should be in the hundredths place.

This time I need two more factors of 2 to have the same number of 2's and 5's, which will make my denominator a power of 10.

6. $\frac{13}{250}$

$$\frac{13}{250} = \frac{13}{2 \times 5^3} = \frac{13 \times 2^2}{2^3 \times 5^3} = \frac{52}{1000} = 0.052$$

I need the decimal farthest to the right to be in the thousandths place, so I need to use a 0 for a place holder.

7. $\frac{21}{175}$

I have to divide out the factor of 7 from the numerator and denominator before I can change the denominator to a power of 10.

$$\frac{21}{175} = \frac{7 \times 3}{7 \times 5^2} = \frac{3}{5^2} = \frac{3 \times 2^2}{5^2 \times 2^2} = \frac{12}{100} = 0.12$$

EUREKA MATH™

G7-M2-Lesson 14: Converting Rational Numbers to Decimals Using Long Division

1. Convert each rational number into its decimal form.

   a. $\frac{3}{12}$

   $$\frac{3}{12} = \frac{3}{2^2 \times 3} = \frac{1}{2^2} = \frac{1 \times 5^2}{2^2 \times 5^2} = \frac{25}{100} = 0.25$$

   $\frac{3}{12} = 0.25$

   > I know the decimal will terminate because the fraction can be rewritten with a denominator that is a power of 10.

   > I notice the remainder continues to repeat, which means the digits in the quotient will also repeat.

   b. $\frac{1}{12}$

   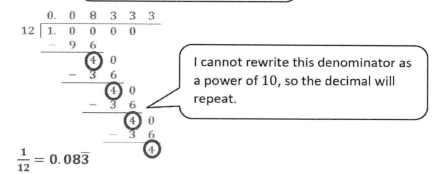

   > I cannot rewrite this denominator as a power of 10, so the decimal will repeat.

   $\frac{1}{12} = 0.08\overline{3}$

2. Josephine thinks $-\frac{5}{15}$ is a terminating decimal. Is Josephine correct? Why or why not?

   $$-\frac{5}{15} = -\frac{1}{3}$$

   Josephine is not correct because the denominator cannot be written as a power of 10, which must be true if the fraction represents a terminating decimal.

© 2015 Great Minds eureka-math.org
G7-M2-HWH-1.3.0-09.2015

EUREKA MATH

G7-M2-Lesson 15: Multiplication and Division of Rational Numbers

1. Charlotte owes her parents $135. If Charlotte pays her parents $15 every week for 7 weeks, how much money will she still owe her parents?

> To determine how much Charlotte pays her parents, I can multiply the size of the payment by the number of payments.

$$135 + 7(-15) = 135 + (-105) = 30$$

Charlotte will still owe her parents $30 after making 7 equal payments of $15.

2. Find at least two sets of values that will make each equation true.

   a. Fill in the blanks with two rational numbers that will make the equation true.

   $$\underline{\quad} \times \left(-\frac{1}{5}\right) \times \underline{\quad} = 10$$

   What must be true about the relationship between the two numbers you choose?

   Two possible answers: -10 and 5 or 10 and -5

   The two numbers must be factors of 50 and have opposite signs.

   > I can use my knowledge of solving equations to determine the product of the two missing values.

   > To get a positive quotient, I need an even number of negative factors. The factor $\left(-\frac{1}{5}\right)$ is already negative, so one of the other two factors needs to be negative.

This part of the equation has a value of 5, which means the missing two factors should have a product of -12.

b. Fill in the blanks with two rational numbers that will make the equation true.

$$(-2.5) \times 50 \div (-25) \times \underline{\hspace{1cm}} \times \underline{\hspace{1cm}} = -60$$

What must be true about the relationship between the two numbers you choose?

Two possible answers: 2 and −6 or −3 and 4

The two numbers must be factors of 12 and have opposite signs.

To have a negative answer, I must have an odd number of negative factors. Two of the factors are already negative, which means one additional factor needs to be negative.

3. Create a word problem that can be represented by the expression, and then represent the quotient as a single rational number.

$$-10 \div 2\tfrac{1}{2}$$

The temperature dropped 10 degrees in $2\tfrac{1}{2}$ hours. If the temperature dropped at a constant rate, how much did the temperature drop each hour?

$$-10 \div 2\tfrac{1}{2}$$
$$-10 \div \tfrac{5}{2}$$
$$-\tfrac{10}{1} \times \tfrac{2}{5}$$
$$-\tfrac{20}{5}$$
$$-4$$

I could have used a different example of a real-world problem, but the answer will still be -4.

The temperature dropped four degrees each hour.

EUREKA MATH

G7-M2-Lesson 16: Applying the Properties of Operations to Multiply and Divide Rational Numbers

1. Evaluate the expression $\left(-\frac{1}{5}\right) \times (-8) \div \left(-\frac{1}{3}\right) \times 15$

    a. Using order of operations only.

    > Using the order of operations to evaluate this expression, I complete the operations from left to right.

    $$\left(-\frac{1}{5}\right) \times (-8) \div \left(-\frac{1}{3}\right) \times 15$$

    $$\frac{8}{5} \div \left(-\frac{1}{3}\right) \times 15$$

    $$\frac{8}{5} \times (-3) \times 15$$

    $$\left(-\frac{24}{5}\right) \times 15$$

    $$-72$$

    b. Using the properties and methods used in Lesson 16.

    > I use the commutative property to change the order of the factors. This allows me to eliminate the fractions.

    $$\left(-\frac{1}{5}\right) \times (-8) \div \left(-\frac{1}{3}\right) \times 15$$

    $$\left(-\frac{1}{5}\right) \times 15 \times (-8) \times (-3)$$

    $$(-3) \times (-8) \times (-3)$$

    $$-72$$

2. Evaluate each expression using the distributive property.

    a. $3\frac{1}{3} \times (-12)$

    $$\left(3 + \frac{1}{3}\right) \times (-12)$$

    > $3\frac{1}{3}$ is equivalent to $3 + \frac{1}{3}$.

    $$3 \times (-12) + \frac{1}{3} \times (-12)$$

    > I distribute the -12 to both values in the parentheses.

    $$-36 + (-4)$$

    $$-40$$

EUREKA MATH™

© 2015 Great Minds eureka-math.org
G7-M2-HWH-1.3.0-09.2015

b. $\frac{3}{4}(-3) + \frac{3}{4}(11)$

$\frac{3}{4}(-3 + 11)$

$\frac{3}{4}(8)$

6

> I use the distributive property to factor out the common factor $\left(\frac{3}{4}\right)$. This allows me to combine the integers before multiplying by the fractional value.

3. Examine the problem and work below. Find and explain the errors, and then find the correct value of the expression.

$(-3) \times 0.4 \times 2 \div \left(-\frac{1}{5}\right) \div 3$

$(-3) \times 0.4 \times 2 \times (-5) \times 3$

$(-3) \times 0.4 \times (-5) \times 2 \times 3$

$(-3) \times (-2) \times 2 \times 3$

-36

> When division is changed to multiplication, the divisor needs to be inverted.

> Two negative factors result in a positive product.

There are two mistakes in the work. First, when changing ÷ 3 to multiplication, it should be changed to $\times \frac{1}{3}$ because we need to invert and multiply. Second, there is an error with the negative signs in the final step. An even number of negative factors will result in a positive product, not a negative product. The correct work is shown below.

$(-3) \times 0.4 \times 2 \times (-5) \times \frac{1}{3}$

$(-3) \times \frac{1}{3} \times 0.4 \times (-5) \times 2$

$-1 \times 0.4 \times (-5) \times 2$

$-1 \times (-2) \times 2$

4

> I can use the commutative property like I did with an earlier problem.

Lesson 16:   Applying the Properties of Operations to Multiply and Divide Rational Numbers

EUREKA MATH

G7-M2-Lesson 17: Comparing Tape Diagram Solutions to Algebraic Solutions

Solve each problem by writing an equation and constructing a tape diagram.

1. Liam always eats 2 servings of fruit every day. He also eats some vegetables every day. He eats 35 servings of fruits and vegetables every week. If Liam eats the same number of vegetables every day, how many servings of vegetables does he eat each day?

Algebraic Equation

Let v represent the number of servings of vegetables Liam eats each day.

I add the number of servings of fruits and vegetables together and then multiply by 7 because there are 7 days in a week, and I know how many servings Liam eats in a week, 35.

$$7(2 + v) = 35$$
$$14 + 7v = 35$$
$$14 - 14 + 7v = 35 - 14$$
$$7v = 21$$
$$\left(\frac{1}{7}\right)(7v) = \left(\frac{1}{7}\right)(21)$$
$$v = 3$$

Here, I apply the distributive property. I could multiply by the multiplicative inverse instead.

I can collect like terms and then multiply by the multiplicative inverse to determine the value of the variable.

Liam eats 3 servings of vegetables each day.

Tape Diagram

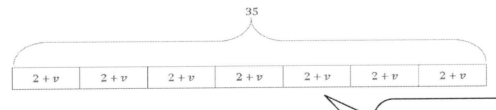

35

| $2 + v$ | $2 + v$ | $2 + v$ | $2 + v$ | $2 + v$ | $2 + v$ | $2 + v$ |

$$7v \qquad\qquad\qquad 35 - 14 = 21$$
$$7(2) = 14 \qquad\qquad 21 \div 7 = 3$$

Liam eats 3 servings of vegetables each day.

I have 7 equal sections, one for each day of the week. Each section shows the number of servings Liam eats each day.

2. Ava bought her first cell phone for $95 and now has a monthly bill. If Ava paid $815 during the first year of having a cell phone, what is the amount of Ava's monthly bill?

Algebraic Equation

Let m represent the amount of Ava's monthly bill.

$$12m + 95 = 815$$
$$12m + 95 - 95 = 815 - 95$$
$$12m = 720$$
$$\left(\frac{1}{12}\right)(12m) = \left(\frac{1}{12}\right)(720)$$
$$m = 60$$

> I know Ava makes 12 equal monthly payments over the course of the year. The sum of her monthly bill and her cell phone will be the amount she paid during the first year.

Ava's monthly bill is $60.

Tape Diagram

> I create a tape diagram that shows 12 equal payments of m plus the cost of the cell phone, $95. The total length of the tape diagram represents the amount Ava paid during the first year, $815.

815

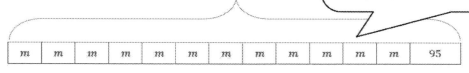

$12m$ $815 - 95 = 720$

                $720 \div 12 = 60$

Ava's monthly bill is $60.

EUREKA
MATH

G7-M2-Lesson 18: Writing, Evaluating, and Finding Equivalent Expressions with Rational Numbers

1. Geraldine receives a weekly allowance. Every week she spends \$2 on snacks at lunch time and saves the rest of her money.

   a. Write an expression that represents the amount Geraldine will save in 8 weeks if she receives a dollars each week for her allowance.

   Let a represent Geraldine's weekly allowance, in dollars.

   $$8(a - 2)$$
   $$8a - 16$$

   > I can apply the distributive property to write an equivalent expression.

   > I know that Geraldine saves her allowance minus the \$2 she spends on snacks for 8 weeks.

   b. If Geraldine receives \$10 each week for her allowance, how much money will she save in 8 weeks?

$8(a - 2)$	**OR**	$8a - 16$
$8(10 - 2)$		$8(10) - 16$
$8(8)$		$80 - 16$
64		64

   Geraldine would save \$64.

   > I now know the value of a and can substitute this value into either of the equivalent expressions.

2. During Nero's last basketball game, he made 6 field goals, 2 three-pointers, and 5 free throws.

   a. Write an expression to represent the total points Nero scored during the game.

   Let f represent the number of points for a field goal, p represent the number of points for a three-pointer, and t represent the number of points for a free throw.

   $$6f + 2p + 5t$$

   > I multiply the number of each type of shot Nero made by the number of points earned for each shot.

b.   Write another expression that is equivalent to the one written above.

$3f + 3f + 2p + 5t$

> There are many options for an equivalent expression. I could have just changed the order of the terms.

c.   If each field goal is worth 2 points, each three-pointer is worth 3 points, and each free throw is worth 1 point, how many total points did Nero score?

$6f + 2p + 5t$

$6(2) + 2(3) + 5(1)$

$12 + 6 + 5$

23

> I substitute each value in for the corresponding variable and use order of operations to evaluate the expression.

Nero scored 23 points.

3.   The seventh grade student council is completing a fundraiser at a track meet. They are selling water bottles for $1.75 but paid $0.50 for each bottle of water. In order to keep the water cold, the student council also purchased a large cooler for $75. The table below shows the earnings, expenses, and profit earned when 80, 90, and 100 water bottles are sold.

Amount of Water Bottles Sold	Earnings (in dollars)	Expenses (in dollars)	Profit (in dollars)
80	$80(1.75) = 140$	$80(0.50) + 75 = 115$	$140 - 115 = 25$
90	$90(1.75) = 157.5$	$90(0.50) + 75 = 120$	$157.5 - 120 = 37.5$
100	$100(1.75) = 175$	$100(0.50) + 75 = 125$	$175 - 125 = 50$

a.   Write an expression that represents the profit (in dollars) the student council earned by selling water bottles at the track meet.

Let w represent the number of water bottles sold.

$$1.75w - 0.5w - 75$$

$$1.25w - 75$$

> The first term shows the earnings. The last two terms are the expenses, so they must be subtracted from the earnings.

> I can collect like terms to write an equivalent expression.

EUREKA MATH

b. How much profit did the student council make if it sold 50 water bottles? What does this mean?
    Explain why this might be the case.

$1.25w - 75$

$1.25(50) - 75$

$62.5 - 75$

-12.5

> The negative value means that the expenses were more than the earnings, which means no profit was made.

The student council did not make any money; in fact, they lost $12.50. Possible reasons could be that it was not too hot and most people brought their own water to the track meet.

c. How much profit did the student council make if it sold 125 water bottles? What does this mean?
    Explain why this might be the case.

$1.25w - 75$

$1.25(125) - 75$

$156.25 - 75$

81.25

> The positive value means that the expenses were less than the earnings, which means a profit was made.

The student council would make a profit of $81.25. The high number of water bottles sold could be explained by extremely hot weather or that most people did not bring enough water to the track meet.

G7-M2-Lesson 19: Writing, Evaluating, and Finding Equivalent Expressions with Rational Numbers

Solve the following problems. If necessary, round to the nearest penny.

1. Viviana is having her birthday party at the movie theater. Eight total people attended the party, and Viviana's parents bough each person a ticket. Viviana's parents also bought all of the drinks and snacks; four people chose a soda, two people chose a slushie, and six people chose a large popcorn.

   a.   Write an expression that can be used to figure out the cost of the birthday party. Include the definitions for the variables Viviana's mom may have used.

   Let t represent the cost of a movie ticket, s represent the cost of a soda, d represent the cost of a slushie, and p represent the cost of a large popcorn.

   $8t + 4s + 2d + 6p$

   > I know that 8 movie tickets were bought, so I multiply 8 by the price of a movie ticket. I follow this same process for the other terms in the expression.

   b.   Viviana's dad wrote down $2(4t + 2s + 3p)$ to determine the total cost of the party. Was he correct? Explain why or why not?

   The expression Viviana's dad wrote is not correct. Although it is possible to apply the distributive property and factor out a 2, he did not complete the process correctly because he dropped a term. There is no longer a term to represent the cost of the slushies. Instead the expression should be $2(4t + 2s + d + 3p)$.

   c.   What is the cost of the party if a movie ticket costs \$9.25, a soda costs \$3.25, a slushie costs \$2.50, and a large popcorn costs \$5.50?

   > I can substitute the known values into the expression from part (a) or the corrected expression in part (b).

   $8t + 4s + 2d + 6p$

   $8(9.25) + 4(3.25) + 2(2.50) + 6(5.50)$

   $74 + 13 + 5 + 33$

   125

   The cost of the birthday party is \$125.

EUREKA MATH™

2. Benson started a resume business. He helps clients create great resumes when they are looking for new jobs. Benson charges each client $50 to create a resume but paid $110 for new computer software to help create fancy resumes.

a. Write an expression to determine Benson's take-home pay after expenses.

Let r represent the number of resumes Benson creates.

$50r - 110$ ⟵ [Benson's only expense is the computer software program.]

b. If Benson help 8 clients create resumes, what was his take-home pay after expenses?

$50r - 110$

$50(8) - 110$

290

Benson's take-home pay would be $290 *after paying his expenses.*

3. Mr. and Mrs. Slater bought some new pillows and used a 10% off coupon that allowed them to save some money. Mr. Slater added the 8% sales tax to the original cost first, and then deducted the coupon savings. Mrs. Slater thought they would save more money if the final cost of the pillows was calculated by deducting the savings from the coupon and then adding the 8% sales tax to the reduced cost.

a. Write an expression to represent each person's scenario if the original price of the pillows was p dollars.

[The sales tax increases the cost of the pillows by 8% of the original cost of the pillows. The coupon decreases the cost of the pillows by 10% of the price of the pillows, including sales tax.]

Mrs. Slater

$(p - 0.10p) + 0.08(p - 0.10p)$

$1.08(p - 0.10p)$

$1.08(0.90p)$

[The coupon decreases the cost of the pillows by 10% of the original cost of the pillows. The sales tax increases the cost of the pillows by 8% of the reduced price of the pillows.]

Mr. Slater

$(p + 0.08p) - 0.10(p + 0.08p)$

$0.90(p + 0.08p)$

$0.90(1.08p)$

b. Explain how both of the expressions are equivalent.

The three factors in the expression are the same, which means the two expressions are equivalent because multiplication is commutative. Both expressions will evaluate to the same value when any number is substituted in for p.

G7-M2-Lesson 20: Investments—Performing Operations with Rational Numbers

A high school basketball team is hosting a family night at one of their games to raise money for new uniforms.

a. The game will be played on January 12, and the cost of admission is $4. Write an expression to represent the total amount of money collected for admission. Evaluate the expression if 476 people attend the basketball game.

Let p represent the number of people who attended the basketball game.

$4p$

$4(476)$

$1,904$ ← This amount represents the deposit in the transaction log in part (c).

If 476 people attend the basketball game, $1,904 would be collected from admission.

b. The following expenses were necessary for the basketball game, and checks were written to pay each company.

   ▪ Referees for the game: *High School Referees Inc.* costs $104 and is paid for on January 8.

   ▪ T-Shirts from *T-Shirt World* for the first 50 fans: Cost of the t-shirts was $5.75 each plus 6% sales tax, and the t-shirts were bought on January 5.

   Write a numerical expression to determine the cost of the t-shirts.

This value represents one of the payments in the transaction log in part (c).

$50(5.75 + 5.75(0.06))$

$50(5.75 + 0.345)$

$50(6.095)$

304.75

I add the sales tax to the original cost of each t-shirt to determine the total cost of each t-shirt and then multiply by the number of shirts needed.

The cost for the t-shirts is $304.75.

EUREKA MATH

c. Complete the transaction log below based on the information presented in parts (a) and (b).

> I subtract the payments from the balance, and I add the deposit to the balance.

Date	Description of Transaction	Payment	Deposit	Balance
	Beginning Balance			876.54
January 5	T-Shirt World	304.75		571.79
January 8	High School Referees Inc.	104.00		467.79
January 12	Game Admission		1,904	2,371.79

Analyze the results.

d. Write an expression to represent the profit earned from the family night. Use the expression to determine the profit if 476 people attend the basketball game.

Let p represent the number of people who attended the basketball game.

$4p - 104 - 304.75$

$4p - 408.75$

> The profit is the amount of money collected in admissions minus all the expenses (cost of the t-shirts and the referees).

$4(476) - 408.75$

$1,495.25$

The profit if 476 people attend the basketball game is $1,495.25.

> The profit matches the transaction log if I calculate the difference between the ending balance and the beginning balance.
>
> $2,371.49 - 876.54 = 1,495.25$

G7-M2-Lesson 21: If-Then Moves with Integer Number Cards

1. Evaluate each expression.

   a. $2 + (-5) + (-8)$ -11

   b. $125 \div (-5) \times 4$ -100

   c. $-10 + 45 \times (-2)$ -100

   > I must follow the order of operations when evaluating expressions.

2. Which expressions from Problem 1 are equivalent?

   Expressions (b) and (c) are equivalent expressions because they both evaluate to the same value.

3. If the two equivalent expressions from Problem 1 are multiplied by 6, write an if-then statement using the properties of equality.

   If $125 \div (-5) \times 4 = -10 + 45 \times (-2)$, *then* $6(125 \div (-5) \times 4) = 6(-10 + 45 \times (-2))$.

   > If I make the same changes to equivalent expressions, then the resulting expressions will still be equivalent.

4. Simplify the expression.

   $3 + (-14) \times 2 \div (-7) - 21$

   $3 + (-28) \div (-7) - 21$

   $3 + 4 - 21$

   -14

   Using the expression, write an equation. $3 + (-14) \times 2 \div (-7) - 21 = -14$

   Rewrite the expression if 4 is subtracted from both expressions.

   $3 + (-14) \times 2 \div (-7) - 21 - 4 = -14 - 4$

   Write an if-then statement using the properties of equality.

   If $3 + (-14) \times 2 \div (-7) - 21 = -14$, *then*

   $3 + (-14) \times 2 \div (-7) - 21 - 4 = -14 - 4.$

© 2015 Great Minds eureka-math.org
G7-M2-HWH-1.3.0-09.2015

EUREKA MATH

G7-M2-Lesson 22: Solving Equations Using Algebra

For each equation below, explain the steps in determining the value of the variable. Then find the value of the variable, showing each step. Write if-then statements to justify each step in solving the equation.

1. $3(y - 2) = -15$

   Multiply both sides of the equation by $\frac{1}{3}$, and then add 2 to both sides of the equation, $y = -3$.

   If: $3(y - 2) = -15$

   Then: $\frac{1}{3}(3(y - 2)) = \frac{1}{3}(-15)$ ◄─── I use the multiplication property of equality using the multiplicative inverse of 3.

   If: $1(y - 2) = -5$ ─── I recognize the multiplicative identity.

   Then: $y - 2 = -5$

   If: $y - 2 = -5$ ─── I use the addition property of equality by using the additive inverse of -2.

   Then: $y - 2 + 2 = -5 + 2$

   If: $y + 0 = -3$ ─── I recognize the additive identity.

   Then: $y = -3$

2. $2 = \frac{3}{4}a + 8$

   Subtract 8 from both sides of the equation, and then multiply both sides of the equation by $\frac{4}{3}$, $a = -8$.

   If: $2 = \frac{3}{4}a + 8$ ─── The variable is on the right side of the equation, so I need to look at the right side of the equation to determine how to solve.

   Then: $2 - 8 = \frac{3}{4}a + 8 - 8$

   If: $-6 = \frac{3}{4}a + 0$

   Then: $-6 = \frac{3}{4}a$

   If: $-6 = \frac{3}{4}a$ ─── The multiplicative inverse of $\frac{3}{4}$ is $\frac{4}{3}$.

   Then: $\frac{4}{3}(-6) = \frac{4}{3}\left(\frac{3}{4}a\right)$

   If: $-8 = 1a$

   Then: $-8 = a$

G7-M2-Lesson 23: Solving Equations Using Algebra

1. Solve the equation algebraically using if-then statements to justify your steps.

$5 = \frac{-5+d}{3}$

If: $5 = \frac{-5+d}{3}$

> Dividing by 3 is the same as multiplying by $\frac{1}{3}$.
> The multiplicative inverse of $\frac{1}{3}$ is 3.

Then: $3(5) = 3\left(\frac{-5+d}{3}\right)$

If: $15 = 1(-5+d)$

Then: $15 = -5+d$

If: $15 = -5+d$

Then: $15+5 = -5+5+d$

If: $20 = 0+d$

Then: $20 = d$

For Problems 2-3, write an equation to represent each word problem. Solve the equation showing the steps, and then state the value of the variable in the context of the situation.

2. Julianne works two part-time jobs. She waters her neighbor's plants every day for 1 hour. Julianne also babysits every day. She continues the same schedule for 8 days and works a total of 32 hours. How many hours does Julianne babysit each day?

    Let b represent the number of hours Julianne babysits each day.

    $8(b+1) = 32$

    If: $8(b+1) = 32$

    > I could have applied the distributive property and then used properties of equality to solve for the missing variable.

    Then: $\frac{1}{8}(8(b+1)) = \frac{1}{8}(32)$

    If: $1(b+1) = 4$

    Then: $b+1 = 4$

    If: $b+1 = 4$

    > If more explanation on solving equations is needed, I can refer back to Lesson 22.

    Then: $b+1-1 = 4-1$

    If: $b+0 = 3$

    Then: $b = 3$

    Julianne babysits for 3 hours each day.

EUREKA
MATH™

3. Vince is thinking of joining a new gym and would have to pay a $55 sign-up fee plus monthly payments of $35. If Vince can only afford to pay $265 for a gym membership, for how many months can he be a member?

   Let m represent the number of months Vince can afford to be a member of the gym.

   $55 + 35m = 265$

   If: $55 + 35m = 265$

   Then: $55 - 55 + 35m = 265 - 55$

   If: $0 + 35m = 210$

   Then: $35m = 210$

   If: $35m = 210$

   Then: $\frac{1}{35}(35m) = \frac{1}{35}(210)$

   If: $1m = 6$

   Then: $m = 6$

   Vince can be a member of the gym for 6 months.

   > I know the sign-up fee is a one-time payment, and then Vince has to pay $35 every month.

Grade 7
Module 3

G7-M3-Lesson 1: Generating Equivalent Expressions

1. Write an equivalent expression by combining like terms. Verify the equivalence of your expression and the given expression by evaluating each for the given value: $m = -3$.

$4m + 7 + m - 9$

$4m + 1m + 7 - 9$

$5m - 2$

> I can rearrange the terms so that I have like terms together. I can also place a 1 in front of the m to make it easier to add $4m + m$.

> Next, I will replace all of the m's in the original expression and the new expression with -3 and evaluate to see if I get the same result.

Check:

$4(-3) + 7 + (-3) - 9$

$-12 + 7 + (-3) + (-9)$

-17

$5(-3) - 2$

$-15 + (-2)$

-17

The expressions $4m + 7 + m - 9$ and $5m - 2$ are equivalent.

2. Use any order and any grouping to write an equivalent expression by combining like terms. Then, verify the equivalence of your expression to the given expression by evaluating for the value(s) given.

$9(2j) + 6(-7k) + 6(-j)$; for $j = \frac{1}{2}$, $k = \frac{1}{3}$

$9(2j) + 6(-7k) + 6(-j)$

$(9)(2)(j) + (6)(-7)(k) + (6)(-1)(j)$

$18j + (-42k) + (-6j)$

$18j + (-6j) + (-42k)$

$12j - 42k$

> I can multiply in any order, which means I can multiply the 9 and 2 together first for the term $9(2j)$.

Check:

$9(2j) + 6(-7k) + 6(-j)$

$9\left(2 \times \dfrac{1}{2}\right) + 6\left(-7 \times \dfrac{1}{3}\right) + 6\left(-\dfrac{1}{2}\right)$

$9(1) + 6\left(-\dfrac{7}{3}\right) + (-3)$

$9 + \left(-\dfrac{42}{3}\right) + (-3)$

$9 + (-14) + (-3)$

-8

> I evaluate both expressions using the given values for each variable. If I don't get the same result, I might have made an error somewhere in my work.

$12j - 42k$

$12\left(\dfrac{1}{2}\right) + (-42)\left(\dfrac{1}{3}\right)$

$6 + (-14)$

-8

> I can go back to Module 2 for a review on how to work with signed rational numbers.

Both expressions are equivalent.

3. Meredith, Jodi, and Clive were finding the sum of $(5x + 8)$ and $-3x$. Meredith wrote the expression $2x + 8$, Jodi wrote $8x + 2$, and Clive wrote $8 + 2x$. Which person(s) was correct and why?

Let $x = 2$

$(5x + 8) + (-3x)$

$5(2) + 8 + (-3(2))$

$10 + 8 + (-6)$

12

> I could test the equivalence by picking any value for x and evaluating each expression.

Meredith

$2x + 8$

$2(2) + 8$

$4 + 8$

12

> I will replace all the x's in the original expression and the three possible expressions to see if I get the same result.

Lesson 1:   Generating Equivalent Expressions

EUREKA MATH™

Jodi

$8x + 2$

$8(2) + 2$

$16 + 2$

18

> Jodi's expression is the only one that did not result in 12 when I evaluated each expression.

Clive

$8 + 2x$

$8 + 2(2)$

$8 + 4$

12

Meredith and Clive are correct. Their expressions are the same, just in different orders. Jodi's expression is incorrect.

G7-M3-Lesson 2: Generating Equivalent Expressions

1. Write each expression in standard form. Verify that your expression is equivalent to the one given by evaluating both expressions for the given value of the variable.

   a. $5x + (4x - 9); x = 3$

   $5x + 4x + (-9)$

   $9x + (-9)$

   $9x - 9$

   > Because I am adding, I need to combine like terms.
   > $$5x + 4x = 9x$$
   > I can't combine $9x$ and (-9) because they are not like terms.

   Check:

$5x + (4x - 9)$	$9x - 9$
$5(3) + (4(3) - 9)$	$9(3) - 9$
$15 + (12 - 9)$	$27 - 9$
$15 + 3$	18
18	

   > To verify that the expressions are equivalent, I replace the x in the original expression and the expression in standard form with a 3 and then evaluate. When I get the same thing for both expressions, I know that they are equivalent.

   Both expressions are equivalent.

   b. $7x - (4 - 2x); x = -5$

   > The opposite of the sum can be written as the sum of the opposites.

   $7x + \left(-(4 + (-2x))\right)$

   $7x + (-4) + 2x$

   $7x + 2x - 4$

   $9x - 4$

   > I can change subtraction to adding the opposite.

   Check:

$7x - (4 - 2x)$	$9x - 4$
$7(-5) - (4 - 2(-5))$	$9(-5) - 4$
$-35 - (4 + 10)$	$-45 - 4$
$-35 - (14)$	$-45 + (-4)$
$-35 + (-14)$	-49
-49	

   > I can look back to Module 2 for help with order of operations and integers.

   These expressions are equivalent.

EUREKA
MATH

c. $(11g + 7h - 8) - (3g - 9h + 6);\ g = -3$ and $h = 4$

$(11g + 7h - 8) + (-(3g + (-9h) + 6))$

$(11g + 7h - 8) + (-3g + 9h - 6)$

$11g + (-3g) + 7h + 9h + (-8) + (-6)$

$8g + 16h + (-14)$

$8g + 16h - 14$

> Even though there are two variables, I can still write the expression in standard form by combining like terms.

> This expression is in standard form because none of the terms are like terms.

> I need to be careful here and use -3 for g and 4 for h. If I put the numbers in the wrong spots, my solution will be incorrect.

Check:

$(11g + 7h - 8) - (3g - 9h + 6)$

$(11(-3) + 7(4) + (-8)) - (3(-3) + (-9(4)) + 6)$

$(-33 + 28 + (-8)) - (-9 + (-36) + 6)$ $8g + 16h - 14$

$(-5 + (-8)) - (-45 + 6)$ $8(-3) + 16(4) + (-14)$

$-13 - (-39)$ $-24 + 64 + (-14)$

$-13 + 39$ $40 + (-14)$

26 26

The expressions are equivalent.

> I can use the same properties when I am verifying that the expressions are equivalent as I did when I was simplifying.

d. $-3(8v) + 2y(15); \; v = \frac{1}{4}, y = \frac{2}{3}$

$(-3)(8)v + 2(15)y$

$-24v + 30y$

> I can multiply in any order. So $2y(15)$ could also be $2(15)y$, giving me $30y$.

Check:

$-3(8v) + 2y(15)$ $-24v + 30y$

$-3\left(8\left(\frac{1}{4}\right)\right) + 2\left(\frac{2}{3}\right)(15)$ $-24\left(\frac{1}{4}\right) + 30\left(\frac{2}{3}\right)$

$-3(2) + 2(10)$ $-6 + 20$

$-6 + 20$ 14

14

The expressions are equivalent.

e. $32xy \div 8y; \; x = -\frac{1}{2}, y = 3$

$32xy \times \left(\frac{1}{8y}\right)$

> Dividing is equivalent to multiplying by the reciprocal. So I can rewrite this problem as a multiplication expression.

$\dfrac{32xy}{8y}$

> I can use the "any order, any grouping" property in order to break apart the factors and simplify.

$\dfrac{32}{8} \cdot \dfrac{x}{1} \cdot \dfrac{y}{y}$

$4x$

Check:

$32xy \div 8y$ $4x$

$32\left(-\frac{1}{2}\right)(3) \div 8(3)$ $4\left(-\frac{1}{2}\right)$

$-48 \div 24$ -2

-2

The expressions are equivalent.

EUREKA
MATH

2. Doug and Romel are placing apples in baskets to sell at the farm stand. They are putting x apples in each basket. When they are finished, Doug has 23 full baskets and has 7 extra apples, and Romel has 19 full baskets and has 3 extra apples. Write an expression in standard form that represents the number of apples the boys started with. Explain what your expression means.

> I can represent the number of apples Doug had with the expression $23x + 7$ because he put x apples in 23 baskets.

> For Romel, I will use $19x + 3$ because he filled 19 baskets with x apples each. Now I need to add together the number of apples each boy had.

$$23x + 7 + 19x + 3$$

$$23x + 19x + 7 + 3$$

$$42x + 10$$

This means that altogether they have 42 baskets with x apples in each, plus another 10 leftover apples.

3. The area of the pictured rectangle below is $36h$ ft^2. Its width is $4h$ ft. Find the height of the rectangle, and name any properties used with the appropriate step.

> I was given the area and the width, so I need to divide to find the height.

$$36h \div 4h$$

Multiplying by the reciprocal $36h \times \dfrac{1}{4h}$

Multiplication $\dfrac{36h}{4h}$

Any order, any grouping $\dfrac{36}{4} \cdot \dfrac{h}{h}$

$9 \cdot 1$

9

The height of the rectangle is 9 feet.

> I need to name the properties that I used with each step. I remember doing this in Lessons 8, 9, and 16 of Module 2 and can reference these lessons for some examples of how I did this before.

(rectangle: width labeled $4h$ ft. across top, height labeled _____ ft. on left, area $36h$ ft^2 inside)

G7-M3-Lesson 3: Writing Products as Sums and Sums as Products

1.

   a. Write two equivalent expressions that represent the rectangular array below.

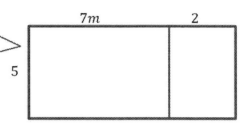

I know that area of a rectangle is length times width. So I can write an expression showing the length, $(7m + 2)$, times the width, 5.

$$5(7m + 2) = 35m + 10$$

I can use the distributive property to rewrite my first expression. I just have to remember to multiply 5 times $7m$ and 5 times 2.

   b. Verify informally that the two expressions are equivalent using substitution.

   Let $m = 2$

$5(7m + 2)$
$5(7(2) + 2)$
$5(14 + 2)$
$5(16)$
80

   $35m + 10$
   $35(2) + 10$
   $70 + 10$
   80

   To verify that these two expressions are equivalent, I can pick any value I want for m and then substitute it into both expressions to make sure they both give me the same value, just like I did in Lesson 2.

   c. Use a rectangular array to write the product $3(2h + 6g + 4k)$ in standard form.

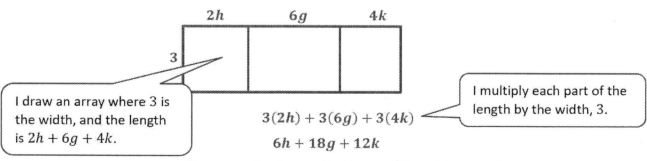

I draw an array where 3 is the width, and the length is $2h + 6g + 4k$.

$3(2h) + 3(6g) + 3(4k)$
$6h + 18g + 12k$

I multiply each part of the length by the width, 3.

The expression in standard form is $6h + 18g + 12k$.

EUREKA
MATH

2. Use the distributive property to write the products in standard form.

a. $(3m + 5n - 6p)4$

This problem is written a little differently than the others. It is still asking me to distribute the 4 to all terms inside the parentheses.

$4(3m + 5n - 6p)$

$4(3m) + 4(5n) + 4(-6p)$

$12m + 20n - 24p$

I can rewrite the problem with the 4 in the front if that makes it easier for me to simplify.

b. $(64h + 40g) \div 8$

I can rewrite the division as multiplication by the reciprocal.

$\dfrac{1}{8}(64h + 40g)$

$\dfrac{1}{8}(64h) + \dfrac{1}{8}(40g)$

$\dfrac{64}{8}h + \dfrac{40}{8}g$

$8h + 5g$

I need to use the distributive property twice in this problem.

c. $7(4x - 1) + 3(5x + 9)$

$7(4x) + 7(-1) + 3(5x) + 3(9)$

$28x + (-7) + 15x + 27$

$28x + 15x + 27 + (-7)$

$43x + 20$

I combine like terms after applying the distributive property.

3. You and your friend are in charge of buying supplies for the next school dance. Each package of balloons costs \$2, and each string of lights costs \$8. Write an equation that represents the total amount spent, S, if b represents the number of packages of balloons purchased and l represents the number of strings of lights purchased. Explain the equation in words.

$$S = 2b + 8l \quad \text{or} \quad S = 2(b + 4l)$$

> I notice that the terms in the first equation have a common factor, which means I can write this equation a second way, by dividing out the common factor from each term and writing it outside the parentheses.

The total amount spent can be determined by multiplying the number of packages of balloons purchased by two and then adding that to the product of the number of strings of lights and eight.

The total amount spent can also be determined by adding the number of packages of balloons purchased to four times the number of strings of lights purchased and then multiplying the sum by two.

EUREKA
MATH

G7-M3-Lesson 4: Writing Products as Sums and Sums as Products

> I need to write my answer showing two expressions that are being multiplied together.

1. Write each expression as the product of two factors.

   a. $k \cdot 5 + m \cdot 5$

      $5(k + m)$

   > I see that both of the addends have a common factor of 5. I can figure out what will still be inside of the parentheses by dividing both terms by 5.

   b. $(d + e) + (d + e) + (d + e) + (d + e)$

      $4(d + e)$

   > I know that repeated addition can be written as multiplication.

   c. $4h + (8 + h) + 3 \cdot 4$

      $4h + 8 + h + 12$

      $5h + 20$

      $5(h + 4)$

   > I must simplify this expression before I can try to write it as the product of two factors.

2. Write each expression in standard form.

   a. $-8(7y - 3z + 5)$

      $-8(7y) + (-8)(-3z) + (-8)(5)$

      $-56y + 24z - 40$

   > To be in standard form, I need to rewrite this expression without the parentheses. I can distribute the -8 to all terms inside.

   b. $4 - 2(-8h - 3)$

      $4 + \left(-2(-8h - 3)\right)$

      $4 + (-2)(-8h) + (-2)(-3)$

      $4 + 16h + 6$

      $10 + 16h$

   > I need to follow the correct order of operations, which means I need to distribute the -2 before I subtract.

3. Use the following rectangular array to answer the questions below.

The height is the greatest common factor of all three products. I determine the greatest common factor and then divide the products by the greatest common factor to determine the lengths.

	$2j$	$7k$	$10m$
5	$10j$	$35k$	$50m$

a. Fill in the missing information.

b. Write the sum represented in the rectangular array.

$$10j + 35k + 50m$$

I can add the area of each section of the array to write the sum.

c. Use the missing information from part (a) to write the sum from part (b) as a product of two factors.

$$5(2j) + 5(7k) + 5(10m)$$

$$5(2j + 7k + 10m)$$

I need to show that 5 is being multiplied by each length without having to write "times 5" three times.

4. Combine like terms to write each expression in standard form.

$$(-m - n) - (m - n)$$

I know I can rewrite all of the subtraction as adding the opposite.

$$-m + (-n) + (-(m - n))$$

$$-m + (-n) + (-m) + n$$

$$-m + (-m) + (-n) + n$$

$$-2m$$

In the end, I have to add opposites.

$$(-n) + n = 0$$

EUREKA MATH

5. Kathy is a professional dog walker. She must walk the dogs 6 days a week. During each day of walking, she drinks 1 bottle of tea and 3 bottles of water. Let t represent the ounces of tea she drinks and w represent the ounces of water she drinks from each bottle of water. Write two different expressions that represent the total number of ounces Kathy drank in one week while walking the dogs. Explain how each expression describes the situation in a different way.

> In one day, Kathy will drink t ounces of tea and $w + w + w$ or $3w$ ounces of water from the three water bottles. That is $t + 3w$ ounces in one day.

$6(t + 3w)$

Kathy drinks tea and water during walks on six different days, so the total ounces is six times the quantity of the water and tea that Kathy drank each day.

$6(t) + 6(3w)$

$6t + 18w$

There are 6 bottles of tea and 18 bottles of water total. The total amount that Kathy drank will be six times the ounces in one bottle of tea plus 18 times the ounces in one bottle of water.

© 2015 Great Minds eureka-math.org
G7-M3-HWH-1.3.0-09.2015

G7-M3-Lesson 5: Using the Identity and Inverse to Write Equivalent Expressions

1. Fill in the missing parts.

The product of $\frac{1}{3}g + 4$ and the multiplicative inverse of $\frac{1}{3}$

> The first part has been set up for me, and it shows that 3 is the multiplicative inverse of $\frac{1}{3}$.

> I see that the column on the left shows the steps, and the column on the right shows the properties that describe the steps.

$$\left(\tfrac{1}{3}g + 4\right)(3)$$
$$\underline{\tfrac{1}{3}g(3) + 4(3)}$$ Distributive property

$$1g + 12$$ *Multiplicative inverse; multiplication*

$$\underline{g + 12}$$ Multiplicative identity property of one

> Here, I can rewrite the expression without the 1 because g and $1g$ are equivalent expressions.

2. Write the sum, and then rewrite the expression in standard form by removing parentheses and collecting like terms.

   a. 13 and $4w - 13$

   $$13 + (4w - 13)$$
   $$13 + 4w + (-13)$$

   > I can rewrite subtraction as adding the opposite so that all terms are being added.

   $$13 + (-13) + 4w$$
   $$4w$$

   > I use the additive inverse property, showing that a number and its inverse have a sum of 0.

   b. The opposite of $5m$ and $9 + 5m$

   $$-5m + (9 + 5m)$$
   $$-5m + 5m + 9$$

   > Because this question says "the opposite of $5m$," I use the opposite sign, making the term $-5m$.

   $$9$$

c. $7y$ and the opposite of $(3 - 8y)$

$7y + \left(-(3 - 8y)\right)$

$7y + \left(-(3 + (-8y))\right)$

$7y + (-3) + (8y)$

$7y + 8y - 3$

$15y - 3$

> I remember that the opposite of a sum is the same as the sum of its opposites.

3. Write the product, and then rewrite the expression in standard form by removing parentheses and collecting like terms.

The multiplicative inverse of -8 and $24g - 8$

> A multiplicative inverse has the same sign of the given number but is the reciprocal.

$-\dfrac{1}{8}(24g - 8)$

$-\dfrac{1}{8}(24g + (-8))$

$-\dfrac{1}{8}(24g) + \left(-\dfrac{1}{8}\right)(-8)$

$-3g + 1$

> When I multiply multiplicative inverses, I get 1.

4. Write the expression in standard form.

$$\dfrac{5}{8}(7x + 4) + 2$$

$$\dfrac{5}{8}(7x) + \dfrac{5}{8}(4) + 2$$

$$\dfrac{5}{8}\left(\dfrac{7}{1}\right)x + \left(\dfrac{5}{8}\right)\left(\dfrac{4}{1}\right) + 2$$

$$\dfrac{35}{8}x + \dfrac{20}{8} + 2$$

$$\dfrac{35}{8}x + \dfrac{5}{2} + \dfrac{4}{2}$$

$$\dfrac{35}{8}x + \dfrac{9}{2}$$

> I only distribute the $\dfrac{5}{8}$ to the terms inside the parentheses.

> I can rewrite the constant terms so they have common denominators in order to add like terms.

G7-M3-Lesson 6: Collecting Rational Number Like Terms

1. Write the indicated expression.

   a. $\frac{2}{5}k$ inches in yards

   $\frac{2}{5}k \times \frac{1}{36}$

   > I know that there are 36 inches in a yard. That means that 1 inch is $\frac{1}{36}$ of a yard.

   $\left(\frac{2}{5}\right)\left(\frac{1}{36}\right)k$

   > Multiplication is commutative, which means I can multiply in any order and still get the same answer.

   $\frac{2}{180}k$

   $\frac{1}{90}k$

   $\frac{2}{5}k$ inches is equal to $\frac{1}{90}k$ yards.

   b. The average speed of a bike rider that travels $3m$ miles in $\frac{5}{8}$ hour

   $$R = \frac{D}{T}$$

   > I know that distance is equal to the rate multiplied by the time. I can write this formula so that I am solving for the rate instead.

   $$R = \frac{3m}{\frac{5}{8}}$$

   > The complex fraction is really showing two values that are being divided.

   $$R = \frac{3m}{1} \div \frac{5}{8}$$

   $$R = \frac{3m}{1} \times \frac{8}{5}$$

   $$R = \frac{24m}{5}$$

   The average speed of the bike rider is $\frac{24m}{5}$ miles per hour.

EUREKA MATH

2. Rewrite the expression by collecting like terms.

a. $\dfrac{b}{5} - \dfrac{3b}{4} + 2$

> Before I can collect like terms, I need to get common denominators.

$\dfrac{4b}{20} - \dfrac{15b}{20} + 2$

$\dfrac{4b}{20} + \left(-\dfrac{15b}{20}\right) + 2$

$-\dfrac{11b}{20} + 2$

> I must collect like terms by combining the terms with the same variable part. To do this, I need to find common denominators for each set of like terms.

b. $\dfrac{2}{3}k - k - \dfrac{5}{6}k + \dfrac{4}{5} - \dfrac{3}{5}m + 3\dfrac{1}{10}m$

$\dfrac{4}{6}k - \dfrac{6}{6}k - \dfrac{5}{6}k + \dfrac{4}{5} - \dfrac{6}{10}m + \dfrac{31}{10}m$

$-\dfrac{7}{6}k + \dfrac{25}{10}m + \dfrac{4}{5}$

> Before I can collect like terms, I must apply the distributive property.

c. $\dfrac{2}{3}(g + 5) - \dfrac{1}{4}(8g + 1)$

$\dfrac{2}{3}(g) + \dfrac{2}{3}(5) + \left(-\dfrac{1}{4}\right)(8g) + \left(-\dfrac{1}{4}\right)(1)$

$\dfrac{2}{3}g + \dfrac{10}{3} + (-2g) + \left(-\dfrac{1}{4}\right)$

> I can apply the commutative property to change the order so that the like terms are together.

$\dfrac{2}{3}g + (-2g) + \dfrac{10}{3} + \left(-\dfrac{1}{4}\right)$

$\dfrac{2}{3}g + \left(-\dfrac{6}{3}g\right) + \dfrac{40}{12} + \left(-\dfrac{3}{12}\right)$

$-\dfrac{4}{3}g + \dfrac{37}{12}$

© 2015 Great Minds eureka-math.org
G7-M3-HWH-1.3.0-09.2015

d. $\dfrac{5y}{3} + \dfrac{2y+1}{4} - \dfrac{y-7}{2}$

$\dfrac{5y}{3} + \dfrac{2y+1}{4} + \left(-\left(\dfrac{y-7}{2} \right) \right)$

> I remember that the opposite of a sum is the same as the sum of its opposites.

$\dfrac{5y}{3} + \dfrac{2y+1}{4} + \dfrac{-y+7}{2}$

> Getting common denominators will make it easier to collect the like terms in the numerator.

$\dfrac{4(5y)}{4(3)} + \dfrac{3(2y+1)}{3(4)} + \dfrac{6(-y+7)}{6(2)}$

$\dfrac{20y}{12} + \dfrac{6y+3}{12} + \dfrac{-6y+42}{12}$

$\dfrac{20y + 6y - 6y + 3 + 42}{12}$

$\dfrac{20y + 45}{12}$

> Or, I could write my answer as $\dfrac{5y}{3} + \dfrac{15}{4}$.

     Lesson 6:   Collecting Rational Number Like Terms

© 2015 Great Minds eureka-math.org
G7-M3-HWH-1.3.0-09.2015

EUREKA MATH

G7-M3-Lesson 7: Understanding Equations

1. Check whether the given value of h is a solution to the equation. Justify your answer.

$$4(2h - 3) = 6 + 2h \qquad h = 3$$

> I need to replace all of the h's with 3 and evaluate each side of the equation.

> Because both expressions are equal to 12 when $h = 3$, I know that $h = 3$ is a solution to the equation. If the value of each expression were not equal, I would know that the number substituted in for h was not a solution.

$$4(2(3) - 3) = 6 + 2(3)$$
$$4(6 - 3) = 6 + 6$$
$$4(3) = 12$$
$$12 = 12$$

Felix is trying to create a number puzzle for his friend to solve. He challenges his friend to find the mystery number. "When 8 is added to one-third of a number, the result is -2." The equation to represent the mystery number is $\frac{1}{3}x + 8 = -2$. Felix's friend tries to guess the mystery number. Her first guess is -18. Is she correct? Why or why not?

$$\frac{1}{3}x + 8 = -2$$
$$\frac{1}{3}(-18) + 8 = -2$$
$$\frac{1}{3}\left(-\frac{18}{1}\right) + 8 = -2$$
$$-\frac{18}{3} + 8 = -2$$
$$-6 + 8 = -2$$
$$2 = -2$$

False

> If I cannot remember how to work with integers, I can go back to the beginning of Module 2 for help.

> I know that 2 and -2 are opposites, which means they are not equal. So, this is not a true statement.

She is not correct. The number -18 will not make a true statement. Therefore, it cannot be a solution.

2. The sum of three consecutive integers is 57.

a. Find the smallest integer using a tape diagram.

> Consecutive means that the numbers follow each other in order, like 4, 5, 6.

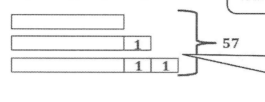

57

> I need to show that each number is one bigger than the number before it.

> After I subtract the "1" pieces, I am left with 3 equal sized unknown pieces, so I divide by 3 to determine the size of each unknown piece.

$57 - 3 = 54$

$54 \div 3 = 18$

The smallest integer would be 18.

b. Let x represent the smallest integer. Write an equation that can be used to find the smallest integer.

Smallest integer: x

2nd integer: $(x + 1)$

3rd integer: $(x + 2)$

> I can use my tape diagram to help me set up expressions for each of the consecutive integers.

Sum of the three consecutive integers: $x + (x + 1) + (x + 2)$

Equation: $x + (x + 1) + (x + 2) = 57$

> Next, I need to show that when I add all of the integers together, I get 57.

c. Will 18 also be a solution to the equation in part (b)?

> I will replace x with 18 and test it out.

$$x + (x + 1) + (x + 2) = 57$$
$$18 + (18 + 1) + (18 + 2) = 57$$
$$18 + 19 + 20 = 57$$
$$57 = 57$$

> Here, I can see that I am finding the sum of three consecutive numbers, 18, 19, and 20.

Yes, 18 is also a solution to the equation.

Lesson 7:   Understanding Equations

© 2015 Great Minds eureka-math.org
G7-M3-HWH-1.3.0-09.2015

EUREKA MATH

G7-M3-Lesson 8: Using If-Then Moves in Solving Equations

1. Four times the sum of three consecutive odd integers is -84. Find the integers.

> Consecutive odd integers would be like $1, 3, 5, \ldots$ Each number is 2 more than the one before.

Let n represent the first odd integer; then $n + 2$ and $n + 4$ represent the next two consecutive odd integers.

$$4(n + (n + 2) + (n + 4)) = -84$$
$$4(3n + 6) = -84$$
$$12n + 24 = -84$$
$$12n + 24 - 24 = -84 - 24$$
$$12n = -108$$
$$n = -9$$

> I need to collect like terms and use the distributive property when solving.

> I can go back to the expressions for each integer and substitute in the -9 for the value of n to determine the other consecutive integers.

$$-9 + 2 = -7$$
$$-9 + 4 = -5$$

The integers are $-9, -7,$ and -5.

EUREKA MATH

© 2015 Great Minds eureka-math.org
G7-M3-HWH-1.3.0-09.2015

2. A number is 11 greater than $\frac{2}{3}$ another number. If the sum of the numbers is 31, find the numbers.

> I only want to use one variable, so I need to write an expression for the first number based on how it is related to the other number.

Let n represent a number; then $\frac{2}{3}n + 11$ represents the other number.

> Rewriting some of the terms in equivalent forms, like n as $\frac{3}{3}n$, will make it easier to collect like terms.

$$n + \left(\frac{2}{3}n + 11\right) = 31$$

$$\left(n + \frac{2}{3}n\right) + 11 = 31$$

$$\left(\frac{3}{3}n + \frac{2}{3}n\right) + 11 = 31$$

$$\frac{5}{3}n + 11 = 31$$

$$\frac{5}{3}n + 11 - 11 = 31 - 11$$

$$\frac{5}{3}n + 0 = 20$$

$$\frac{5}{3}n = 20$$

$$\frac{3}{5} \cdot \frac{5}{3}n = \frac{3}{5} \cdot 20$$

$$1n = 3 \cdot 4$$

$$n = 12$$

Since the numbers sum to 31, they are 12 and 19.

EUREKA MATH

3. Lukas filled 6.5 more boxes than Charlotte, and Xin filled 8 fewer than Lukas. Together, they filled 50 boxes. How many boxes did each person fill?

> There are three different people mentioned here. Lukas is being compared to Charlotte, but I don't know anything about how many Charlotte filled, so I will call it n.

Let n represent the number of boxes Charlotte filled.

Then, $(n + 6.5)$ will represent the number of boxes Lukas filled.

And $\left((n + 6.5) - 8\right)$ or $(n - 1.5)$ will represent the number of boxes Xin filled.

> Simplifying the expression for Xin now will make it easier to work with later.

$$n + (n + 6.5) + (n - 1.5) = 50$$
$$n + n + n + 6.5 - 1.5 = 50$$
$$3n + 5 = 50$$
$$3n + 5 - 5 = 50 - 5$$
$$3n = 45$$
$$\left(\frac{1}{3}\right)(3n) = \left(\frac{1}{3}\right)(45)$$
$$n = 15$$

> The equation I write should be Charlotte's expression + Lukas' expression + Xin's expression = 50. Then I replace the people's names with expressions that represent how many boxes they filled.

$15 + 6.5 = 21.5$

$15 - 1.5 = 13.5$

$15 + 21.5 + 13.5 = 50$

If the total number of boxes filled was 50, then Charlotte filled 15 boxes, Lukas filled 21.5 boxes, and Xin filled 13.5 boxes.

© 2015 Great Minds eureka-math.org
G7-M3-HWH-1.3.0-09.2015

4. A preschool teacher plans her class to include 30 minutes on the playground, $\frac{1}{4}$ of the daily class time on a craft/project, and the remaining practice time working on skills, reading, and math. The teacher planned 75 minutes for the playground and craft/project time. How long, in hours, is a day of preschool?

The duration of the entire preschool day: x hours

The problem says to give the time in hours. I know that there are 60 minutes in an hour. I can write the minutes given in terms of hours by placing them in a fraction with 60 in the denominator.

I can simplify fractions to have common denominators to make it easier to collect the like terms.

$$\frac{1}{4}x + \frac{30}{60} = \frac{75}{60}$$

$$\frac{1}{4}x + \frac{2}{4} = \frac{5}{4}$$

$$\frac{1}{4}x + \frac{2}{4} - \frac{2}{4} = \frac{5}{4} - \frac{2}{4}$$

$$\frac{1}{4}x = \frac{3}{4}$$

$$\left(\frac{4}{1}\right)\left(\frac{1}{4}x\right) = \frac{3}{4}\left(\frac{4}{1}\right)$$

$$x = \frac{12}{4}$$

$$x = 3$$

Preschool is 3 hours long each day.

EUREKA MATH™

G7-M3-Lesson 9: Using If-Then Moves in Solving Equations

1. Holly's grandfather is 52 years older than her. In 7 years, the sum of their ages will be 70. Find Holly's present age.

    Let x represents Holly's age now in years.

	Now	*7 years later*
Holly	x	$x + 7$
Grandfather	$x + 52$	$(x + 52) + 7$

    The question mentions now and 7 years later. I can make a table to organize the information provided to help me create an equation to model the situation.

    $$x + 7 + x + 52 + 7 = 70$$
    $$x + x + 7 + 52 + 7 = 70$$
    $$2x + 66 = 70$$
    $$2x + 66 - 66 = 70 - 66$$
    $$2x = 4$$
    $$\left(\frac{1}{2}\right)(2x) = \left(\frac{1}{2}\right)(4)$$
    $$x = 2$$

    I was given the sum after 7 years, so I will use the third column in the table to form the equation.

    Holly's present age is 2 years old.

2. The sum of two numbers is 63, and their difference is 7. Find the numbers.

Let x represent one of the two numbers.

Let 63 − x represent the other number.

This question tells me about the sum and the difference. I use the sum to set up the "let" statements and the difference to write the equation that models the situation.

If two numbers have a sum of 63, and I take one number away from 63, I will get the other number. I can check this by adding them together.

$$x + (63 - x) = x - x + 63 = 63$$

$$x - (63 - x) = 7$$
$$x + \left(-(63 - x)\right) = 7$$
$$x + (-63 + x) = 7$$
$$x + (-63) + x = 7$$
$$2x - 63 = 7$$
$$2x - 63 + 63 = 7 + 63$$
$$2x = 70$$
$$\left(\frac{1}{2}\right)(2x) = \left(\frac{1}{2}\right)(70)$$
$$x = 35$$

$63 - 35 = 28$

The numbers are 35 and 28.

EUREKA MATH

3. Carmen is planning a party to introduce people to her new products for sale. She bought 500 gifts bags to hold party favors and 500 business cards. Each gift bag costs 57 cents more than each business card. If Carmen's total order costs $315, find the cost of each gift bag and business card.

> This question gives money in cents and money in dollars, but I need common units, so I write both of the amounts in dollars.

Let b represent the cost of a business card.

Then, the cost of a gift bag in dollars is $b + 0.57$.

> Because she bought 500 of both items, I can use the distributive property to write this equation.

$$500(b + b + 0.57) = 315$$
$$500(2b + 0.57) = 315$$
$$1,000b + 285 = 315$$
$$1,000b + 285 - 285 = 315 - 285$$
$$1,000b = 30$$
$$\left(\frac{1}{1,000}\right)(1,000b) = \left(\frac{1}{1,000}\right)(30)$$
$$b = 0.03$$

> Because this question deals with money, it will be helpful to convert from fraction to decimal.

$0.03 + 0.57 = 0.60$

A business card costs $0.03, and a gift bag costs $0.60.

4. A group of friends left for vacation in two vehicles at the same time. One car traveled an average speed of 4 miles per hour faster than the other. When the first car arrived at the destination after $8\frac{1}{4}$ hours of driving, both cars had driven a total of 1,006.5 miles. If the second car continues at the same average speed, how much time, to the nearest minute, will it take before the second car arrives?

> The 1,006.5 miles doesn't represent the total miles driven for the whole trip. Instead, this is the amount that both cars drove in $8\frac{1}{4}$ hours. The second car hasn't arrived at the destination yet.

Let r represent the speed in miles per hour of the faster car; then $r - 4$ represents the speed in miles per hour of the slower car.

$$8\frac{1}{4}(r) + 8\frac{1}{4}(r - 4) = 1,006.5$$

$$8\frac{1}{4}(r + r - 4) = 1,006.5$$

$$8\frac{1}{4}(2r - 4) = 1,006.5$$

$$\frac{33}{4}(2r - 4) = 1,006.5$$

$$\frac{4}{33} \cdot \frac{33}{4}(2r - 4) = \frac{4}{33} \cdot 1,006.5$$

$$2r - 4 = 122$$

$$2r - 4 + 4 = 122 + 4$$

$$2r = 126$$

$$\left(\frac{1}{2}\right)(2r) = \left(\frac{1}{2}\right)(126)$$

$$r = 63$$

> I can use the formula
> distance = rate × time to help me set up an equation for this problem. This will first help me to determine how fast each vehicle was going.

> I can think of 1,006.5 as $\frac{1,006.5}{1}$ so that I can multiply the two factors.

The average speed of the faster car is 63 miles per hour, so the average speed of the slower car is 59 miles per hour.

$$d = 59 \cdot 8\frac{1}{4}$$

$$d = 59 \cdot \frac{33}{4}$$

$$d = 486.75$$

EUREKA
MATH

The slower car traveled 486.75 *miles in* $8\frac{1}{4}$ *hours.*

$1,006.5 - 486.75 = 519.75$

The faster car traveled 519.75 *miles in* $8\frac{1}{4}$ *hours.*

The slower car traveled 486.75 *miles in* $8\frac{1}{4}$ *hours.*

The remainder of the slower car's trip is 33 *miles because* $519.75 - 486.75 = 33$.

Now that I know the rate and distance the second car still needs to travel, I can use $d = rt$ again to solve for the time.

$$33 = 59\,(t)$$
$$\frac{1}{59}(33) = \frac{1}{59}(59)(t)$$
$$\frac{33}{59} = t$$

This time is in hours. To convert to minutes, multiply by 60 *because there are* 60 *minutes in an hour.*

$$\frac{33}{59} \cdot 60 = \frac{1980}{59} \approx 34$$

The slower car will arrive approximately 34 *minutes after the faster car.*

EUREKA MATH™

© 2015 Great Minds eureka-math.org
G7-M3-HWH-1.3.0-09.2015

5. Lucien bought a certain brand of fertilizer for his garden at a unit price of $1.25 per pound. The total cost of the fertilizer left him with $5. He wanted to buy the same weight of a better brand of fertilizer, but at $2.10 per pound, he would have been $80 short of the total amount due. How much money did Lucien have to buy fertilizer?

> From the word problem, I can determine the difference in how much money is left between buying the cheaper or the more expensive product.
>
> $$5 - (-80) = 5 + 80 = 85.$$

The difference in the costs is $85.00 for the same weight in fertilizer.

Let w represent the weight in pounds of fertilizer.

$$2.10w - 1.25w = 85$$
$$0.85w = 85$$
$$\frac{85}{100}w = 85$$
$$\frac{100}{85} \cdot \frac{85}{100}w = 85 \cdot \frac{100}{85}$$
$$1w = 100$$
$$w = 100$$

> I can use the difference in the price per pound with the difference in the amount of money Lucien will have to help me determine how much was bought.

Lucien bought 100 pounds of fertilizer.

$$\text{Cost} = \text{unit price} \cdot \text{weight}$$
$$\text{Cost} = (\$1.25 \text{ per pound}) \cdot (100 \text{ pounds})$$
$$\text{Cost} = \$125.00$$

Lucien paid $125 for 100 pounds of fertilizer. Lucien had $5 left after his purchase, so he started with $125 + $5 = $130.

> If he would have had $5 left after paying, I need to add that to the $125 he paid for the fertilizer to determine how much he started with.

EUREKA MATH

© 2015 Great Minds eureka-math.org
G7-M3-HWH-1.3.0-09.2015

G7-M3-Lesson 10: Angle Problems and Solving Equations

For each question, use angle relationships to write an equation in order to solve for each variable. Determine the indicated angles.

1. In a complete sentence, describe the relevant angle relationships in the following diagram. Find the measurements of $\angle ABE$ and $\angle EBD$.

   $\angle ABE$, $\angle EBD$, and $\angle DBC$ are angles on a line and their measures sum to $180°$.

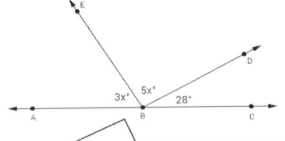

   $$3x + 5x + 28 = 180$$
   $$8x + 28 = 180$$
   $$8x + 28 - 28 = 180 - 28$$
   $$8x = 152$$
   $$\left(\frac{1}{8}\right)8x = \left(\frac{1}{8}\right)152$$
   $$x = 19$$

   I can see that all three of these angles form a straight line, which means the sum of these three angles must be $180°$.

   $$m\angle ABE = 3(19°) = 57°$$
   $$m\angle EBD = 5(19°) = 95°$$

   Finding the value of x is not the answer. I need to go one step further and plug x back into the expressions and evaluate to determine the measure of each angle.

2. In a complete sentence, describe the relevant angle relationships in the following diagram. Find the measurement of $\angle WSV$.

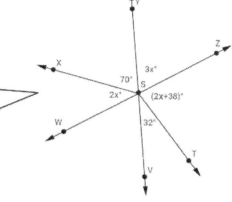

I can see that $\angle WSV$ and $\angle ZSY$ are formed by the same two lines. So they are vertical angles and are congruent. That means $m\angle WSV$ must also be $3x°$.

All of the angles in the diagram are angles at a point, and their measures sum to $360°$. $\angle ZSY$ and $\angle WSV$ are vertical angles and are of equal measurement.

I need to be sure to include another $3x$ term for the missing vertical angle when I set up my equation.

$$3x + 70 + 2x + 3x + (2x + 38) + 32 = 360$$
$$3x + 2x + 3x + 2x + 70 + 38 + 32 = 360$$
$$10x + 140 = 360$$
$$10x + 140 - 140 = 360 - 140$$
$$10x = 220$$
$$\left(\frac{1}{10}\right)10x = \left(\frac{1}{10}\right)220$$
$$x = 22$$

$$m\angle WSV = 3x° = 3(22°) = 66°$$

EUREKA MATH

3. The ratio of the measures of three adjacent angles on a line is $1 : 4 : 7$.

a. Find the measures of the three angles.

$m\angle 1 = x^\circ, m\angle 2 = 4x^\circ, m\angle 3 = 7x^\circ$

$x + 4x + 7x = 180$

$12x = 180$

$\left(\dfrac{1}{12}\right) 12x = \left(\dfrac{1}{12}\right) 180$

$x = 15$

> I can use the ratio to set up an expression for each angle. I also know the measure of adjacent angles on a line must have a sum of 180°.

$m\angle 1 = 15^\circ$

$m\angle 2 = 4(15^\circ) = 60^\circ$

$m\angle 3 = 7(15^\circ) = 105^\circ$

b. Draw a diagram to scale of these adjacent angles. Indicate the measurements of each angle.

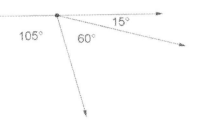

> I can use my protractor to measure the angles accurately.

G7-M3-Lesson 11: Angle Problems and Solving Equations

In a complete sentence, describe the angle relationships in each diagram. Write an equation for the angle relationship(s) shown in the figure, and solve for the indicated unknown angle.

1. Find the measure of $\angle HLG$.

$\angle BLC$, $\angle CLD$, and $\angle DLE$ have a sum of $90°$.

$\angle ALK$, $\angle KLJ$, $\angle JLH$, $\angle HLG$, and $\angle GLF$ are angles on a line and have a sum of $180°$.

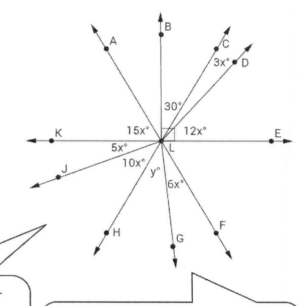

$$3x + 12x + 30 = 90$$
$$15x + 30 = 90$$
$$15x + 30 - 30 = 90 - 30$$
$$15x = 60$$
$$\left(\frac{1}{15}\right)15x = \left(\frac{1}{15}\right)60$$
$$x = 4$$

> I look for the small box in the corner showing me 90° angles, and I also look for angles that form a straight line because their measures have a sum of 180°.

> In order to solve for y, I must solve for x first. The value of x can be used to help determine the value of y.

$$15x + 5x + 10x + y + 6x = 180$$
$$15(4) + 5(4) + 10(4) + y + 6(4) = 180$$
$$60 + 20 + 40 + y + 24 = 180$$
$$144 + y = 180$$
$$144 - 144 + y = 180 - 144$$
$$y = 36$$

$$m\angle HLG = 36°$$

EUREKA
MATH

2. Find the measures of $\angle TWV$ and $\angle ZWV$.

The measures of $\angle XWY$ and $\angle YWZ$ have a sum of $90°$. The measures of $\angle TWV$, $\angle VWZ$, and $\angle ZWY$ have a sum of $180°$.

$90 - 65 = 25$

$m\angle ZWY = 25°$

> I know that $\angle XWY$ and $\angle ZWY$ have a sum of $90°$. I can work backwards to determine the unknown angle.

$$24x + 7x + 25 = 180$$
$$31x + 25 = 180$$
$$31x + 25 - 25 = 180 - 25$$
$$31x = 155$$
$$\left(\frac{1}{31}\right)31x = \left(\frac{1}{31}\right)155$$
$$x = 5$$

> I don't have all the information to use the angles on a line to solve for x yet, but I can get the measure of $\angle ZWY$ by knowing that there are two angles that have a sum of $90°$ first.

$m\angle TWV = 24(5°) = 120°$

$m\angle VWZ = 7(5°) = 35°$

3. Find the measure of $\angle BAC$.

Adjacent angles $6x°$ and $36°$ together are vertically opposite from and are equal to angle $108°$.

$$6x + 36 = 108$$
$$6x + 36 - 36 = 108 - 36$$
$$6x = 72$$
$$\left(\frac{1}{6}\right)6x = \left(\frac{1}{6}\right)72$$
$$x = 12$$

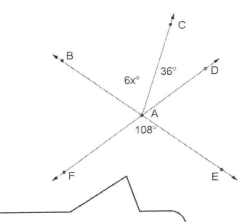

$m\angle BAC = 6(12°) = 72°$

> These angles are not on a line, about a point, or forming a right angle. Instead, I have vertical angles that are formed by two intersecting lines.

EUREKA MATH

© 2015 Great Minds eureka-math.org
G7-M3-HWH-1.3.0-09.2015

4. The measures of three angles at a point are in the ratio of $2 : 7 : 9$. Find the measures of the angles.

> I can use the ratio to write expressions to represent each of the angles.

$m\angle A = 2x°, m\angle B = 7x°, m\angle C = 9x°$

$$2x + 7x + 9x = 360$$
$$18x = 360$$
$$\left(\frac{1}{18}\right)18x = \left(\frac{1}{18}\right)360$$
$$x = 20$$

> Since these three angles are at a point, their measures have a sum of $360°$.

$m\angle A = 2(20°) = 40°$

$m\angle B = 7(20°) = 140°$

$m\angle C = 9(20°) = 180°$

EUREKA
MATH

G7-M3-Lesson 12: Properties of Inequalities

1. For each problem, use the properties of inequalities to write a true inequality statement.
    The two integers are -8 and -3.

    a. Write a true inequality statement.

    $-8 < -3$

    > I can picture a number line to help me write the inequality. On a number line, -8 would be to the left of -3, which means it is less than -3.

    b. Add -4 to each side of the inequality. Write a true inequality statement.

    $-12 < -7$

    > I need to add $-8 + -4$ and $-3 + -4$ and then write another inequality. I can always look back at Module 2 for help working with signed numbers.

    c. Multiply each number in part (a) by -5. Write a true inequality statement.

    $40 > 15$

    > I need to multiply -8×-5 and -3×-5 and then write another inequality. I notice that I must reverse the inequality sign in order to write a true statement.

    d. Subtract $-c$ from each side of the inequality in part (a). Assume that c is a positive number. Write a true inequality statement.

    $-8 - (-c) < -3 - (-c)$
    $-8 + c < -3 + c$

    > I know that adding or subtracting an integer from both sides of the inequality preserves the inequality sign.

© 2015 Great Minds eureka-math.org
G7-M3-HWH-1.3.0-09.2015

e. Divide each side of the inequality in part (a) by $-c$, where c is positive. Write a true inequality statement.

$$\frac{-8}{-c} > \frac{-3}{-c}$$

$$\frac{8}{c} > \frac{3}{c}$$

> I know that when I divide by a negative, the inequality symbol is reversed.

2. Kyla and Pedro went on vacation in northern Vermont during the winter. On Monday, the temperature was $-30°F$, and on Wednesday the temperature was $-8°F$.

    a. Write an inequality comparing the temperature on Monday and the temperature on Wednesday.

        $-30 < -8$

        > I need to compare these temperatures using less than or greater than.

    b. If the temperatures felt 12 degrees colder each day with the wind chill, write a new inequality to show the comparison of the temperatures they actually felt.

        $-42 < -20$

        > I could show the temperature with the wind chill by adding -12 to both sides.

    c. Was the inequality symbol preserved or reversed? Explain.

        The inequality symbol was preserved because the number was added or subtracted from both sides of the inequality.

© 2015 Great Minds eureka-math.org
G7-M3-HWH-1.3.0-09.2015

EUREKA
MATH

G7-M3-Lesson 13: Inequalities

I notice that the problem states that x is a positive integer, which means that x could be $1, 2, 3, 4, 5, 6, \ldots$.

1. If x represents a positive integer, find the solutions to the following inequalities.

a. $x + 9 \leq 5$

$$x + 9 \leq 5$$
$$x + 9 - 9 \leq 5 - 9$$
$$x \leq -4$$

There are no positive integers that are a solution.

I determined that the only values of x that will make the inequality true are less than or equal to -4, but there are no positive integers that are less than or equal to -4.

b. $5 + \dfrac{x}{7} > 12$

I can solve inequalities similar to how I solve equations, but I remember that there are times when I have to reverse the inequality symbol.

$$5 - 5 + \frac{x}{7} > 12 - 5$$
$$\frac{x}{7} > 7$$
$$7\left(\frac{x}{7}\right) > 7(7)$$
$$x > 49$$

The possible solutions for x would include all integers greater than 49.

If x is greater than 49, then it cannot be exactly 49. Instead, x may be $50, 51, 52, 53, \ldots$ or any larger integer.

© 2015 Great Minds eureka-math.org
G7-M3-HWH-1.3.0-09.2015

For each part, I need to determine if any negative integer will be a possible solution, if only some negative integers are solutions, or if no negative integer could ever be a solution.

2. Recall that the symbol ≠ means not equal to. If x represents a negative integer, state whether each of the following statements is always true, sometimes true, or false.

a. $x > 3$

False

The only possible integer solutions that make this statement true are those greater than 3, which would only be positive numbers like $4, 5, 6, \ldots$.

b. $x \neq 0$

Always True

This inequality states that x is not 0. This would always be true, because if x is all integers less than 0, x will never equal 0.

c. $x \leq 2$

Always True

All negative numbers are less than 2, and I know x represents a negative integer, so it must be less than 2.

d. $x < -9$

Sometimes True

Although there are some negative numbers that are less than -9, there are also some negative integers that would not be less than -9, like -7 or -1.

Lesson 13: Inequalities

© 2015 Great Minds eureka-math.org
G7-M3-HWH-1.3.0-09.2015

EUREKA MATH

3. Three times the smaller of two consecutive even integers increased by the larger integer is at least 26.

> Consecutive even integers are two apart, so I use x to represent the first number and $x + 2$ to represent the second number.

Model the problem with an inequality, and determine which of the given values 4 and 6 are solutions. Then, find the smallest number that will make the inequality true.

$3x + x + 2 \geq 26$

> I know that "at least" means that the sum will be 26 or more. So the sum will be greater than or equal to 26.

For 4:

$3(4) + (4) + 2 \geq 26$

$12 + 4 + 2 \geq 26$

$18 \geq 26$

False, 4 is not a solution.

For 6:

$3(6) + (6) + 2 \geq 26$

$18 + 6 + 2 \geq 26$

$26 \geq 26$

True, 6 is a solution.

$3x + x + 2 \geq 26$

$4x + 2 \geq 26$

$4x + 2 - 2 \geq 26 - 2$

$4x \geq 24$

$x \geq 6$

> To determine if a number is a solution of an inequality, I can just substitute the number in for x and evaluate to see if the result is a true statement.

The smallest number that will make the inequality true is 6.

> "At most" tells me that she can use 74 feet of fencing or less. So the total must be less than or equal to 74.

4. Rochelle has, at most, 74 feet of fencing to put around her veggie garden. She plans to create a rectangular garden that has a length that is 3 feet longer than the width. Write an inequality to model the situation. Then solve to determine the dimensions of the garden with the largest perimeter Rochelle can make.

   Let x represent the width.

   Let $x + 3$ represent the length.

> The perimeter is the sum of all 4 sides of a rectangle. I must include all 4 sides when writing my inequality.

$$x + x + x + 3 + x + 3 \le 74$$
$$4x + 6 \le 74$$
$$4x + 6 - 6 \le 74 - 6$$
$$4x \le 68$$
$$\left(\frac{1}{4}\right)(4x) \le \left(\frac{1}{4}\right)(68)$$
$$x \le 17$$

$17 + 3 = 20$

In order to get the largest perimeter, the width would be 17 feet, and the length would be 20 feet.

> Once I solve, I need to use the "let" statements I wrote at the beginning to help me determine the meaning of my answer.

EUREKA
MATH

G7-M3-Lesson 14: Solving Inequalities

1. Ethan earns a commission of 5% of the total amount he sells. In addition, he is also paid $380 per week. In order to stick to his budget, he needs to earn at least $975 this week. Write an inequality with integer coefficients for the total sales needed to earn at least $975, and describe what the solution represents.

> Because he has to earn at least $975, I know that I should use greater than or equal to 975 because Ethan needs to earn $975 or more.

Let the variable p represent the purchase amount.

> Since percent means out of 100, I can show 5% as $\frac{5}{100}$.

$$\frac{5}{100}p + 380 \geq 975$$

$$(100)\left(\frac{5}{100}p\right) + 100(380) \geq 100(975)$$

> Now that I have gotten rid of the fraction, this would be my inequality with integer coefficients.

$$5p + 38000 \geq 97500$$

$$5p + 38000 - 38000 \geq 97500 - 38000$$

$$5p \geq 59500$$

$$\left(\frac{1}{5}\right)(5p) \geq \left(\frac{1}{5}\right)(59500)$$

$$p \geq 11900$$

Ethan's total sales must be at least $11,900 if he wants to earn $975 or more.

2. Katie and Kane were exercising on Saturday. Kane was riding a bicycle 12 miles per hour faster than Katie was walking. Katie walked for $3\frac{1}{2}$ hours, and Kane bicycled for 2 hours. Altogether, Katie and Kane traveled no more than 57 miles. Find the maximum speed of each person.

	Rate	Time	Distance
Kane	$x + 12$	2	$2(x + 12)$
Katie	x	$3\frac{1}{2}$	$3\frac{1}{2}x$

> I can organize all the information in a table and use the relationship $d = rt$.

$$2(x + 12) + 3\frac{1}{2}x \le 57$$

I know that sum of the two distances presented in the table must be no more than 57 miles, which means the sum must be less than or equal to 57.

$$2x + 24 + 3\frac{1}{2}x \le 57$$

$$5\frac{1}{2}x + 24 \le 57$$

$$5\frac{1}{2}x + 24 - 24 \le 57 - 24$$

$$5\frac{1}{2}x \le 33$$

Rewriting mixed numbers as fractions greater than one can help make it easier to solve.

$$\frac{11}{2}x \le 33$$

$$\left(\frac{2}{11}\right)\left(\frac{11}{2}x\right) \le (33)\left(\frac{2}{11}\right)$$

$$x \le 6$$

$$6 + 12 = 18$$

The maximum speed Katie was walking was 6 miles per hour, and the maximum speed Kane was riding the bike was 18 miles per hour.

3. Systolic blood pressure is the higher number in a blood pressure reading. It is measured as the heart muscle contracts. Ramel is having his blood pressure checked. The nurse told him that the upper limit of his systolic blood pressure is equal to a third of his age increased by 117. If Ramel is 42 years old, write and solve an inequality to determine what is normal for his systolic blood pressure.

An upper limit provides the maximum number for Ramel's systolic blood pressure. That means that Ramel's systolic blood pressure must be less than or equal to the expression showing a third of his age increased by 117.

Let p represent the systolic blood pressure in millimeters of mercury (mmHg).

Let a represent Ramel's age.

$p \le \frac{1}{3}a + 117$, where $a = 42$.

I can just substitute in Ramel's age for a in order to solve for p.

$$p \le \frac{1}{3}(42) + 117$$

$$p \le 14 + 117$$

$$p \le 131$$

The normal upper limit for Ramel is 131, which means that Ramel's systolic blood pressure should be 131 mmHg or lower.

EUREKA MATH

G7-M3-Lesson 15: Graphing Solutions to Inequalities

> Because this problem says at least 15 hours, I know that he must read 15 hours or more. I use the greater than or equal to symbol in my inequality to represent this relationship.

1. Doug has decided that he should read for at least 15 hours a week. On Monday and Tuesday, his days off from work, he reads for a total of $6\frac{1}{4}$ hours. For the remaining 5 days, he reads for the same amount of time each day. Find t, the amount of time he reads for each of the 5 days. Graph your solution.

Let t represent the time, in hours, he spends reading on each of the remaining days.

$$5t + 6\frac{1}{4} \geq 15$$

$$5t + 6\frac{1}{4} - 6\frac{1}{4} \geq 15 - 6\frac{1}{4}$$

> I can unbundle to rewrite 15 as $14\frac{4}{4}$, when trying to subtract.

$$5t \geq 8\frac{3}{4}$$

$$\left(\frac{1}{5}\right)(5t) \geq \left(\frac{1}{5}\right)\left(8\frac{3}{4}\right)$$

$$t \geq \left(\frac{1}{5}\right)\left(\frac{35}{4}\right)$$

$$t \geq \frac{35}{20}$$

$$t \geq 1.75$$

Doug must read for 1.75 hours or more on each of the remaining days.

Graph:

> Because I want to include 1.75 as a possible solution, I use a solid circle. The arrow indicates that all numbers greater than 1.75 are also included in the solution.

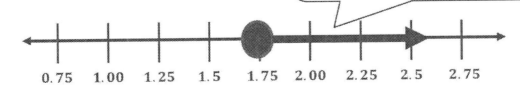

2. The length of a parallelogram is 70 centimeters, and its perimeter is less than 360 centimeters. Cherise writes an inequality and graphs the solution below to find the width of the parallelogram. Is she correct? If yes, write and solve the inequality to represent the problem and graph. If no, explain the error(s) Cherise made.

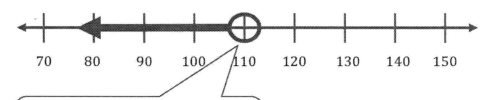

This graph shows the width must be less than 110, and it doesn't include 110 because there is an open circle.

Let w represent the width of the parallelogram.

$$2w + 2(70) < 360$$
$$2w + 140 < 360$$
$$2w + 140 - 140 < 360 - 140$$
$$2w < 220$$
$$\left(\frac{1}{2}\right)(2w) < \left(\frac{1}{2}\right)(220)$$
$$w < 110$$

A parallelogram has two lengths and two widths. The sum of all four sides will be the perimeter. I can use this information to set up my inequality.

Yes, Cherise is correct.

The width must be less than 110 in order for the perimeter to be less than 360. To graph this relationship, I do need an open circle because 110 is not included in the solution.

EUREKA
MATH™

© 2015 Great Minds eureka-math.org
G7-M3-HWH-1.3.0-09.2015

G7-M3-Lesson 16: The Most Famous Ratio of All

1. Find the circumference.

   a. Give the exact answer in terms of π.

   $d = 10$ in.

   $C = \pi d$

   $C = 10\pi$ in.

   > I know that the diameter of every circle is twice the length of the radius, which is given in the diagram.

   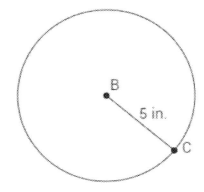

   B

   5 in.

   C

   b. Use $\pi \approx \frac{22}{7}$, and express your answer as a fraction in lowest terms.

   $C \approx \frac{22}{7}(10 \text{ in.})$

   $C \approx 31\frac{3}{7}$ in.

   > I use that the formula for circumference ($C = \pi d$) and use $\frac{22}{7}$ as the approximation for π.

   c. Use the π button on your calculator, and express your answer to the nearest hundredth.

   $C = \pi(10 \text{ in.})$

   $C \approx 31.42$ in.

   > In my calculator I type 10 and then press the multiplication and π buttons to calculate the circumference of the given circle.

2. Consider the diagram shown.

   a. Explain in words how to determine the perimeter of the diagram.

   The perimeter would be the sum of two side lengths (a) and (c) and the circumference of half a circle with radius d.

   > To calculate the circumference of a half circle, I use the formula $C = \frac{1}{2}\pi d$.

   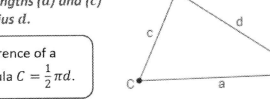

   A

   c

   d

   C   a   B

   b. Write an algebraic equation that will result in the perimeter of the diagram.

   $P = \frac{1}{2}\pi d + a + c$

   > I know the perimeter is the length around the outside of the diagram. It can be used to determine the amount of fencing or edging needed.

© 2015 Great Minds eureka-math.org
G7-M3-HWH-1.3.0-09.2015

c. Find the perimeter of the figure if the diameter of the semicircle is 9 m, side length c is 6 m, and side length a is 10 m. Use 3.14 for π.

$$P = \frac{1}{2}\pi d + a + c$$

$$P \approx \frac{1}{2}(3.14)(9) + 10 + 6$$

> I can use the given side lengths and the equation I wrote in part (b) to calculate the perimeter of the diagram.

$$P \approx 14.13 + 10 + 6$$

$$P \approx 30.13$$

The perimeter of the diagram is about 30.13 m.

3. Dan wants to go on the longest bike ride possible. If he plans to complete a loop where he starts at point D and ends back at point D, which route is the longest: following the semicircle path or following the path of the two smaller semicircles? Explain your reasoning. Let $\pi \approx 3.14$.

Length of the single semicircle path:

Let d represent the diameter of the semicircle.

$$P = \frac{1}{2}\pi d + d$$

> In order to find the length of this entire path, I add the circumference of the semicircle and the length of the diameter.

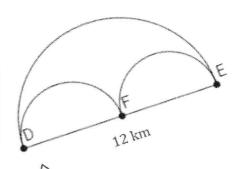

12 km

$$P \approx \frac{1}{2}(3.14)(12) + 12$$

$$P \approx 18.84 + 12$$

$$P \approx 30.84$$

The length of the semicircle path is about 30.84 km.

> If Dan was only riding his bike from point D to point E, he could either travel around the semicircle or follow the diameter of the circle.

Length of the two smaller semicircles path:

Let a represent the diameter of the smaller semicircles.

$$P = \frac{1}{2}\pi a + \frac{1}{2}\pi a + a + a$$

$$P \approx \frac{1}{2}(3.14)(6) + \frac{1}{2}(3.14)(6) + 6 + 6$$

> The two smaller semicircles each have a diameter of 6 km. I also have to add the diameter of each smaller semicircle to provide the length of segment DE.

$$P \approx 9.42 + 9.42 + 6 + 6$$

$$P \approx 30.84$$

The length of the two smaller semicircles path is about 30.84 km.

Dan can bike ride on either path because they cover the same distance. Neither path is longer than the other one.

Lesson 16:   The Most Famous Ratio of All

EUREKA MATH

© 2015 Great Minds eureka-math.org
G7-M3-HWH-1.3.0-09.2015

G7-M3-Lesson 17: The Area of a Circle

1. Find the area of the circle. Use $\frac{22}{7}$ as an approximation for π.

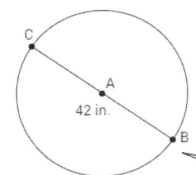

$r = 21$ in.

$A = \pi r^2$

$A \approx \left(\frac{22}{7}\right)(21 \text{ in.})^2$

$A \approx \left(\frac{22}{7}\right)(441 \text{ in}^2)$

$A \approx 1,386 \text{ in}^2$

> The diameter is given, but I need to determine the length of the radius to calculate the area. I know the length of the radius is half the length of the diameter.

2. A circle has a diameter of 14 cm.

    a. Find the exact area, and find an approximate area using $\pi \approx 3.14$.

    $r = 7 \text{ cm}$

    Exact Area:

    $A = \pi r^2$

    $A = \pi(7 \text{ cm})^2$

    $A = 49\pi \text{ cm}^2$

    > π is an irrational number, so I must leave π in my answer to provide the exact area.

    Approximate Area:

    $A \approx 49(3.14) \text{ cm}^2$

    $A \approx 153.86 \text{ cm}^2$

    > Using the approximation of 3.14 for π provides an approximate area.

    b. What is the circumference of the circle using $\pi \approx 3.14$?

    $d = 14 \text{ cm}$

    $C \approx (3.14)(14 \text{ cm})$

    $C \approx 43.96 \text{ cm}$

    > I remember from the previous lesson that the formula for circumference is $C = \pi d$, which means I need to use the given diameter.

© 2015 Great Minds eureka-math.org
G7-M3-HWH-1.3.0-09.2015

3. A circle has a circumference of 264 ft. Approximate the area of the circle. Use $\pi \approx \frac{22}{7}$.

$$C = \pi d$$

> I can use the circumference to determine the diameter the circle.

$$264 \approx \frac{22}{7}d$$

$$\left(\frac{7}{22}\right)(264) \approx \left(\frac{7}{22}\right)\left(\frac{22}{7}d\right)$$

$$84 \approx d$$

> Now that I know the approximated diameter, I need to determine the radius to calculate the area of the circle.

$$42 \approx r$$

$$A \approx \left(\frac{22}{7}\right)(42^2)$$

$$A \approx \left(\frac{22}{7}\right)(1,764)$$

$$A \approx 5,544$$

The area of the circle is approximately $5,544$ ft^2.

4. The area of a circle is 81π in^2. Find its circumference.

$$A = \pi r^2$$

$$81\pi = \pi r^2$$

> I can use the area to determine the radius of the circle.

$$\left(\frac{1}{\pi}\right)(81\pi) = \left(\frac{1}{\pi}\right)(\pi r^2)$$

> I know the radius is 9 because $9^2 = 81$.

$$81 = r^2$$

$$9 = r$$

$$18 = d$$

> Now that I know the length of the diameter, I can calculate the circumference of the circle.

$$C = \pi d$$

$$C = 18\pi$$

The circumference of the circle is 18π in.

5. Find the ratio of the area of two circles with radii 5 in. and 6 in.

The area of the circle with radius 5 in. is 25π in^2. The area of the circle with radius 6 in. is 36π in^2. The ratio of the area of the two circles is $25\pi: 36\pi$ or $25: 36$.

> I calculate the area of each circle and then write the two areas as a ratio.

Lesson 17:   The Area of a Circle

© 2015 Great Minds eureka-math.org
G7-M3-HWH-1.3.0-09.2015

EUREKA
MATH

G7-M3-Lesson 18: More Problems on Area and Circumference

1. Frederick is replacing a broken window that has a semicircle on top and a square on the bottom. He knows that the semicircular region has an area of 100.48 in^2.

   a. Draw a picture to represent the window.

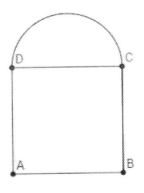

   > I can use the information I know to calculate the length of the radius of the semicircle.

   b. What is the length of the square? Use $\pi \approx 3.14$.

   > The given area is for the semicircle, so I need to multiply the area formula by $\frac{1}{2}$.

   $$A = \frac{1}{2}\pi r^2$$

   $$100.48 \approx \frac{1}{2}(3.14)(r^2)$$

   $$100.48 \approx 1.57r^2$$

   $$\left(\frac{1}{1.57}\right)(100.48) \approx \left(\frac{1}{1.57}\right)(1.57r^2)$$

   $$64 \approx r^2$$

   $$8 \approx r$$

   > I know the radius is about 8 because $8 \times 8 = 64$.

   The length of the diameter is approximately 16 in., which means the length of the side of the square is approximately 16 in.

   > The side length of the square is the same length as the diameter of the semicircle.

© 2015 Great Minds eureka-math.org
G7-M3-HWH-1.3.0-09.2015

2. The diagram below is comprised of two squares and one quarter circle. It has a total length of 30 cm. What is the approximate area of the diagram? Use $\pi \approx 3.14$.

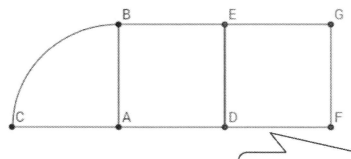

I know the total length is 30 cm, which means each section has a length of 10 cm.

Area of the quarter circle:

$A = \frac{1}{4}\pi r^2$

$A \approx \frac{1}{4}(3.14)(10^2)$

$A \approx 78.5$

I must multiply the area formula by $\frac{1}{4}$ since I am calculating the area of a quarter circle.

Area of one square:

$A = s^2$

$A = 10^2$

$A = 100$

I know that both squares will have the same area.

The total area of the diagram will be the sum of the area of the quarter circle and the area of the two squares.

$78.5 + 100 + 100 \approx 278.5$

Therefore, the sum of the diagram is approximately 278.5 cm^2.

3. The image below is the top of a unique end table. Help David determine the area of the table, so he can purchase a glass cover for the table. Approximate π as 3.14.

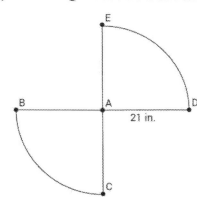

Each part of the table represents a quarter circle, so I multiply the area formula by $\frac{1}{4}$.

$A = \frac{1}{4}\pi r^2$

$A \approx \frac{1}{4}(3.14)(21 \text{ in.})^2$

$A \approx 346.185 \text{ in}^2$

21 in.

There are two quarter circles with the same area.

$A \approx 2(346.185 \text{ in}^2) \approx 692.37 \text{ in}^2$

The area of the entire table is approximately 692.37 in^2.

EUREKA MATH™

© 2015 Great Minds eureka-math.org
G7-M3-HWH-1.3.0-09.2015

4. Delecia is painting polk-a-dots in her daughter's room. Her daughter wants each one to have a purple center and a pink outline. Use the diagram below to determine the area of the pink paint. Use $\pi \approx 3.14$.

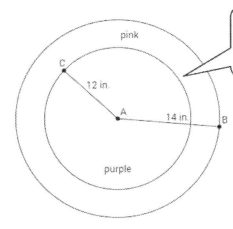

To find the area of pink paint, I need to find the area of the outside circle and the area of the inside circle.

Area of the outside circle:

$A = \pi r^2$

$A = \pi (14 \text{ in.})^2$

$A = 196\pi \text{ in}^2$

I use the exact area through all the calculations.

Area of the inside circle:

$A = \pi r^2$

$A = \pi (12 \text{ in.})^2$

$A = 144\pi \text{ in}^2$

To determine the area of just the pink paint, I need to find the difference of the two areas.

$196\pi \text{ in}^2 - 144\pi \text{ in}^2 = 52\pi \text{ in}^2$

The exact area of the pink circle is $52\pi \text{ in}^2$.

$A \approx 52(3.14) \text{ in}^2 \approx 163.28 \text{ in}^2$

The approximate area of the pink circle is 163.28 in^2.

G7-M3-Lesson 19: Unknown Area Problems on the Coordinate Plane

1. Find the area of each figure. When necessary, use 3.14 as an approximation for π.

a.

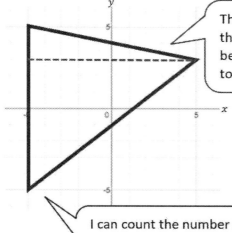

This dashed line represents the height of the triangle because it is perpendicular to the base.

$A = \frac{1}{2}bh$

$A = \frac{1}{2}(10 \text{ units})(10 \text{ units})$

$A = 50 \text{ sq. units}$

I can count the number of units to determine the length of the base and height of the acute triangle.

I notice that the semicircle's diameter has the same length as the rectangle's width (6 units). Therefore, the radius of the semicircle is 3 units.

b. $A = $ *area of the rectangle + area of the semicircle*

$A = (6 \text{ units} \times 8 \text{ units}) + \left(\frac{1}{2}\pi(3 \text{ units})^2\right)$

$A = 48 \text{ units}^2 + 4.5\pi \text{ units}^2$

$A \approx 48 \text{ units}^2 + 14.13 \text{ units}^2$

$A \approx 62.13 \text{ units}^2$

The area of the region is approximately 62.13 units^2.

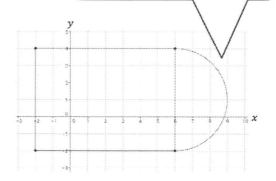

EUREKA MATH

c.

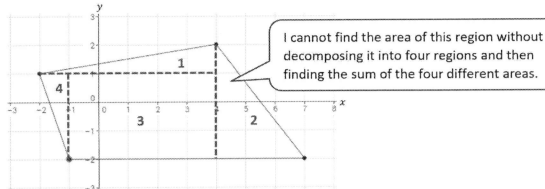

I cannot find the area of this region without decomposing it into four regions and then finding the sum of the four different areas.

A = area of region 1 + area of region 2 + area of region 3 + area of region 4

$A = \left(\frac{1}{2} \times 1 \text{ unit} \times 6 \text{ units}\right) + \left(\frac{1}{2} \times 4 \text{ units} \times 3 \text{ units}\right) + (5 \text{ units} \times 3 \text{ units}) + \left(\frac{1}{2} \times 1 \text{ unit} \times 3 \text{ units}\right)$

$A = 3 \text{ units}^2 + 6 \text{ units}^2 + 15 \text{ units}^2 + 1.5 \text{ units}^2$

$A = 25.5 \text{ units}^2$

To calculate the area of a triangle, I use the formula $A = \frac{1}{2}bh$. The area formula of rectangles is $A = lw$.

2. Draw a figure in the coordinate plane that matches the description.

A triangle with an area of 10 sq. units.

$A = \frac{1}{2}bh$

$10 \text{ sq. units} = \frac{1}{2}bh$

$\frac{2}{1}(10 \text{ sq. units}) = \frac{2}{1}\left(\frac{1}{2}bh\right)$

$20 \text{ sq. units} = bh$

One possible answer is a right triangle with a height of 5 units and a base of 4 units, which results in a product of 20 sq. units.

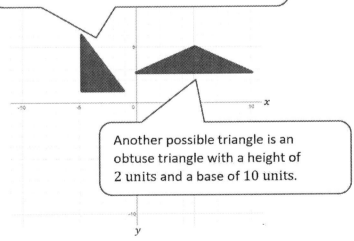

I can use my knowledge of solving equations to determine that the bh must equal 20 sq. units. This means that the base and the height must be factors of 20.

Another possible triangle is an obtuse triangle with a height of 2 units and a base of 10 units.

3. Find the area of triangle DEF.

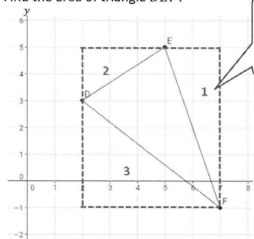

> I am unable to determine the base and height of the triangle, which is needed to calculate the area. Therefore, I compose a rectangle around triangle DEF.

Area of the rectangle:

$A = 6$ units $\times 5$ units

$A = 30$ sq. units

> The rectangle is composed of three right triangles and triangle DEF.

Area of triangle 1:

$A = \frac{1}{2} \times 6$ units $\times 2$ units

$A = 6$ sq. units

Area of triangle 2:

$A = \frac{1}{2} \times 2$ units $\times 3$ units

$A = 3$ sq. units

Area of triangle 3:

$A = \frac{1}{2} \times 4$ units $\times 5$ units

$A = 10$ sq. units

Area of triangle $DEF = 30$ sq. units $- (6$ sq. units $+ 3$ sq. units $+ 10$ sq. units$)$

Area of triangle $DEF = 30$ sq. units $- 19$ sq. units

Area of triangle $DEF = 11$ sq. units

> To determine the area of triangle DEF, I must subtract the areas of the three right triangles from the composed rectangle.

The area of triangle DEF is 11 sq. units.

Lesson 19:   Unknown Area Problems on the Coordinate Plane

© 2015 Great Minds eureka-math.org
G7-M3-HWH-1.3.0-09.2015

EUREKA
MATH

4. Find the area of the quadrilateral using two different methods.

> When I decompose, I break the shape into smaller shapes and then calculate the sum of these areas.

Method 1: Decompose

Area of the rectangle:

$A = 5 \text{ units} \times 4 \text{ units}$

$A = 20 \text{ sq. units}$

Area of the triangle:

$A = \frac{1}{2} \times 2 \text{ units} \times 4 \text{ units}$

$A = 4 \text{ sq. units}$

$A = 20 \text{ sq. units} + 4 \text{ sq. units}$

$A = 24 \text{ sq. units}$

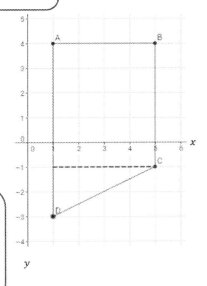

> I compose a larger shape that surrounds the original quadrilateral. I then calculate the difference of the area of the larger shape and the shape that is not included in the original quadrilateral.

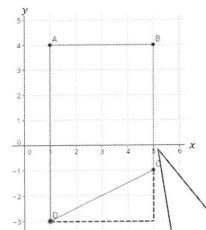

Method 2: Compose

Area of the rectangle

$A = 7 \text{ units} \times 4 \text{ units}$

$A = 28 \text{ sq. units}$

Area of the triangle:

$A = \frac{1}{2} \times 2 \text{ units} \times 4 \text{ units}$

$A = 4 \text{ sq. units}$

$A = 28 \text{ sq. units} - 4 \text{ sq. units}$

$A = 24 \text{ sq. units}$

> I could also recognize the original shape as a trapezoid and use the formula to calculate the area of a trapezoid:
> $A = \frac{1}{2} (\text{base 1} + \text{base 2}) \times \text{height}$.

G7-M3-Lesson 20: Composite Area Problems

1. The figure shows two semicircles. Find the area of the shaded region. Use 3.14 for π.

> I remember from previous lessons how to calculate the area of a circular region.

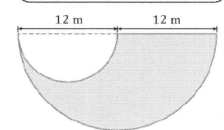

Area of the larger semicircle:

$A = \frac{1}{2}\pi r^2$

> The radius of the larger semicircle is 12 m.

$A \approx \frac{1}{2}(3.14)(12 \text{ m})^2$

$A \approx 226.08 \text{ m}^2$

Area of the smaller semicircle:

$A = \frac{1}{2}\pi r^2$

> The radius of the smaller semicircle is 6 m.

$A \approx \frac{1}{2}(3.14)(6 \text{ m})^2$

$A \approx 56.52 \text{ m}^2$

> The area of the shaded region is the difference between the area of each semicircle.

Area of the shaded region:

$A \approx 226.08 \text{ m}^2 - 56.52 \text{ m}^2$

$A \approx 169.56 \text{ m}^2$

The approximate area of the shaded region is 169.56 m^2*.*

© 2015 Great Minds eureka-math.org
G7-M3-HWH-1.3.0-09.2015

2. Find the area of the shaded region. Use 3.14 for π.

Area of the square:

$18 \text{ in.} \times 18 \text{ in.} = 324 \text{ in}^2$

In order to determine the area of the shaded region, I need to subtract the area of the semicircle from the area of the square.

Area of the semicircle:

$A = \frac{1}{2}\pi r^2$

$A \approx \frac{1}{2}(3.14)(9 \text{ in.})^2$

$A \approx 127.17 \text{ in}^2$

The diameter of the semicircle is the same length as a side of the square (18 in.), which means the radius of the semicircle is 9 in. because it is half of the diameter.

18 in.

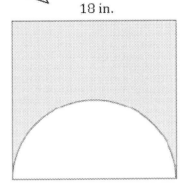

Area of the shaded region:

$A \approx 324 \text{ in}^2 - 127.17 \text{ in}^2$

$A \approx 196.83 \text{ in}^2$

The area of the shaded region is approximately 196.83 in^2.

3. Sydney created a flower petal stencil to use to decorate the walls of her new daycare center. Sydney needs to calculate the area of each petal in order to plan the pattern on the wall. What is the area of Sydney's stencil. Provide your answer in terms of π.

Area of Region 1:

> The radius of Region 1 is half the diameter of 28 in.

> I decompose the petal into two different regions to make it easier to calculate the area.

$A = \frac{1}{2}\pi r^2$

$A = \frac{1}{2}\pi(14 \text{ in.})^2$

$A = 98\pi \text{ in}^2$

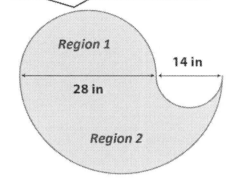

> Region 2 is the larger semicircle that has a smaller semicircle cut out of it. Therefore, I need to find the area of each semicircle and then calculate the difference.

Area of Region 2:

> The diameter of the larger semicircle is 28 in. +14 in., or 42 in., which makes the radius 21 in.

Let a represent the radius of the larger semicircle in region 2.
Let b represent the radius of the smaller semicircle in region 2.

$A = \frac{1}{2}\pi a^2 - \frac{1}{2}\pi b^2$

$A = \frac{1}{2}\pi(21 \text{ in.})^2 - \frac{1}{2}\pi(7 \text{ in.})^2$

$A = 220.5\pi \text{ in}^2 - 24.5\pi \text{ in}^2$

$A = 196\pi \text{ in}^2$

Area of the flower petal:

$A = 98\pi \text{ in}^2 + 196\pi \text{ in}^2$

$A = 294\pi \text{ in}^2$

> Now that I know the area of each region, I find the total area by calculating the sum of the areas of the two regions.

The exact area of the flower petal is $294\pi \text{ in}^2$.

EUREKA MATH

© 2015 Great Minds eureka-math.org
G7-M3-HWH-1.3.0-09.2015

4. The figure is formed by five rectangles. Find the area of the unshaded rectangular region.

area of the entire rectangle — area of the shaded rectangles = area of the unshaded rectangular region

$A = 27 \text{ ft.} \times 17 \text{ ft.} - ((27 \text{ ft.} \times 5 \text{ ft.}) + 2(12 \text{ ft.} \times 5 \text{ ft.}) + (12 \text{ ft.} \times 10 \text{ ft.}))$

$A = 459 \text{ ft}^2 - (135 \text{ ft}^2 + 120 \text{ ft}^2 + 120 \text{ ft}^2)$

$A = 459 \text{ ft}^2 - 375 \text{ ft}^2$

$A = 84 \text{ ft}^2$

The area of the unshaded rectangular region is 84 ft².

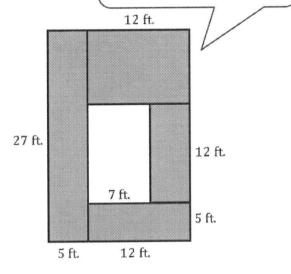

I know this missing length is 10 ft. because the entire side length must be 27 ft.

5. The figure is a rectangle made out of triangles. Find the area of the shaded region.

area of the shaded region = area of the rectangle — area of the unshaded triangles

$A = 44 \text{ in.} \times 36 \text{ in.} - \left(\left(\frac{1}{2}\right)(18 \text{ in.} \times 44 \text{ in.}) + \left(\frac{1}{2}\right)(18 \text{ in.} \times 36 \text{ in.})\right)$

$A = 1,584 \text{ in}^2 - (396 \text{ in}^2 + 324 \text{ in}^2)$

$A = 1,584 \text{ in}^2 - 720 \text{ in}^2$

$A = 864 \text{ in}^2$

The area of the unshaded region is 864 in².

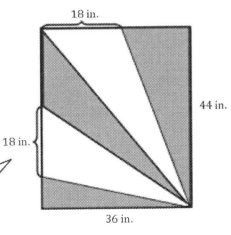

The two unshaded regions are obtuse triangles, so I use the formula $A = \frac{1}{2}bh$ to calculate their areas.

G7-M3-Lesson 21: Surface Area

Surface Area of Nets

1. For the following net, draw a solid represented by the net, indicate the type of solid, and then find the solid's surface area.

Right triangular prism

$SA = LA + 2B$

> The figure has two identical bases, which means the net represents a prism. Since both of the bases are triangles, the figure is a triangular prism.

> In order to find the surface area, I find the area of the lateral faces and then add that to the area of both bases.

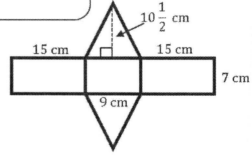

$LA = P \cdot h$

$LA = (15 \text{ cm} + 9 \text{ cm} + 15 \text{ cm})(7 \text{ cm})$

$LA = (39 \text{ cm})(7 \text{ cm})$

$LA = 273 \text{ cm}^2$

$B = \frac{1}{2}(9 \text{ cm})(10\frac{1}{2} \text{ cm})$

$B = 47.25 \text{ cm}^2$

$SA = 273 \text{ cm}^2 + 2(47.25 \text{ cm}^2)$

$SA = 273 \text{ cm}^2 + 94.5 \text{ cm}^2$

$SA = 367.5 \text{ cm}^2$

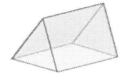

(3-Dimensional Form)

EUREKA
MATH

Surface Area of Cubes

2. Given the cube with edges that are $\frac{1}{2}$ inch long.

   a. Find the surface area of the cube.

   $SA = 6s^2$

   $SA = 6\left(\frac{1}{2}\text{ in.}\right)^2$

   $SA = 6\left(\frac{1}{4}\text{ in}^2\right)$

   $SA = 1\frac{1}{2}\text{ in}^2$

   > A cube has 6 identical faces, so the area of all the faces will be the same.

   b. Maria makes a scale drawing of the cube using a scale factor of 8. Find the surface area of the cube that Maria drew.

   $\frac{1}{2}$ in.$\cdot$ 8 = 4 in.; *the edge lengths of Maria's drawing would be* 4 in.

   > I use the scale factor to determine the length of the edges in the scale drawing.

   $SA = 6(4\text{ in.})^2$

   $SA = 6(16\text{ in}^2)$

   $SA = 96\text{ in}^2$

   c. What is the ratio of the surface area of the scale drawing to the surface area of the actual cube, and how does the value of the ratio compare to the scale factor?

   $96 \div 1\frac{1}{2}$

   > I divide the two surface areas to determine the ratio.

   $96 \div \frac{3}{2}$

   $96 \times \frac{2}{3}$

   > The value of the ratio is $\frac{x}{y}$ or $\frac{64}{1}$, which is the same as the scale factor squared.

   64

   The ratio of the surface area of the scale drawing to the surface area of the actual cube is 64: 1. *The value of the ratio is* 64. *The scale factor of the drawing is* 8, *and the value of the ratio of the surface area of the drawing to the surface area of the actual cube is* 8^2, *or* 64.

Surface Area of Prisms

3. Find the surface area of each of the following right prisms using the formula $SA = LA + 2B$.

    a. Trapezoidal Prism

    $$SA = LA + 2B$$

    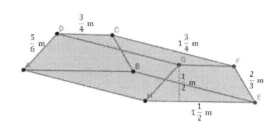

$$LA = \left(\frac{2}{3}\,\text{m} + \frac{3}{4}\,\text{m} + \frac{5}{6}\,\text{m} + 1\frac{1}{2}\,\text{m}\right)\left(1\frac{3}{4}\,\text{m}\right)$$

$$LA = \left(\frac{8}{12}\,\text{m} + \frac{9}{12}\,\text{m} + \frac{10}{12}\,\text{m} + 1\frac{6}{12}\,\text{m}\right)\left(1\frac{3}{4}\,\text{m}\right)$$

> I need common denominators before I can add fractions.

$$LA = \left(3\frac{3}{4}\,\text{m}\right)\left(1\frac{3}{4}\,\text{m}\right)$$

$$LA = \left(\frac{15}{4}\,\text{m}\right)\left(\frac{7}{4}\,\text{m}\right)$$

$$LA = \frac{105}{16}\,\text{m}^2$$

$$B = \frac{1}{2}(b_1 + b_2)h$$

> The base of the prism is a trapezoid, so I use the area formula for a trapezoid to determine the area of each base.

$$LA = 6\frac{9}{16}\,\text{m}^2$$

$$B = \frac{1}{2}\left(\frac{3}{4}\,\text{m} + 1\frac{1}{2}\,\text{m}\right)\left(\frac{1}{2}\,\text{m}\right)$$

$$B = \frac{1}{2}\left(2\frac{1}{4}\,\text{m}\right)\left(\frac{1}{2}\,\text{m}\right)$$

$$B = \frac{9}{16}\,\text{m}^2$$

$$SA = 6\frac{9}{16}\,\text{m}^2 + \frac{2}{1}\left(\frac{9}{16}\,\text{m}^2\right)$$

$$SA = 6\frac{9}{16}\,\text{m}^2 + \frac{18}{16}\,\text{m}^2$$

$$SA = 6\frac{9}{16}\,\text{m}^2 + 1\frac{2}{16}\,\text{m}^2$$

> When I multiply, I change the whole number to a fraction $\left(\frac{2}{1}\right)$ and then multiply the numerators and the denominators.

$$SA = 7\frac{11}{16}\,\text{m}^2$$

© 2015 Great Minds eureka-math.org
G7-M3-HWH-1.3.0-09.2015

EUREKA
MATH

b.   Kite Prism

$$SA = LA + 2B$$

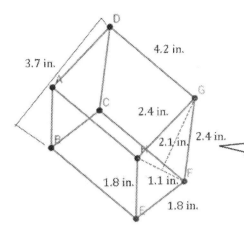

To find the area of the base, I decompose the base into two triangles.

$LA = (2.4 \text{ in.} + 2.4 \text{ in.} + 1.8 \text{ in.} + 1.8 \text{ in.})(4.2 \text{ in.})$

$LA = (8.4 \text{ in.})(4.2 \text{ in.})$

$LA = 35.28 \text{ in}^2$

$B = \frac{1}{2}(2.1 \text{ in.} \times 1.1 \text{ in.}) + \frac{1}{2}(1.6 \text{ in.} \times 1.1 \text{ in.})$

$B = \frac{1}{2}(2.31 \text{ in}^2 + 1.76 \text{ in}^2)$

$B = \frac{1}{2}(4.07 \text{ in}^2)$

$B = 2.035 \text{ in}^2$

I need to use the given measurements to determine the height of the second triangle.

3.7 in. − 2.1 in. = 1.6 in.

$SA = 35.28 \text{ in}^2 + 2(2.035 \text{ in}^2)$

$SA = 35.28 \text{ in}^2 + 4.07 \text{ in}^2$

$SA = 39.35 \text{ in}^2$

© 2015 Great Minds eureka-math.org
G7-M3-HWH-1.3.0-09.2015

4. The surface area of the right rectangular prism is $164\frac{1}{2}$ ft². The dimensions of its base are 5 ft. and 8 ft. Use the formulas $SA = LA + 2B$ and $LA = Ph$ to find the unknown height, h, of the prism.

$SA = LA + 2B$

$SA = Ph + 2B$

> I know $LA = Ph$, so I can substitute Ph into the equation for LA.

$$164\frac{1}{2} \text{ ft}^2 = (5 \text{ ft.} + 8 \text{ ft.} + 5\text{ft.} + 8 \text{ ft.})h + 2(5 \text{ ft.} \times 8 \text{ ft.})$$

$$164\frac{1}{2} \text{ ft}^2 = (26 \text{ ft.})h + 80 \text{ ft}^2$$

$$164\frac{1}{2} \text{ ft}^2 - 80 \text{ ft}^2 = (26 \text{ ft.})h + 80 \text{ ft}^2 - 80 \text{ ft}^2$$

$$84\frac{1}{2} \text{ ft}^2 = (26 \text{ ft.})h$$

$$\left(\frac{1}{26 \text{ ft.}}\right)\left(84\frac{1}{2} \text{ ft}^2\right) = \left(\frac{1}{26 \text{ ft.}}\right)(26 \text{ ft.})h$$

$$3\frac{1}{4} \text{ ft.} = h$$

> I substitute all the values I know into the equation. However, I do not know the value of h.

> I use my knowledge of solving equations to determine the height of the prism.

The height of the prism is $3\frac{1}{4}$ ft.

EUREKA MATH

G7-M3-Lesson 22: Surface Area

Surface Area of Nets

1. For the following net, draw (or describe) the solid represented by the net, and find its surface area. Each of the triangular faces is identical.

The net represents a square pyramid where the four lateral faces are identical triangles. The base is square.

> The pyramid only has one base, so the formula for surface area should reflect this.

$$SA = LA + B$$

> The lateral area is the area of the four identical triangles. The area of the base is the area of the square base.

$$LA = 4\left(\tfrac{1}{2} \times 8 \text{ cm} \times 6 \text{ cm}\right)$$

$$LA = 4(24 \text{ cm}^2)$$ $$B = 6 \text{ cm} \times 6 \text{ cm}$$

$$LA = 96 \text{ cm}^2$$ $$B = 36 \text{ cm}^2$$

$$SA = 96 \text{ cm}^2 + 36 \text{ cm}^2$$

$$SA = 132 \text{ cm}^2$$

(Net diagram: 10 cm, 10 cm, 8 cm, 6 cm)

© 2015 Great Minds eureka-math.org
G7-M3-HWH-1.3.0-09.2015

Surface Area of Multiple Cubes

> I know the volume of a cube is s^3, which means each edge length is $\frac{1}{3}$ cm because $\left(\frac{1}{3} \text{ cm}\right)^3 = \frac{1}{27} \text{ cm}^3$.

2. In the diagram, there are 14 cubes glued together to form a solid. Each cube has a volume of $\frac{1}{27}$ cm³. Find the surface area of the solid.

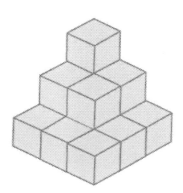

Each cube has edges that are $\frac{1}{3}$ cm long.

The cube faces have an area of $\left(\frac{1}{3} \text{ cm}\right)^2$ or $\frac{1}{9}$ cm².

There are 42 cube faces that make up the surface of the solid.

$$SA = 42\left(\frac{1}{9} \text{ cm}^2\right)$$

$$SA = 4\frac{2}{3} \text{ cm}^2$$

> I also have to remember that there are faces that I cannot see.

Surface Area of Prisms with Shapes Cut Out

3. Find the surface area of the solid shown in the diagram. The solid is a right triangular prism (with right triangular bases) with a smaller right triangular prism removed from it.

$$SA = LA + 2B$$

$$LA = Ph$$

$$LA = \left(7 \text{ m} + 7 \text{ m} + 9\frac{9}{10} \text{ m}\right)(3 \text{ m})$$

$$LA = \left(23\frac{9}{10} \text{ m}\right)(3 \text{ m})$$

$$LA = 71\frac{7}{10} \text{ m}^2$$

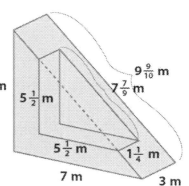

> The $7\frac{7}{9}$ m by $1\frac{1}{4}$ m rectangle has to be taken away from the lateral area.

$$A = 7\frac{7}{9} \text{ m} \times 1\frac{1}{4} \text{ m}$$

$$A = 9\frac{13}{18} \text{ m}^2$$

$$LA = 71\frac{7}{10} \text{ m}^2 - 9\frac{13}{18} \text{ m}^2$$

$$LA = 61\frac{44}{45} \text{ m}^2$$

© 2015 Great Minds eureka-math.org
G7-M3-HWH-1.3.0-09.2015

EUREKA MATH

Two lateral faces of the smaller triangular prisms must be added.

The bases of the larger triangular prism are isosceles triangles.

$$SA = 61\frac{44}{45}\ \text{m}^2 + 2\left(5\frac{1}{2}\ \text{m} \times 1\frac{1}{4}\ \text{m}\right) + 2\left(\frac{1}{2} \times 7\ \text{m} \times 7\ \text{m}\right)$$

$$SA = 61\frac{44}{45}\ \text{m}^2 + 13\frac{3}{4}\ \text{m}^2 + 49\ \text{m}^2$$

$$SA = 124\frac{131}{180}\ \text{m}^2$$

4. The diagram below shows a cube that has had three square holes punched completely through the cube on three perpendicular axes. Find the surface area of the remaining solid.

The exterior is a cube with a square hole on each of its six faces.

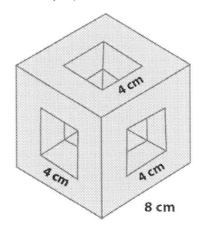

Surface area of the exterior:

$$SA = 6(8\ \text{cm} \times 8\ \text{cm}) - 6(4\ \text{cm} \times 4\ \text{cm})$$

$$SA = 6\left(64\ \text{cm}^2\right) - 6\left(16\ \text{cm}^2\right)$$

$$SA = 384\ \text{cm}^2 - 96\ \text{cm}^2$$

$$SA = 288\ \text{cm}^2$$

Surface area of the holes:

Each of the holes is a square with a depth of 2 cm.

$$SA = 6(LA)$$

$$SA = 6\big((4\ \text{cm} + 4\ \text{cm} + 4\ \text{cm} + 4\ \text{cm}) \times 2\ \text{cm}\big)$$

$$SA = 6(16\ \text{cm} \times 2\ \text{cm})$$

$$SA = 6\left(32\ \text{cm}^2\right)$$

$$SA = 192\ \text{cm}^2$$

The total surface area would be the sum of the exterior surface area and the area of the holes.

Total surface area:

$$SA = 288\ \text{cm}^2 + 192\ \text{cm}^2$$

$$SA = 480\ \text{cm}^2$$

G7-M3-Lesson 23: The Volume of a Right Prism

1. Calculate the volume of each right prism using the formula $V = Bh$.

a.

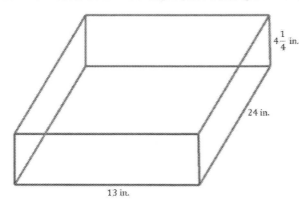

To calculate the volume of the prism, I find the product of the area of the base and the height of the prism.

$V = Bh$

$V = (13 \text{ in.} \times 24 \text{ in.}) \times 4\frac{1}{4} \text{ in.}$

$V = 312 \text{ in}^2 \times 4\frac{1}{4} \text{ in.}$

$V = 1,326 \text{ in}^3$

The volume of the solid is $1,326 \text{ in}^3$.

b. $B = A_{\text{lg rectangle}} - A_{\text{sm rectangle}}$

$B = \left(8\frac{1}{3} \text{ cm} \times 5 \text{ cm}\right) - (3 \text{ cm} \times 2 \text{ cm})$

$B = \left(\frac{25}{3} \text{ cm} \times 5 \text{ cm}\right) - 6 \text{ cm}^2$

$B = 41\frac{2}{3} \text{ cm}^2 - 6 \text{ cm}^2$

$B = 35\frac{2}{3} \text{ cm}^2$

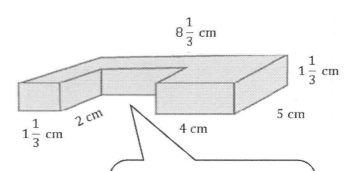

There is a section cut out of the prism. I can find the area of the entire base and then subtract the area that has been cut out of the prism.

$V = Bh$

$V = 35\frac{2}{3} \text{ cm}^2 \left(1\frac{1}{3} \text{ cm}\right)$

$V = \frac{107}{3} \text{ cm}^2 \left(\frac{4}{3} \text{ cm}\right)$

$V = \frac{428}{9} \text{ cm}^3$

$V = 47\frac{5}{9} \text{ cm}^3$

Once I calculate the area of the base, I still multiply it by the height of the prism to calculate the volume of the entire prism.

The volume of the solid is $47\frac{5}{9} \text{ cm}^3$.

EUREKA MATH

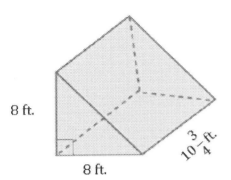

c.

$$B = \frac{1}{2}bh_{\text{triangle}}$$

$$B = \frac{1}{2}(8\text{ ft.})(8\text{ ft.})$$

$$B = 32\text{ ft}^2$$

> The base of the prism is a triangle, so I use the area formula for a triangle to calculate the area of the base.

$$V = Bh_{\text{prism}}$$

$$V = 32\text{ ft}^2 \times 10\frac{3}{4}\text{ ft.}$$

$$V = 32\text{ ft}^2 \times \frac{43}{4}\text{ ft.}$$

$$V = 344\text{ ft}^3$$

> The height of the prism is the distance between the two triangular bases.

The volume of the solid is 344 ft^3.

> I can decompose the trapezoidal base into a rectangle and a triangle. I could also choose to use the area formula for a trapezoid, which is $A = \frac{1}{2}(b_1 + b_2)h$.

d.

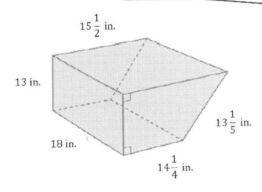

$$B = A_{\text{rectangle}} + A_{\text{triangle}}$$

$$B = \left(14\frac{1}{4}\text{ in.} \times 13\text{ in.}\right) + \left(\frac{1}{2} \times 1\frac{1}{4}\text{ in.} \times 13\text{ in.}\right)$$

$$B = \left(\frac{57}{4}\text{ in.} \times 13\text{ in.}\right) + \left(\frac{1}{2} \times \frac{5}{4}\text{ in.} \times 13\text{ in.}\right)$$

$$B = \frac{741}{4}\text{ in}^2 + \frac{65}{8}\text{ in}^2$$

$$B = \frac{1482}{8}\text{ in}^2 + \frac{65}{8}\text{ in}^2$$

$$B = \frac{1547}{8}\text{ in}^2$$

$$V = Bh$$

$$V = \frac{1547}{8}\text{ in}^2 \times 18\text{ in.}$$

$$V = 3,480\frac{3}{4}\text{ in}^3$$

> I wait to convert this fraction into a mixed number until I am done with all of my calculations.

The volume of this solid is $3,480\frac{3}{4}\text{ in}^3$.

EUREKA MATH™

© 2015 Great Minds eureka-math.org
G7-M3-HWH-1.3.0-09.2015

2. Let l represent the length, w the width, and h the height of a right rectangular prism. Find the volume of the prism when $l = 12$ m, $w = \frac{5}{6}$ m, $h = 6\frac{1}{10}$ m.

$V = Bh$

$V = lwh$

$V = 12 \text{ m} \times \frac{5}{6} \text{ m} \times 6\frac{1}{10} \text{ m}$

$V = 10 \text{ m}^2 \times 6\frac{1}{10} \text{ m}$

$V = 61 \text{ m}^3$

> I multiply the length and width to calculate the area of the base of a right rectangular prism. Therefore, I can substitute lw in for B in the volume formula.

3. Find the length of the edge indicated in the diagram if the volume of the prism is 432 cm^3.

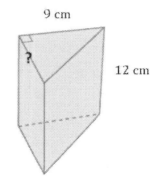

9 cm

12 cm

Let h represent the number of centimeters in the height of the triangular base of the prism.

$$V = Bh$$

$$V = \left(\frac{1}{2}bh_{\text{triangle}}\right)(h_{\text{prism}})$$

$$432 \text{ cm}^3 = \left(\frac{1}{2} \cdot 9 \text{ cm} \cdot h\right)(12 \text{ cm})$$

$$432 \text{ cm}^3 = \frac{1}{2} \cdot 108 \text{ cm}^2 \cdot h$$

$$432 \text{ cm}^3 = 54 \text{ cm}^2 \cdot h$$

$$\left(\frac{1}{54 \text{ cm}^2}\right)(432 \text{ cm}^3) = \left(\frac{1}{54 \text{ cm}^2}\right)54 \text{ cm}^2 \cdot h$$

$$8 \text{ cm} = h$$

> I substitute the information I know into the volume formula and then use my knowledge of solving equations to determine the height of the prism.

The height of the triangle is 8 cm.

EUREKA MATH

4. Given a right rectangular prism with a volume of 36 in³, a length of 8 in., and a width of 3 in., find the height of the prism.

Let h represent the number of inches in the height of the prism.

$$V = lwh$$
$$36 \text{ in}^3 = 8 \text{ in.} \times 3 \text{ in.} \times h$$
$$36 \text{ in}^3 = 24 \text{ in}^2 \times h$$
$$\left(\frac{1}{24 \text{ in}^2}\right) 36 \text{ in}^3 = \left(\frac{1}{24 \text{ in}^2}\right) \times 24 \text{ in}^2 \times h$$
$$1\frac{1}{2} \text{ in.} = h$$

> I can use $V = lwh$ because the bases of the prism are rectangles. Using this formula, I can use my knowledge of solving equations to determine the height.

The height of the prism is $1\frac{1}{2}$ in.

G7-M3-Lesson 24: The Volume of a Right Prism

> If I did not know the inside dimensions, I would not be able to calculate the correct volume because the thickness of the walls has an impact on the volume when using dimensions on the outside of the tank.

1. Whitney bought an aquarium that is a right rectangular prism. The inside dimensions of the aquarium are 75 cm long, by 50 cm, by 70 cm deep. She plans to put water in the aquarium before purchasing any pet fish. How many liters of water does she need to put in the aquarium so that the water level is 8 cm from the top?

$V = lwh$

$V = 75 \text{ cm} \times 50 \text{ cm} \times 62 \text{ cm}$

$V = 232,500 \text{ cm}^3$

> The height of the water is only 62 cm because the water level is 8 cm below the top of the aquarium.

$232,500 \text{ cm}^3 = 232.5 \ L$

> I know that there are 1,000 cubic centimeters in 1 liter.

The volume of the water needed is $232.5 \ L$.

2. The insides of two different water tanks are shown below. Which tank has the smaller capacity? Justify your answer.

$V_1 = Bh$

$V_1 = (9 \text{ ft.} \times 2.8 \text{ ft.}) \times 4 \text{ ft.}$

$V_1 = 25.2 \text{ ft}^2 \times 4 \text{ ft.}$

$V_1 = 100.8 \text{ ft}^3$

> I need to determine the volume of each tank in order to determine which one has a smaller capacity.

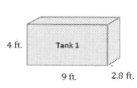
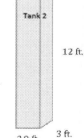

$V_2 = (2.8 \text{ ft.} \times 3 \text{ ft.}) \times 12 \text{ ft.}$

$V_2 = 8.4 \text{ ft}^2 \times 12 \text{ ft.}$

$V_2 = 100.8 \text{ ft}^3$

Each prism has a volume of 100.8 ft^3, *which means that both tanks have the same capacity so neither one has a smaller capacity.*

EUREKA MATH

© 2015 Great Minds eureka-math.org
G7-M3-HWH-1.3.0-09.2015

3. The inside base of a right rectangular prism-shaped tank is 42 cm by 59 cm. What is the minimum height inside the tank if the volume of the liquid in the tank is 74.34 L?

In order to find the height, all the known dimensions must have the same units. I know 74.34 L is equivalent to 74,340 cm^3.

$$V = Bh$$
$$74,340 \text{ cm}^3 = (42 \text{ cm} \times 59 \text{ cm}) \times h$$
$$74,340 \text{ cm}^3 = 2,478 \text{ cm}^2 \times h$$
$$\left(\frac{1}{2,478 \text{ cm}^2}\right)(74,340 \text{ cm}^3) = \left(\frac{1}{2,478 \text{ cm}^2}\right)(2,478 \text{ cm}^2 \times h)$$
$$30 \text{ cm} = h$$

The minimum height of the tank is 30 cm.

4. The inside of a right rectangular prism-shaped tank has a base that is 18 cm by 30 cm and a height of 42 cm. The tank is filled to its capacity with water, and then 4.32 L of water was removed. How far did the water level drop?

$$V = Bh$$
$$V = (18 \text{ cm} \times 30 \text{ cm}) \times 42 \text{ cm}$$
$$V = 540 \text{ cm}^2 \times 42 \text{ cm}$$
$$V = 22,680 \text{ cm}^3$$

I need to determine the maximum capacity of the tank before I can worry about letting water out.

The capacity of the tank is 22,680 cm^3 *or* 22.68 L.

$$22.68 \text{ L} - 4.32 \text{ L} = 18.36 \text{ L}$$

When 4.32 L are removed from the tank, 18.36 L, or 18,360 cm^3, are left.

I can use the new volume of the water to determine the height of the water left in the tank.

$$V = Bh$$
$$18,360 \text{ cm}^3 = (18 \text{ cm} \times 30 \text{ cm}) \times h$$
$$18,360 \text{ cm}^3 = 540 \text{ cm}^2 \times h$$
$$\left(\frac{1}{540 \text{ cm}^2}\right)(18,360 \text{ cm}^3) = \left(\frac{1}{540 \text{ cm}^2}\right)(540 \text{ cm}^2 \times h)$$
$$34 \text{ cm} = h$$

$$42 \text{ cm} - 34 \text{ cm} = 8 \text{ cm}$$
The water level has dropped 8 cm.

I know the original height of the water was 42 cm. After some water was removed, the height is now 34 cm.

EUREKA MATH

Lesson 24:   The Volume of a Right Prism

75

© 2015 Great Minds eureka-math.org
G7-M3-HWH-1.3.0-09.2015

5. A tank in the shape of a right rectangular prism has inside dimensions of $35\frac{1}{2}$ cm long and $42\frac{1}{5}$ cm wide. The tank is $\frac{3}{4}$ full of water. It contains 89.886 L of water. Find the height of the container.

$$V = lwh$$

$$89,886 \text{ cm}^3 = \left(35\frac{1}{2} \text{ cm} \times 42\frac{1}{5} \text{ cm}\right) \times h$$

$$89,886 \text{ cm}^3 = 1,498.1 \text{ cm}^2 \times h$$

$$\left(\frac{1}{1,498.1 \text{ cm}^2}\right)(89,886 \text{ cm}^3) = \left(\frac{1}{1,498.1 \text{ cm}^2}\right)(1,498.1 \text{ cm}^2 \times h)$$

$$60 \text{ cm} = h$$

> If I determine the height of the water, I can use this information to determine the height of the tank.

Let d represent the depth of the container in centimeters.

$$60 \text{ cm} = \frac{3}{4} \cdot d$$

$$\left(\frac{4}{3}\right)(60 \text{ cm}) = \left(\frac{4}{3}\right)\left(\frac{3}{4} \cdot d\right)$$

$$80 \text{ cm} = d$$

> I know the water only fills $\frac{3}{4}$ of the tank, so the height of the tank should be larger than the height of the water.

The depth of the container is 80 cm.

Lesson 24:   The Volume of a Right Prism

EUREKA
MATH

G7-M3-Lesson 25: Volume and Surface Area

1. The dimensions of two right rectangular fish tanks are listed below. Find the volume in cubic centimeters, the capacity in liters, and the surface area in square centimeters for each tank. What do you observe about the change in volume compared with the change in surface area between the two tanks?

Tank Size	Length (cm)	Width (cm)	Height (cm)
Small	20	14	11
Large	32	20	21

$V_s = 20 \text{ cm} \times 14 \text{ cm} \times 11 \text{ cm} = 3,080 \text{ cm}^3$

$V_l = 32 \text{ cm} \times 20 \text{ cm} \times 21 \text{ cm} = 13,440 \text{ cm}^3$

> Once I know the volume, I can calculate the capacity by converting the cubic centimeters into liters.

$SA_s = 2(20 \text{ cm} \times 14 \text{ cm}) + 2(14 \text{ cm} \times 11 \text{ cm}) + 2(20 \text{ cm} \times 11 \text{cm})$

$SA_s = 2(280 \text{ cm}^2) + 2(154 \text{ cm}^2) + 2(220 \text{ cm}^2)$

$SA_s = 560 \text{ cm}^2 + 308 \text{ cm}^2 + 440 \text{ cm}^2$

$SA_s = 1,308 \text{ cm}^2$

> I remember how to calculate the surface area from Lessons 21 and 22.

$SA_l = 2(32 \text{ cm} \times 20 \text{ cm}) + 2(20 \text{ cm} \times 21 \text{ cm}) + 2(32 \text{ cm} \times 21 \text{ cm})$

$SA_l = 2(640 \text{ cm}^2) + 2(420 \text{ cm}^2) + 2(672 \text{ cm}^2)$

$SA_l = 1,280 \text{ cm}^2 + 840 \text{ cm}^2 + 1,344 \text{ cm}^2$

$SA_l = 3,464 \text{ cm}^2$

Tank Size	Volume (cm^3)	Capacity (L)	Surface Area (cm^2)
Small	3,080	3.08	1,308
Large	13,440	13.44	3,464

The volume of the large tank is about four times the volume of the small tank. However, the surface area of the large tank is only about two and half times the surface area of the small tank.

© 2015 Great Minds eureka-math.org
G7-M3-HWH-1.3.0-09.2015

2. A rectangular container 30 cm long by 20 cm wide contains 12 L of water.

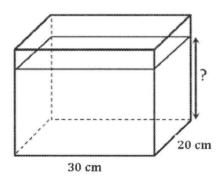

20 cm

30 cm

a. Find the height of the water level in the container.

$$12 \, L = 12,000 \, cm^3$$

> I have to convert the capacity of the water to cm^3 before finding the height of the water.

$$12,000 \, cm^3 = 30 \, cm \times 20 \, cm \times h$$
$$12,000 \, cm^3 = 600 \, cm^2 \times h$$
$$\left(\frac{1}{600 \, cm^2}\right)(12,000 \, cm^3) = \left(\frac{1}{600 \, cm^2}\right)(600 \, cm^2 \times h)$$
$$20 \, cm = h$$

The height of the water is 20 cm.

b. If the height of the container is 24 cm, how many more liters of water would it take to completely fill the container?

$$V = 30 \, cm \times 20 \, cm \times 24 \, cm = 14,400 \, cm^3$$
$$14.4 \, L - 12 \, L = 2.4 \, L$$

> The total capacity of the container is 14.4 L.

> I need to find the difference between the total capacity and the capacity of the water to determine the amount of water needed to fill the container.

To completely fill the tank, 2.4 L of water would have to be added to the tank.

Lesson 25:   Volume and Surface Area

© 2015 Great Minds eureka-math.org
G7-M3-HWH-1.3.0-09.2015

EUREKA
MATH

c.   What percentage of the tank is filled when it contains 12 L of water?

$$\frac{12\ L}{14.4\ L} = 0.8\overline{3} = 83\frac{1}{3}\%$$

> I divide the part by the whole in order to find the percent.

3.   Two tanks are shown below. Both are filled to capacity, but the owner decides to drain them. Tank 1 is draining at a rate of 6 liters per minute. Tank 2 is draining at a rate of 7 liters per minute. Which tank empties first?

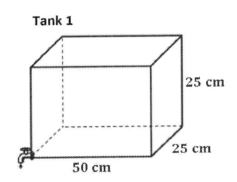

Tank 1

25 cm
25 cm
50 cm

Tank 2

60 cm
15 cm
65 cm

Tank 1 Volume: $50\ cm \times 25\ cm \times 25\ cm = 31,250\ cm^3$

Tank 2 Volume: $65\ cm \times 15\ cm \times 60\ cm = 58,500\ cm^3$

> Before finding the time it takes to drain the tank, I need to calculate the capacity of each tank.

Tank 1 Capacity: $31.25\ L$ *Tank 2 Capacity:* $58.5\ L$

Time to drain Tank 1: $\dfrac{31.25\ L}{6\frac{L}{min}} \approx 5.2$ min.   *Time to drain Tank 2:* $\dfrac{58.5\ L}{7\frac{L}{min}} \approx 8.4$ min.

> I divide the capacity of each tank by the rate at which the tank drains to determine how long it takes to drain each tank.

Tank 1 will be empty first because it will drain in about 5.2 *minutes, and Tank 2 drains in about* 8.4 *minutes.*

4. Two tanks have equal volumes. The tops are open. The owner wants to cover one tank with a glass top. The cost of glass is $0.08 per square inch. Which tank would be less expensive to cover? How much less?

   Dimensions of Tank 1: 14 in. long by 6 in. wide by 9 in. high

   Dimensions of Tank 2: 12 in. long by 9 in. wide by 7 in. high

   > I need to know the surface area of the top of each tank before I can determine how much it costs for the glass.

   $$SA_1 = 14 \text{ in.} \times 6 \text{ in.} = 84 \text{ in}^2 \qquad\qquad SA_2 = 12 \text{ in.} \times 9 \text{ in.} = 108 \text{ in}^2$$

   > To determine the total cost, I multiply the cost of the glass by the number of square inches needed for each top.

   Tank 1 Cost: $\dfrac{\$0.08}{\text{in}^2} \cdot 84 \text{ in}^2 = \$6.72$ *Tank 2 Cost:* $\dfrac{\$0.08}{\text{in}^2} \cdot 108 \text{ in}^2 = \$8.64$

   The second tank is $1.92 cheaper to cover than the first tank.

© 2015 Great Minds eureka-math.org
G7-M3-HWH-1.3.0-09.2015

G7-M3-Lesson 26: Volume and Surface Area

1. A child's toy is constructed by cutting a right triangular prism out of a right rectangular prism. The image is not drawn to scale.

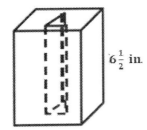

Top View

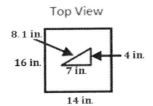

8.1 in.

16 in.

4 in.

7 in.

14 in.

$6\frac{1}{2}$ in.

a. Calculate the volume of the right rectangular prism.

$V = 14 \text{ in.} \times 16 \text{ in.} \times 6\frac{1}{2} \text{ in.} = 1,456 \text{ in}^3$

> I use the area formula for a triangle to calculate the area of the base of the triangular prism.

b. Calculate the volume of the triangular prism.

$V = \frac{1}{2}(7 \text{ in.} \times 4 \text{ in.}) \times 6\frac{1}{2} \text{ in.} = 14 \text{ in}^2 \times 6\frac{1}{2} \text{ in.} = 91 \text{ in}^3$

c. Calculate the volume of the material remaining in the rectangular prism.

$V = 1,456 \text{ in}^3 - 91 \text{ in}^3 = 1,365 \text{ in}^3$

> The remaining volume is the difference between the volumes of the rectangular prism and the triangular prism.

d. What is the largest number of triangular prisms that can be cut from the rectangular prism?

$\dfrac{1,456 \text{ in}^3}{91 \text{ in}^3} = 16$

> I calculate the quotient of the two volumes to determine how many triangular prisms will fit inside the rectangular prism.

e. What is the surface area of the triangular prism (assume there is no top or bottom)?

$SA = 7 \text{ in.} \times 6\frac{1}{2} \text{ in.} + 4 \text{ in.} \times 6\frac{1}{2} \text{ in.} + 8.1 \text{ in.} \times 6\frac{1}{2} \text{ in.}$

$SA = 45.5 \text{ in}^2 + 26 \text{ in}^2 + 52.65 \text{ in}^2$

$SA = 124.15 \text{ in}^2$

> I only have to find the area of the three faces of the triangle since there is no top or bottom.

EUREKA MATH

© 2015 Great Minds eureka-math.org
G7-M3-HWH-1.3.0-09.2015

2. A landscape designer is constructing a flower bed in the shape of a right trapezoidal prism. He needs to run three identical square prisms through the bed for drainage.

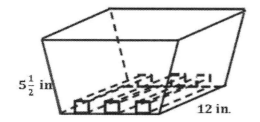
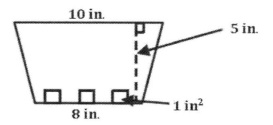

a. What is the volume of the bed without the drainage pipes?

$$V = \frac{1}{2}(8 \text{ in.} + 10 \text{ in.}) \times 5 \text{ in.} \times 12 \text{ in.} = 9 \text{ in.} \times 5 \text{ in.} \times 12 \text{ in.} = 540 \text{ in}^3$$

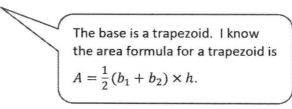

The base is a trapezoid. I know the area formula for a trapezoid is $A = \frac{1}{2}(b_1 + b_2) \times h$.

b. What is the total volume of the drainage pipes?

$$V = 3(1 \text{ in}^2 \times 12 \text{ in.}) = 3(12 \text{ in}^3) = 36 \text{ in}^3$$

c. What is the volume of the soil if the planter is filled to $\frac{3}{5}$ of its total capacity with the pipes in place?

$$V = \frac{3}{5}(540 \text{ in}^3) - 36 \text{ in}^3 = 288 \text{ in}^3$$

I know the volume of the soil is $\frac{3}{5}$ of the total volume minus the volume of the drainage pipes.

d. What is the height of the soil? If necessary, round to the nearest tenth.

$$288 \text{ in}^3 = \frac{1}{2}(8 \text{ in.} + 10 \text{ in.}) \times h \times 12 \text{ in.}$$

$$288 \text{ in}^3 = 108 \text{ in}^2 \times h$$

$$\left(\frac{1}{108 \text{ in}^2}\right)(288 \text{ in}^3) = \left(\frac{1}{108 \text{ in}^2}\right)(108 \text{ in}^2 \times h)$$

$$2.67 \text{ in.} \approx h$$

The soil has a height of about 2.67 in.

EUREKA MATH

Homework Helpers

Grade 7
Module 4

G7-M4-Lesson 1: Percent

1. Create a model to represent the following percents.

a.   75%

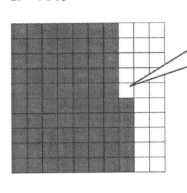

> Each box represents 1% because there are 100 boxes. Therefore, I can shade in any 75 boxes to represent 75%.

b.   0.5%

> I will have to shade in less than one box because the percent given is less than 1.

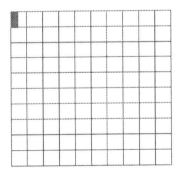

c.   350%

> 350% is greater than 100%, so I will need more than one grid to model the given percent.

  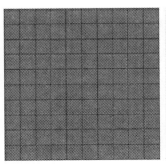 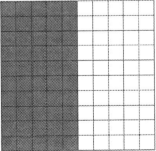

2. Complete the table by converting among fractions, decimals, and percents.

> To convert a fraction to a decimal, I can either use long division or find an equivalent fraction with a denominator as a multiple of 10.

> To convert a fraction to a percent, I find an equivalent fraction with a denominator of 100.

Fraction	Decimal	Percent
$\dfrac{1}{5}$	$\dfrac{1}{5} = \dfrac{2}{10} = 0.2$	$\dfrac{1}{5} = \dfrac{20}{100} = 20\%$

> To convert a decimal to a fraction, I use the place value of the digit furthest to the right to determine my denominator.

> The 5 is in the thousandths place.

> To convert a decimal to a percent, I write the decimal as a fraction with a denominator of 100.

$\dfrac{815}{1000}$	0.815	$\dfrac{81.5}{100} = 81.5\%$

> To convert a percent to a fraction, I write the percent as a fraction with a denominator of 100 and change to a mixed number if necessary.

> To convert a percent to a decimal, I write the percent as a fraction with a denominator of 100 and then use place value to write the value as a decimal.

$\dfrac{225}{100} = 2\dfrac{25}{100} = 2\dfrac{1}{4}$	$\dfrac{225}{100} = 2\dfrac{25}{100} = 2.25$	225%

3. Order the following from least to greatest.

$200\%, \quad 2.1, \quad \dfrac{1}{50}, \quad 0.2, \quad \dfrac{20{,}000}{1{,}000}, \quad 0.02\%, \quad 0.002$

> I can rewrite every term as a decimal to make the comparison easier:
> $2, \quad 2.1, \quad 0.02, \quad 0.2, \quad 20, \quad 0.0002, \quad 0.002$

$0.02\%, \quad 0.002, \quad \dfrac{1}{50}, \quad 0.2, \quad 200\%, \quad 2.1, \quad \dfrac{20{,}000}{1{,}000}$

EUREKA MATH™

G7-M4-Lesson 2: Part of a Whole as a Percent

I know that "is" means "equals" and that "of" means "multiply." Using this knowledge, I can translate the words into an equation.

Represent each situation using an equation.

1. What number is 20% of 80?

   Let n represent the unknown number.

   $n = 20\%(80)$

   Before I can solve for n, I need to convert the percent to a decimal or a fraction.

   $n = 0.2(80)$

   $n = 16$

   This means 16 is 20% of 80.

2. 28 is 40% of what number?

   Let n represent the unknown number.

   $$28 = 40\%(n)$$
   $$28 = \frac{40}{100}n$$
   $$\left(\frac{100}{40}\right)(28) = \left(\frac{100}{40}\right)\left(\frac{40}{100}n\right)$$
   $$70 = n$$

   Therefore, 28 is 40% of 70.

   In order to solve for n, I multiply both sides of the equation by the multiplicative inverse of $\frac{40}{100}$.

3. 40 is what percent of 50?

   Let p represent the unknown percent.

   $$40 = p(50)$$
   $$40\left(\frac{1}{50}\right) = p(50)\left(\frac{1}{50}\right)$$
   $$0.8 = p$$

   $p = 0.8 = 80\%$

   Therefore, 40 is 80% of 50.

Use percents to solve the following real-world problems.

> When solving real-world problems, I can use the formula Part = Percent × Whole.

4. Michael spent 40% of his money on new shoes. If Michael spent $85 on his new shoes, how much money did Michael have at the beginning?

    $$Part = Percent \times Whole$$

    > I know the percent and the part; I need to calculate the whole.

    Let w represent the amount of money Michael had at the beginning.

    $$85 = 40\% \times w$$

    > Michael spent 40% of his money, w, on shoes.

    $$85 = 0.4 \times w$$
    $$85\left(\frac{1}{0.4}\right) = 0.4w\left(\frac{1}{0.4}\right)$$
    $$212.5 = w$$

    This means that Michael had $212.50 before he bought new shoes.

5. McKayla took 30 shots during her last basketball game, but only made 18 baskets. What percent of her shots did McKayla make?

    $$Part = Percent \times Whole$$

    > I know the whole is the number of shots McKayla took, and the part is the 18 baskets she made.

    Let p represent the percent of the shots McKayla made.

    $$18 = p \times 30$$
    $$18\left(\frac{1}{30}\right) = p(30)\left(\frac{1}{30}\right)$$
    $$0.6 = p$$

    $$p = 0.6 = 60\%$$

    This means that McKayla made 60% of the baskets she shot.

Lesson 2:   Part of a Whole as a Percent

© 2015 Great Minds eureka-math.org
G7-M4-HWH-1.3.0-10.2015

EUREKA
MATH

G7-M4-Lesson 3: Comparing Quantities with Percent

> When solving real-world problems with percents, I can use the formula Quantity = Percent × Whole.

> I am being asked to find the percent of the old number of participants. Therefore, the old number of participants is the whole.

1. The number of participants in the city choir decreased from 40 to 25.

    a. Express the new number of participants as a percent of the old number of participants.

    Let p represent the unknown percent.

    $$\text{Quanitity} = \text{Percent} \times \text{Whole}$$
    $$25 = p \times 40$$

    > The question is asking for a percent, so I need to convert this decimal to a percent.

    $$25\left(\frac{1}{40}\right) = p(40)\left(\frac{1}{40}\right)$$

    > In Lesson 2, I solved equations similar to this one.

    $$0.625 = 1p$$
    $$0.625 = p$$

    The new number of participants is 62.5% of the old number of participants.

    > The question has changed, and now the new number of participants is the whole.

    b. Express the old number of participants as a percent of the new number of participants.

    Let p represent the unknown percent.

    $$\text{Quantity} = \text{Percent} \times \text{Whole}$$
    $$40 = p \times 25$$
    $$40\left(\frac{1}{25}\right) = p(25)\left(\frac{1}{25}\right)$$
    $$1.6 = 1p$$
    $$1.6 = p$$

    The old number of participants is 160% of the new number of participants.

> The number of students who attend Berry is the whole, and the number of students who attend Newton is the quantity.

2. The number of students who attend Newton Elementary School is 75% of the number of students who attend Berry Middle School.

   a. Find the number of students who attend Newton if 500 students attend Berry.

   $$\text{Quantity} = \text{Percent} \times \text{Whole}$$
   I know the percent and the whole; I have to determine the quantity.

   Let n represent the number of students who attend Newton.

   $n = 75\%(500)$
   Before solving the equation, I need to convert the percent to a decimal.

   $n = 0.75(500)$
   In order to solve for n, multiply the two factors together.

   $n = 375$

   This means that 375 students attend Newton Elementary School.

   b. Find the number of students who attend Berry if 150 students attend Newton.

   $$\text{Quantity} = \text{Percent} \times \text{Whole}$$

   Let b represent the number of students who attend Berry.

   > The question has changed. I now know the percent and the quantity. I need to calculate the whole.

   $$150 = 75\% \times b$$
   $$150 = 0.75b$$
   $$150\left(\frac{1}{0.75}\right) = 0.75b\left(\frac{1}{0.75}\right)$$
   $$200 = b$$

   Therefore, 200 students attend Berry Middle School.

EUREKA
MATH™

G7-M4-Lesson 4: Percent Increase and Decrease

> This is the original price, so it represents the whole.

1. A store is advertising 20% off a new Blu-ray Player that regularly sells for $60.

    a. What is the sale price of the item?

    $100\% - 20\% = 80\%$

    Therefore, I am paying 80% of the original price.

    > In order to solve this problem, I determine the percent of the original price I have to pay.

    Let n represent the sale price.

    $n = 80\% \times 60$

    $n = 0.8(60)$

    $n = 48$

    The sale price is $48.

    > Percent increase and decrease problems are still percent problems in the real-world, so I use the formula
    > Quantity = Percent × Whole.

    b. If 6% sales tax is charged on the sale price, what is the total with tax?

    $100\% + 6\% = 106\%$

    I pay 106% of the sale price ($48), which will represent the whole since I am finding the sale price with tax.

    > Sales tax increases the price, so I have to pay 100% of the sale price, plus the extra 6% for tax.

    Let t represent the sale price with tax.

    $t = 106\% \times 48$

    $t = 1.06 \times 48$

    $t = 50.88$

    The sale price with tax is $50.88.

2. The Parent-Teacher Organization had 30 participants attend the first meeting of the school year and only 24 participants attend the second meeting. Find the percent decrease in the participants from the first meeting to the second meeting.

$$\textbf{Quantity} = \textbf{Percent} \times \textbf{Whole}$$

> I only want to determine the percent decrease; therefore, the quantity is the amount of decrease, which is 6 because $30 - 24 = 6$.

> The number of participants who attended the first meeting represents the whole.

Let p represent the percent decrease.

$$6 = p \times 30$$
$$6\left(\frac{1}{30}\right) = p \times 30\left(\frac{1}{30}\right)$$
$$0.2 = p$$
$$20\% = p$$

Therefore, the percent decrease is 20%.

3. Chelsey is keeping a diary to keep track of the number of days she goes running. In the first 40 days, she ran 40% of the days. She kept recording for another 20 days and then found that the total number of days she ran increased to 50%. How many of the final 20 days did Chelsey go running?

Let r represent the number of days Chelsey ran during the first 40 days.

$r = 40(40\%)$

> I know I can find the number of days Chelsey ran during the first 40 days where 40 represents the whole.

$r = (40)(0.40)$

$r = 16$

Chelsey ran 16 days in the first 40 days.

Let d represent the total number of days Chelsey went running.

$d = 60(50\%)$

> $40 + 20 = 60$ This means that Chelsey kept the diary for a total of 60 days.

$d = 60(0.50)$

$d = 30$

Chelsey ran a total of 30 days.

$30 - 16 = 14$

> I know the number of days Chelsey ran during the last 20 days is the difference between the total number of days she ran and the number of days she ran during the first 40 days.

Chelsey ran 14 days during the last 20 days.

© 2015 Great Minds eureka-math.org
G7-M4-HWH-1.3.0-10.2015

EUREKA MATH

G7-M4-Lesson 5: Finding One Hundred Percent Given Another Percent

Use a model to answer the problem.

1. The number of students who attended the spring school dance was a 20% decrease from the number of students who attended the fall dance. If 424 students attended the spring dance, how many students attended the fall dance?

> 100% represents the number of students who attended the fall dance and 80% represents the number of students who attended the spring dance. The greatest common factor of 100 and 80 is 20. Therefore, I split the number line into five equal sections each representing 20%.

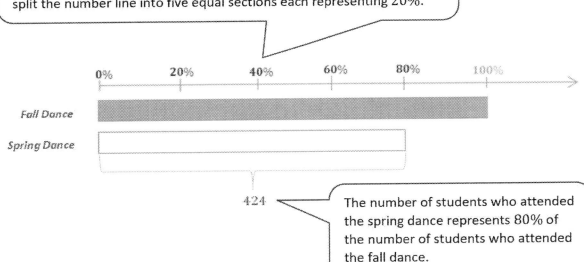

> The number of students who attended the spring dance represents 80% of the number of students who attended the fall dance.

There are four equal sections of 20% *in* 80%.

$424 \div 4 = 106$

Therefore, each of these sections would represent 106.

$106 \times 5 = 530$

There are five equal sections of 20% *in* 100%. *I know that each section of* 20% *represents* 106 *students. The number of students who attended the fall dance was* 530.

Use any method to solve the problem.

2. A middle school ordered new calculators. The science teachers received 40% of the calculators, and the math teachers received 75% of the remaining calculators. There were 60 calculators that were not given to either science or math teachers. How many calculators were given to the science teachers? Math teachers? How many calculators were originally ordered?

I know that 40% of the calculators were given to science teachers, which means 60% of the calculators were given to other teachers.

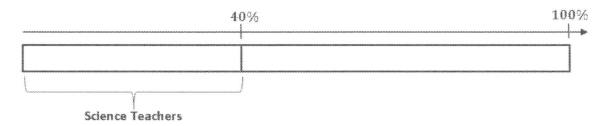

Of the remaining 60% of calculators, math teachers received 75% of them.

$60\% \times 75\% = 45\%$

Therefore, math teachers received 45% of the original amount of calculators.

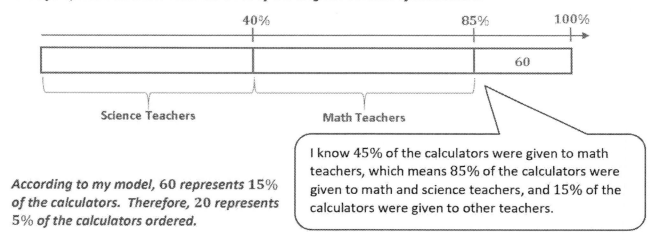

According to my model, 60 represents 15% of the calculators. Therefore, 20 represents 5% of the calculators ordered.

I know 45% of the calculators were given to math teachers, which means 85% of the calculators were given to math and science teachers, and 15% of the calculators were given to other teachers.

If I know 20 represents 5%, I can multiply both values by eight in order to determine how many calculators represents 40% of the calculators ordered. For the same reason, I need to multiply both values by nine to determine the number of calculators the math teachers received.

EUREKA
MATH™

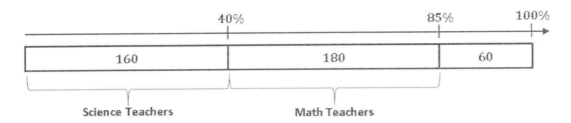

Science teachers received 160 calculators. Math teachers received 180 calculators.

$160 + 180 + 60 = 400$

The school originally ordered 400 calculators.

G7-M4-Lesson 6: Fluency with Percents

1. Monroe Middle School has 564 students, which is 60% of the number of students who attend Wilson Middle School. How many student attend Wilson Middle School?

$$\textbf{Quantity} = \textbf{Percent} \times \textbf{Whole}$$

Let s represent the number of students who attend Wilson Middle School.

$$564 = 60\% \times s$$
$$564 = 0.6 \times s$$
$$\left(\frac{1}{0.6}\right)(564) = \left(\frac{1}{0.6}\right)(0.6)s$$
$$940 = s$$

> I know the number of students who attend Wilson Middle School represents the whole because it is the value being compared to the percent.

940 students attend Wilson Middle School.

2. In a school-wide survey, students could either choose basketball or soccer as their favorite sport. The number of people who chose basketball as their favorite sport was 20% greater than the number of people who chose soccer. If 450 students chose basketball as their favorite sport, how many people took the survey?

Let s represent the number of people who chose soccer as their favorite sport.

$$450 = 120\% \times s$$
$$450 = 1.2s$$
$$\left(\frac{1}{1.2}\right)(450) = \left(\frac{1}{1.2}\right)(1.2s)$$
$$375 = s$$

> The number of people who chose basketball is 120% of those who chose soccer because the number of people who chose basketball is equal to the number of people who chose soccer plus an extra 20% of the people.

The number of people who chose soccer as their favorite sport is 375.

$$375 + 450 = 825$$

The total number of people who completed the survey was 825.

EUREKA
MATH™

3. Electricity City increases the price of televisions by 25%. If a television now sells for $425, what was the original price?

$$\text{Quantity} = \text{Percent} \times \text{Whole}$$

Let p represent the original price, in dollars, of the television.

$$425 = 125\% \times p$$
$$425 = 1.25p$$
$$\left(\frac{1}{1.25}\right)(425) = \left(\frac{1}{1.25}\right)(1.25)p$$
$$340 = p$$

> I know the television sold for 125% of the original price because the cost would be 100% of the original price plus the 25% increase.

The original price of the television is $340.

> I can do a quick check to make sure my answer makes sense. I know that my answer is the original price, which means it should be a smaller value than the price the television sold for.

4. Christopher spent 20% of his paycheck at the mall, and 35% of that amount was spent on a new video game. Christopher spent a total of $21.35 on the video game. How much money was in Christopher's paycheck?

Let m represent the amount Christopher spent at the mall.

$$21.35 = \frac{35}{100}m$$
$$\left(\frac{100}{35}\right)(21.35) = \left(\frac{100}{35}\right)\left(\frac{35}{100}m\right)$$
$$61 = m$$

> The amount Christopher spent at the mall is the whole, and I can determine the amount he spent on a video game.

Christopher spent $61.00 at the mall. Let p represent the amount of money in Christopher's paycheck.

> I can use the information I found in the previous equation to determine the amount of money in Christopher's paycheck.

$$61 = \frac{20}{100}p$$
$$\left(\frac{100}{20}\right)(61) = \left(\frac{100}{20}\right)\left(\frac{20}{100}p\right)$$
$$305 = p$$

Christopher's paycheck was $305.00.

© 2015 Great Minds eureka-math.org
G7-M4-HWH-1.3.0-10.2015

G7-M4-Lesson 7: Markup and Markdown Problems

1. A school is conducting a fundraiser by selling sweatshirts. The school marks up the price of the sweatshirts by 40% in order to make a large profit. The school sells each sweatshirt for $28.

    a. What is the original cost of the sweatshirts?

    Selling Price = 140%(Original Cost)

    Let c represent the original cost.

    > There was a markup of 40%; therefore, the selling price is 140% of the original price because I have to pay 100% of the original price and the 40% markup.

    $$28 = 140\%(c)$$
    $$28 = 1.4c$$
    $$\frac{1}{1.4}(28) = \left(\frac{1}{1.4}\right)(1.4)(c)$$
    $$20 = c$$

    Therefore, the original cost of each sweatshirt was $20.

    b. How much did the school earn on each sweatshirt due to the markup?

    $28 − $20 = $8

    The school earned $8 *due to the markup.*

    > Due to the discount, I will pay 100% − 25%, or 75%, of the original price. However, the sales tax will force me to pay 100% + 6%, or 106%, of the discounted price.

2. A tool bench costs $650 but is marked 25% off. If sales tax is 6%, what is the final cost of the tool bench?

    Let c represent the final cost of the tool bench.

    $$c = (\text{original cost})(\text{percentage paid})(\text{sales tax})$$
    $$c = (650)(0.75)(1.06)$$
    $$c = 516.75$$

    > The commutative and associative properties can help me calculate the product.

    Therefore, the final price of the tool bench is $516.75.

EUREKA MATH

3. A local store sells a small television for $185. However, the local store buys the same television from a wholesaler for $100. What is the markup rate?

Let p represent the percent of the original price.

$$\textbf{Selling Price} = \textbf{Percent} \times \textbf{Original Price}$$

$$185 = p \times 100$$

The selling price is $185, and the original price is $100.

$$\left(\frac{1}{100}\right)(185) = \left(\frac{1}{100}\right)(p \times 100)$$

$$1.85 = p$$

This means that the selling price is 185% of the wholesale price, but this is not the markup rate.

$$185\% - 100\% = 85\%$$

The markup rate is 85%.

4. The sale price for a computer is $450. The original price was first discounted by 25% and then discounted an additional 20%. Find the original price of the computer.

Let c represent the cost of the computer before the additional 20% discount.

$$450 = 0.80c$$

$$\left(\frac{1}{0.80}\right)(450) = \left(\frac{1}{0.80}\right)(0.80c)$$

$$562.5 = c$$

I need to work backward and first find the cost of the computer before the second discount.

Now, I can use the price of the computer after the first discount to determine the original cost.

The cost of the computer before the second discount was $562.50.

A discount of 25% means I pay 75% of the original price.

Let p represent the original cost of the computer.

$$562.5 = 0.75p$$

$$\left(\frac{1}{0.75}\right)(562.5) = \left(\frac{1}{0.75}\right)(0.75p)$$

$$750 = p$$

The original cost of the computer was $750.

G7-M4-Lesson 8: Percent Error Problems

1. Lincoln High School just installed a new basketball court. The length of the new court is 90 feet, and the width of the court is 49 feet. However, the regulation length and width of a basketball court are 94 ft. and 50 ft.

    a. What is the percent error of the width of the basketball court?

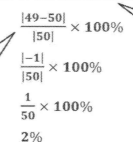

> I know the exact value is 50 ft., and the approximate value is 49 ft.

> I complete the operations within the absolute value before calculating the absolute value, or distance from 0.

$$\frac{|49-50|}{|50|} \times 100\%$$

$$\frac{|-1|}{|50|} \times 100\%$$

$$\frac{1}{50} \times 100\%$$

$$2\%$$

The percent error of the width is 2%.

    b. The percent error of the area of the basketball court must be less than 5%. If the percent error is larger, the court will have to be re-installed. Does Lincoln High School have to re-install its new basketball court? Why or why not?

Exact Area: $94 \text{ ft.} \times 50 \text{ ft.} = 4,700 \text{ ft}^2$

> In order to find the percent error of the area, I first calculate the exact area and the approximate area.

Approximate Area: $90 \text{ ft.} \times 49 \text{ ft.} = 4,410 \text{ ft}^2$

Percent Error: $\frac{|4,410-4,700|}{|4,700|} \times 100\%$

$$\frac{|-290|}{|4,700|} \times 100\%$$

$$\frac{29}{470} \times 100\%$$

$$6.17\%$$

Lincoln High School needs to re-install its basketball court because the area of the new court has more than a 5% percent error.

EUREKA
MATH

2. Michael volunteered his mom to bring snacks for the seventh grade dance. Michael said that the school is expecting anywhere from 100 to 125 students at the dance. At most, what is the percent error?

The approximate value is 125, *and the exact value is* 100.

$$\frac{|100-125|}{|125|} \times 100\%$$

$$\frac{|-25|}{|125|} \times 100\%$$

I know that the percent error is the largest value when the exact value is the smallest value.

$$\frac{25}{125} \times 100\%$$

$$20\%$$

The largest percent error is 20%.

3. In the school choir, 76% of the members are female. If there are 350 members in the school choir, how many members are male?

$$100\% - 76\% = 24\%$$

If 76% of the members of female, then the remaining 24% of the members are male.

Let m *represent the number of choir members who are male.*

$$m = 0.24(350)$$

$$m = 84$$

There are 84 *males in the school choir.*

G7-M4-Lesson 9: Problem Solving When the Percent Changes

Use models to solve each problem.

1. The number of video games Scott has is 125% of the number of Doug's video games. However, Scott's mother forced him to donate 8 video games. Now, Scott and Doug have the same number of video games. How many video games did each boy start with?

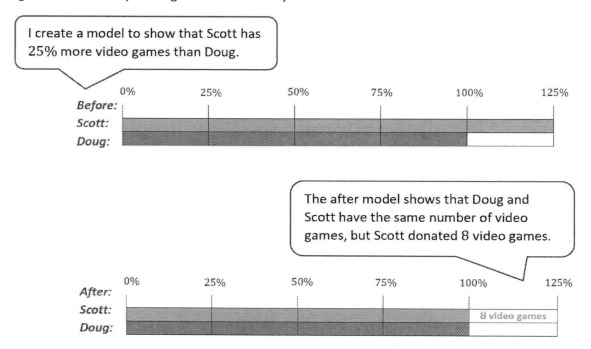

I create a model to show that Scott has 25% more video games than Doug.

The after model shows that Doug and Scott have the same number of video games, but Scott donated 8 video games.

The models show that each bar represents 8 video games.

Scott started with 40 video games because his original tape diagram has 5 bars that each represent 8 video games.

Doug started with 32 video games because his original tape diagram has 4 bars that, again, each represent 8 video games.

EUREKA
MATH™

2. Genesis and Kyle went to the store to buy school supplies. Genesis bought 75% as many pencils as Kyle. Kyle ended up giving 10 of his pencils to his friend, and now the number of pencils Genesis has is 50% more than Kyle. How many pencils did each person have at the beginning?

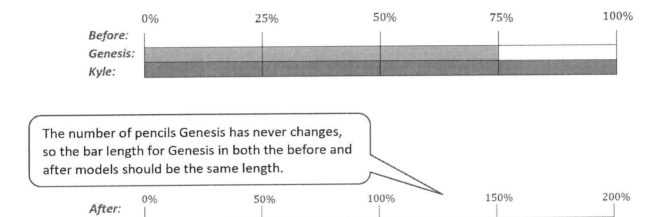

The number of pencils Genesis has never changes, so the bar length for Genesis in both the before and after models should be the same length.

10 pencils

The models show that each bar represents 5 pencils because two bars represent 10 pencils.

Genesis started with 15 pencils because her tape diagram has 3 bars where each represents 5 pencils.

Kyle started with 20 pencils because his tape diagram has 4 bars where each represents 5 pencils.

© 2015 Great Minds eureka-math.org
G7-M4-HWH-1.3.0-10.2015

3. Janaye and Nevaeh compared their money and noticed Janaye had 50% more money than Nevaeh. After Nevaeh earned an extra $20, Janaye had 20% more money. How much more money did Janaye have than Nevaeh at first?

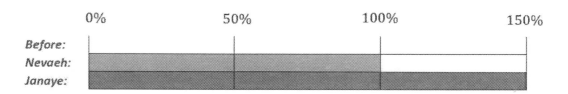

Each model has a different size bars; in order to solve the problem the bars must all be the same size.

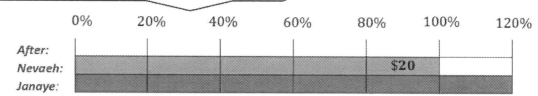

The bars in the first model need to be split in half in order to be the same size as the bars in the after model. This is shown below.

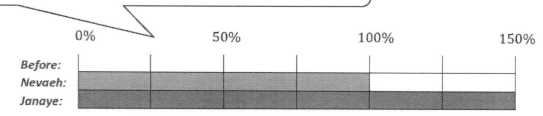

Now that the bars on both models are the same size, I know each bar represents $20.

Therefore, Nevaeh had $80 at the beginning because her tape diagram has 4 bars where each represents $20, and Janaye had $120 at first.

In order to answer the question, I have to determine how much each girl had at the beginning.

$120 − $80 = $40

This means that Janaye had $40 more than Nevaeh at the start.

© 2015 Great Minds eureka-math.org
G7-M4-HWH-1.3.0-10.2015

EUREKA
MATH™

G7-M4-Lesson 10: Simple Interest

1. Joy borrowed $2,000 from the bank and agreed to pay an annual interest rate of 6% for 24 months. What is the amount of interest she will pay on this loan?

$$I = Prt$$

$$I = (2,000)(6\%)\left(\frac{24}{12}\right)$$

$$I = (2,000)(0.06)(2)$$

$$I = 240$$

> I have annual interest, which means the time must be represented in years.

Joy will pay $240 in interest.

2. Xavier opened a new savings account by putting $300 into the account. At the end of the year, the savings account pays an annual interest of 5.25% on the amount he put into the account.

   a. How much will Xavier earn if he leaves his money in the savings account for 15 years?

   > I know the principal amount is $300, the annual interest rate is 5.25%, and the time is 15 years.

   > Before multiplying, I must convert the percent to a decimal.

   $$I = Prt$$

   $$I = (300)(5.25\%)(15)$$

   $$I = (300)(0.0525)(15)$$

   $$I = 236.25$$

   Xavier will earn $236.25 in interest.

   b. If Xavier does not add any money to his account, how much money will Xavier have in his account after the 15 years?

   $$\$300 + \$236.25 = \$536.25$$

   After 15 years, Xavier will have $536.25 in his account.

EUREKA
MATH™

3. Mr. Brown had to take out a loan to help pay rent. He borrowed $800 and agreed to pay an annual interest rate of 6%. If Mr. Brown was able to pay the loan back in just 6 months, how much interest did Mr. Brown pay?

12 months = 1 year

If we divide both sides by 2, we find that 6 months is equal to $\frac{1}{2}$ year.

$I = Prt$

$I = 800(0.06)\left(\dfrac{1}{2}\right)$

$I = 24$

Mr. Brown paid $24 in interest.

> The rate and time are not compatible. The rate is annual, which means time must be converted to years.

4. Stefani received a loan for $2,000 and now has acquired $720 in interest. If she pays an annual interest of 4.5% on the amount borrowed, how much time has elapsed since Stefani received the loan?

Let t represent the time, in years, that has elapsed since Stefani received the loan.

$$I = Prt$$
$$720 = 2000(0.045)t$$
$$720 = 90t$$
$$\left(\dfrac{1}{90}\right)(720) = \left(\dfrac{1}{90}\right)90t$$
$$8 = t$$

> This time, I know the interest and need to calculate the time (in years).

Therefore, Stefani received the loan 8 years ago.

© 2015 Great Minds eureka-math.org
G7-M4-HWH-1.3.0-10.2015

EUREKA MATH

G7-M4-Lesson 11: Tax, Commissions, Fees, and Other Real-World Percent Applications

1. In order for Josue to pay all of his bills, he needs to make $1,900 a month. Josue earns $10 an hour, plus 8% commission on his insurance sales. If Josue worked 160 hours each month, what is the least amount in insurance Josue would have to sell in order to have enough money to pay his bills?

   Let s represent the amount, in dollars, sold in insurance.

   > These factors will tell me how much Josue gets paid each month, without commission.

   > The 1900 represents the amount Josue needs to earn each month.

   $$1900 = 160(10) + 8\%(s)$$
   $$1900 = 1600 + 0.08s$$
   $$1900 - 1600 = 1600 + 0.08s - 1600$$
   $$300 = 0.08s$$
   $$\left(\frac{1}{0.08}\right)(300) = \left(\frac{1}{0.08}\right)(0.08)s$$
   $$3750 = s$$

   > These factors will tell me the amount of commission Josue will earn.

   Therefore, Josue would have to sell $3,750 worth of insurance in order to pay his monthly bills.

2. A dealership sells a car to an average of 12% of the daily customers.

   a. Write an equation that shows the proportional relationship between the number of customers who go to the dealership, c, and the number of customers who actually buy a car, b.

   $$b = 0.12c$$

   > I will multiply the percent of customers who buy a car by the number of daily customers in order to determine the number of customers who buy a car.

b. Use your equation to complete the table. List 5 possible values for b and c.

c	b
50	6
100	12
150	18
200	24
250	30

I can choose any numbers for c because this is the independent variable.

In order to determine my b values, I have to use my equation. For example, $b = 0.12(50)$. After multiplying, I find $b = 6$.

c. Identify the constant of proportionality, and explain what it means in the context of the situation.

The constant of proportionality is 0.12, or 12%. On average, for every 100 customers who go to the car dealership, 12 will buy a car.

EUREKA MATH

G7-M4-Lesson 12: The Scale Factor as a Percent for a Scale Drawing

> The scale factor is less than 100%, which means the scale drawing will be smaller than the original diagram.

1. Use the diagram below to create a scale drawing using a scale factor of 80%. Write numerical equations to find the horizontal and vertical distances in the scale drawing.

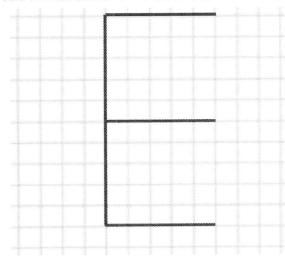

Scale Factor: $80\% = \frac{80}{100} = \frac{4}{5}$

Horizontal Distance: 5 *units*

Vertical Distance: 10 *units (broken into two equal sections of 5 units).*

> To determine the dimensions of the scale drawing, I multiply each dimension by the scale factor of 80%, or $\frac{4}{5}$.

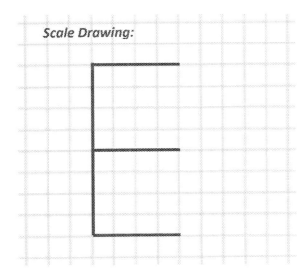

Scale Drawing:

Horizontal Distance of Scale Drawing:
$(5 \text{ units}) \left(\frac{4}{5}\right) = 4 \text{ units}$

Vertical Distance of Scale Drawing:
$(10 \text{ units}) \left(\frac{4}{5}\right) = 8 \text{ units}$ *(broken into two equal sections of 4 units).*

I have two different scale factors this time. The horizontal distance will be enlarged, and the vertical distance will be reduced.

2. Create a scale drawing of the original drawing given below using a horizontal scale factor of 150% and a vertical scale factor of 50%. Write numerical equations to find the horizontal and vertical distances.

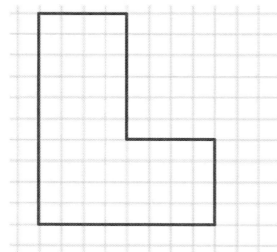

Horizontal Scale Factor: $150\% = \frac{150}{100} = \frac{3}{2}$

Vertical Scale Factor: $50\% = \frac{50}{100} = \frac{1}{2}$

Horizontal Distance: 8 units

The top is broken into two sections of 4 units.

Vertical Distance: 10 units

The right side is broken into two sections, where one section is 6 units and the other is 4 units.

Horizontal Distance of Scale Drawing:

$(8 \text{ units})(150\%) = (8 \text{ units})\left(\frac{3}{2}\right) = 12 \text{ units}$

However, the top will be broken into two sections of 6 units.

When finding the distances for the scale drawing, I need to make sure I use the correct scale factor for the horizontal distances and the vertical distances.

Vertical Distance of Scale Drawing:

$(10 \text{ units})(50\%) = (10 \text{ units})\left(\frac{1}{2}\right) = 5 \text{ units}$

However, the right side will be broken into two sections, where one section is
$(6 \text{ units})\left(\frac{1}{2}\right) = 3 \text{ units}$ *and the other section is* $(4 \text{ units})\left(\frac{1}{2}\right) = 2 \text{ units}.$

Scale Drawing:

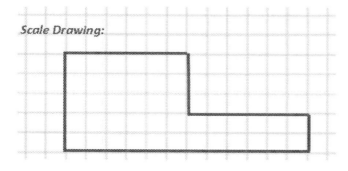

Lesson 12:   The Scale Factor as a Percent for a Scale Drawing

EUREKA MATH

G7-M4-Lesson 13: Changing Scales

1. The scale factor from Drawing 1 to Drawing 2 is 150%. Justify why Drawing 1 is a scale drawing of Drawing 2 and why it is a reduction of Drawing 2. Include the scale factor in your justification.

Drawing 1   Drawing 2

$$\text{Length of Drawing 1} = \text{Percent} \times \text{Length of Drawing 2}$$

$$100\% = \text{Percent} \times 150\%$$

> The lengths of the original drawings always represent 100%.

$$\left(\frac{1}{150\%}\right)(100\%) = \left(\frac{1}{150\%}\right)(\text{Percent} \times 150\%)$$

$$66\frac{2}{3} = \text{Percent}$$

Drawing 1 is a scale drawing of Drawing 2 because the lengths of Drawing 1 would be smaller than the corresponding lengths in Drawing 2.

Since the scale factor from Drawing 2 to Drawing 1 is $66\frac{2}{3}\%$, Drawing 1 is a reduction of Drawing 2.

> I know a scale drawing is a reduction when the scale factor is less than 100%. If the scale factor is greater than 100%, then the scale drawing is an enlargement.

2. The scale factor from Drawing 2 (presented in the first problem) to Drawing 3 is 125%. What is the scale factor from Drawing 1 to Drawing 3? Explain your reasoning, and check your answer using an example.

$(150\%)(125\%) = (1.50)(1.25) = 1.875$

Therefore, the scale factor from Drawing 1 to Drawing 3 is 187.5%.

Drawing 3

> I can choose any length for the length in Drawing 1 when I am checking the scale factors.

Check: Assume that one of the lengths in Drawing 1 is 8 cm.

$(8 \text{ cm})(1.50) = 12 \text{ cm}$

The corresponding length in Drawing 2 would be 12 cm.

$(12 \text{ cm})(1.25) = 15 \text{ cm}$

The corresponding length in Drawing 3 would be 15 cm.

> I use the scale factor for Drawing 1 to Drawing 2 and then take the new length and use the scale factor for Drawing 2 to Drawing 3. The result will be the corresponding side length for Drawing 3.

> I use the same length that I originally chose for Drawing 1 and use the scale factor for Drawing 1 to Drawing 3 to determine if the side length for Drawing 3 is the same as when I used the two different scale factors.

$(8 \text{ cm})(1.875) = 15 \text{ cm}$

If I use the scale factor from Drawing 1 to Drawing 3, I find that the corresponding length in Drawing 3 will still be 15 cm.

EUREKA
MATH

3. Cooper drew a picture in the size of a 6-inch by 6-inch square. He wanted to enlarge the original drawing to a size of 7 inches by 7 inches and 11 inches by 11 inches.

a. Sketch the different sizes of the drawing.

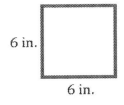

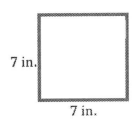

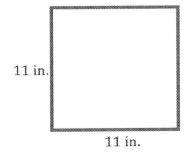

b. What was the scale factor from the original drawing to the drawing that is 7 inches by 7 inches?

$$\frac{7}{6} = 1.1\overline{6} = 116\frac{2}{3}\%$$

The scale factor from the original drawing to the drawing that is 7 inches by 7 inches was $116\frac{2}{3}\%$.

I can check to make sure my answer makes sense because I know the 7 × 7 is an enlargement of the original drawing. Therefore, the scale factor must be greater than 100%.

c. What was the scale factor from the original drawing to the drawing that is 11 inches by 11 inches?

$$\frac{11}{6} = 1.8\overline{3} = 183\frac{1}{3}\%$$

The scale factor from the original drawing to the drawing that is 11 inches by 11 inches was $183\frac{1}{3}\%$.

d. What was the scale factor from the 7 × 7 drawing to the 11 × 11 drawing?

$$\frac{11}{7} = 1.\overline{571428} = 157\frac{1}{7}\%$$

The scale factor from the 7 × 7 drawing to the 11 × 11 drawing is $157\frac{1}{7}\%$.

e. Write an equation to verify how the scale factor from the original drawing to the enlarged 11×11 drawing can be calculated using the scale factors from the original drawing to the 7×7 drawing.

Scale factor from original to 7×7*:* $116\frac{2}{3}\%$

Scale factor from the 7×7 *to* 11×11*:* $157\frac{1}{7}\%$

$$6\left(116\frac{2}{3}\%\right) = 6(1.1\overline{6}) = 7$$

$$7\left(157\frac{1}{7}\%\right) = 7(1.\overline{571428}) = 11$$

> Similar to Problem 2, I apply two scale factors and see if the final result is the same as only applying the scale factor from the original drawing to the 11×11 drawing.

Scale Factor from 6×6 *to* 11×11*:* $183\frac{1}{3}\%$

$$6\left(183\frac{1}{3}\%\right) = 6(1.8\overline{3}) = 11$$

This verifies that the scale factor of $183\frac{1}{3}\%$ *is equivalent to a scale factor of* $116\frac{2}{3}\%$ *followed by a scale factor of* $157\frac{1}{7}\%$*.*

EUREKA MATH™

G7-M4-Lesson 14: Computing Actual Lengths from a Scale Drawing

1. A drawing of a toy car is a two-dimensional scale drawing of an actual toy car. The length of the drawing is 1.8 inches, and the width is 0.55 inches. If the length of an actual toy car is 6.12 inches, use an equation to find the width of the actual toy car.

> I can use the corresponding lengths to create an equation that will tell me the scale factor that relates the drawing to the actual toy car.

The length of the drawing of the toy car is 1.8 inches.

The length of the actual toy car is 6.12 inches.

Scale factor:

$$6.12 = \text{Percent} \times 1.8$$

$$\left(\frac{1}{1.8}\right)(6.12) = \text{Percent} \times 1.8 \times \frac{1}{1.8}$$

$$3.4 = \text{Percent}$$

$$3.4 = 340\%$$

> The length of the actual toy car is larger than the length of the drawing. Therefore, the scale factor is greater than 1, and the percent is over 100%.

Width of the actual toy car:

$$(0.55)(3.4) = 1.87$$

> I can use the scale factor to determine the width of the actual toy car.

The width of the actual toy car is 1.87 inches.

2. The larger quadrilateral is a scale drawing of the smaller quadrilateral. If the distance around the larger quadrilateral is 36.18 units, what is the distance around the smaller quadrilateral? Use an equation to find the distance, and interpret your solution in the context of the problem.

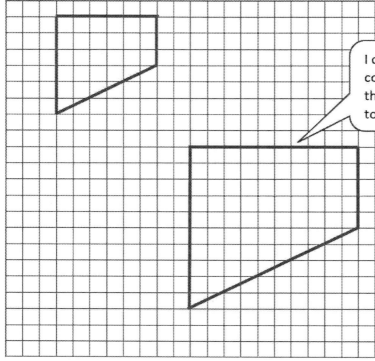

> I can use the drawings and count the boxes to determine the horizontal length across the top of each quadrilateral.

The horizontal distance of the smaller quadrilateral is 6 units.

The horizontal distance of the larger quadrilateral is 10 units.

Scale factor:

> I can write an equation to determine the scale factor. Once I know the scale factor of the horizontal distances, I am able to determine the distance around the smaller quadrilateral.

$$6 = \text{Percent} \times 10$$

$$\left(\frac{1}{10}\right)(6) = \text{Percent} \times 10 \times \frac{1}{10}$$

$$0.6 = \text{Percent}$$

$$0.6 = 60\%$$

The distance around the smaller quadrilateral:

$$(36.18)(0.6) = 21.708$$

> The lengths of the smaller object are 60% of the lengths of the larger object. So I will multiply the distance around the larger object by 60% to determine the distance around the smaller object.

The distance around the smaller quadrilateral is 21.708 units.

EUREKA
MATH

G7-M4-Lesson 15: Solving Area Problems Using Scale Drawings

1. Use the diagram of the circles to answer the following questions.

   a. What percent of the area of the larger circle is shaded?

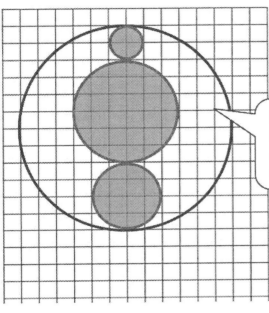

> I can use the diagram to determine the radius of each of the circles. There are four circles in this diagram, three on the inside and one outside circle.

Shaded small circle: radius = 1 unit

Shaded medium circle: radius = 2 units

Shaded large circle: radius = 3 units

Outside circle: radius = 6 units

Let A represent the area of the outside circle.

> I can compare the area of each shaded circle to the area of the outside circle. Because we are working with area, I need to square the scale factor that compares the side lengths.

Area of small circle: $\left(\frac{1}{6}\right)^2 A = \frac{1}{36} A$

Area of medium circle: $\left(\frac{2}{6}\right)^2 A = \frac{4}{36} A$

Area of large circle: $\left(\frac{3}{6}\right)^2 A = \frac{9}{36} A$

Area of shaded region: $\frac{1}{36} A + \frac{4}{36} A + \frac{9}{36} A = \frac{14}{36} A = \frac{14}{36} A \times 100\% = \left(38\frac{8}{9}\%\right) A$

The area of the shaded region is $38\frac{8}{9}\%$ of the area of the entire circle.

b. Using 3.14 as an estimate for π, the area of the outside circle is approximately 113.04 in^2. Determine the area of the shaded region.

If A represents the area of the outside circle, then the total shaded area:

$$\frac{14}{36}A = \frac{14}{36}(113.04) = 43.96$$

The area of the shaded region is approximately 43.96 in^2.

> I can use the expression that I came up with in part (a) to determine the area. I just need to replace the A with the actual area of the outside circle.

c. What percent of the outside circle is unshaded?

$$113.04 - 43.96 = 69.08$$

> I know the total area and the area of the shaded region. I can use this to determine the area of the unshaded region. Then, I can use that area to determine the percent.

Therefore, the area of the unshaded region is approximately 69.08 in^2.

The percent of the outside circular region that is unshaded is

$$\frac{69.08}{113.04} = 0.6\overline{1} = 61\frac{1}{9}\%.$$

> I could have subtracted the percent the shaded region represents ($38\frac{8}{9}\%$) from 100% because I know the entire area represents 100%.

d. What percent of the area of the medium circle is the area of the large circle?

Scale factor: $\frac{3}{2}$

Area: $\left(\frac{3}{2}\right)^2 = \frac{9}{4} = \frac{9}{4} \times 100\% = 225\%$

> To determine the percent, I will first write out the scale factor, comparing the radius of the large circle to the radius of the medium circle.

The area of the large circle is 225% of the area of the medium circle.

EUREKA MATH™

2. On the square page of a menu shown below, five 3-in. by 3-in. squares are cut out for pictures. If these cut-out regions make up $\frac{5}{36}$ of the area of the entire page, what are the dimensions of the page?

Since the cut-out regions make up $\frac{5}{36}$ of the entire page, each cut-out region makes up $\frac{\frac{5}{36}}{5} = \frac{1}{36}$ of the entire page.

> To figure out what part of the area is covered by just one square, I can divide by the number of squares.

$$\left(\frac{1}{6}\right)^2 = \frac{1}{36}$$

The scale factor is $\frac{1}{6}$.

> In this question, I was given information about the areas, but I need to work backward to determine the side lengths. Because the scale factor was squared to determine the areas, I need to determine what number was squared to determine the scale factor and work toward the side lengths.

To find the dimensions of the square page:

$$\textbf{Quantity} = \textbf{Percent} \times \textbf{Whole}$$

$$\textbf{Small square side length} = \textbf{Percent} \times \textbf{Page length}$$

$$3 \text{ in.} = \frac{1}{6} \times \textbf{Page length}$$

> I can write a percent as a fraction to use in the formula.

$$6(3) \text{ in.} = 6\left(\frac{1}{6}\right) \times \textbf{Page length}$$

$$18 \text{ in.} = \textbf{Page length}$$

The dimensions of the square menu page are 18 in. by 18 in.

G7-M4-Lesson 16: Population Problems

1. During a school fundraiser, 70% of customers ordered vanilla ice cream, and 30% of customers ordered chocolate ice cream. Of the customers who ordered vanilla, 80% asked for sprinkles as well. Of the customers who ordered chocolate, 50% asked for sprinkles. What is the percent of customers who ordered sprinkles with their ice cream?

   Let c represent the number of customer orders.

   > I don't know how many customers bought ice cream, so I need to use a variable to represent this value.

   Vanilla Orders: $70\% \times c = 0.7c$

   Chocolate Orders: $30\% \times c = 0.3c$

   Vanilla Orders with Sprinkles: $0.7c \times 0.8 = 0.56c$

   Chocolate Orders with Sprinkles: $0.3c \times 0.5 = 0.15c$

   > I need to multiply the number of orders by the percent of orders that included sprinkles.

   Orders with Sprinkles: $0.56c + 0.15c = 0.71c$

   > I know the percent of vanilla orders with sprinkles and chocolate orders with sprinkles; now I need to determine the total percent of orders with sprinkles.

   Therefore, the percent of customers who ordered sprinkles is 71%.

© 2015 Great Minds eureka-math.org
G7-M4-HWH-1.3.0-10.2015

EUREKA
MATH™

2. The city zoo keeps records on the number of guests they have throughout the year. Last year, 40% of the guests were adults, and 60% of the guests were children. This year, there was an 8% decrease in adult guests and a 3% increase in children guests. What is the percent increase or decrease in guests this year?

Let g represent the number of guests last year.

Adults Decrease: $(0.4g)(0.92) = 0.368g$

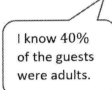

> I know 40% of the guests were adults.

> An 8% decrease means 92% of the number of adult guests from last year went to the zoo this year.

Children Increase: $(0.6g)(1.03) = 0.618g$

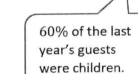

> 60% of the last year's guests were children.

> A 3% increase means 103% of last year's children guests went to the zoo this year.

$0.368g + 0.618g = 0.986g$

$100\% - 98.6\% = 1.4\%$

Therefore, the number of guests decreased by 1.4%.

3. A seventh grade math class is made up of 40% girls and 60% boys, and 35% of the entire class is earning an A in the class. If 50% of the girls are earning an A, what is the percent of boys who are earning an A?

Let b represent the percent of boys who are earning an A.

$$0.4(0.5) + 0.6b = 1(0.35)$$
$$0.2 + 0.6b = 0.35$$
$$0.2 + 0.6b - 0.2 = 0.35 - 0.2$$
$$0.6b = 0.15$$
$$\left(\frac{1}{0.6}\right)(0.6b) = \left(\frac{1}{0.6}\right)0.15$$
$$b = 0.25$$

> I know the total percentage of A's is 35%. Therefore, the sum of percentages of the girls A's and the boys A's is 35%.

> I use the additive inverse of 0.2 in order to isolate the variable.

> I use the multiplicative inverse of 0.6 in order to isolate the variable.

Therefore, 25% of the boys are earning an A.

G7-M4-Lesson 17: Mixture Problems

1. A 3-liter container is filled with a liquid that is 40% juice. A 5-liter container is filled with a liquid that is 60% juice. What percent of juice is obtained by putting the two mixtures together?

    Let x represent the percent of juice in the resulting mixture.

    $$3(0.4) + 5(0.6) = 8x$$

    > I know there will be a total of 8 liters in the resulting mixture because there is a 3-liter container and a 5-liter container.

    $$1.2 + 3 = 8x$$
    $$4.2 = 8x$$

    > In order to solve for x, I must collect the like terms.

    $$\left(\frac{1}{8}\right)(4.2) = \left(\frac{1}{8}\right)8x$$
    $$0.525 = x$$

    > I multiply by the multiplicative inverse of 8 in order to isolate the variable.

    Therefore, the resulting mixture will have 52.5% juice.

2. Solution A contains 50 liters of a solution that is 75% hydrochloric acid. How many liters of Solution B containing 50% hydrochloric acid must be added to get a solution that is 60% hydrochloric acid?

    Let b represent the amount of Solution B, in liters, to be added.

    $$50(0.75) + (0.50)b = (0.60)(50 + b)$$

    > The final solution will have 50 liters of Solution A and b liters of Solution B.

    $$37.5 + 0.5b = 30 + 0.6b$$
    $$37.5 + 0.5b - 30 = 30 + 0.6b - 30$$
    $$7.5 + 0.5b = 0.6b$$
    $$7.5 + 0.5b - 0.5b = 0.6b - 0.5b$$
    $$7.5 = 0.1b$$

    > I know that I need to collect like terms, even when they are on opposite sides of the equal sign.

    $$\left(\frac{1}{0.1}\right)(7.5) = \left(\frac{1}{0.1}\right)(0.1b)$$
    $$75 = b$$

    In order to get the desired solution, 75 liters of Solution B needs to be added.

EUREKA MATH

3. Miguel is consolidating two containers of trail mix. The first container has 2.5 cups and is 70% nuts. The second container is 3 cups. If the resulting trail mix is 50% nuts, what percent of the second container is nuts?

> I am trying to determine the percent of nuts in the second container of trail mix.

Let n represent the percent of nuts in the second container of trail mix.

$$2.5(0.7) + 3n = 5.5(0.5)$$
$$1.75 + 3n = 2.75$$
$$1.75 + 3n - 1.75 = 2.75 - 1.75$$
$$3n = 1$$
$$\left(\frac{1}{3}\right)3n = \left(\frac{1}{3}\right)(1)$$
$$n = \frac{1}{3}$$

> After consolidating, Miguel will have 5.5 cups of trail mix.

> I use my algebraic knowledge to isolate the variable.

The second container of trail mix had $33\frac{1}{3}$% nuts.

4. Veronica wants to create a 20-cup mixture of candy with 80% of the candy being chocolate by mixing two bags of candy. The first bag of candy contains 50% chocolate candy, and the second bag contains 100% chocolate candy. How much of each bag should she use?

Let x represent the amount, in cups, in the first bag of candy.

> If the first bag of candy has x cups and the total is 20 cups, then I know the second bag will have $20 - x$ cups.

$$0.5x + 1(20 - x) = 0.8(20)$$
$$0.5x + 20 - 1x = 16$$
$$-0.5x + 20 = 16$$
$$-0.5x + 20 - 20 = 16 - 20$$
$$-0.5x = -4$$
$$\left(-\frac{1}{0.5}\right)(-0.5x) = \left(-\frac{1}{0.5}\right)(-4)$$
$$x = 8$$

> Use the distributive property.

> Collect like terms.

Therefore, Veronica needs to use 8 cups of candy from the first bag and 12 cups of candy from the second bag to get her desired mixture.

G7-M4-Lesson 18: Counting Problems

1. A carnival game requires you to roll a six-sided number cube two times. To determine if you win a prize, you must calculate the product of the two rolls. The possible products are

1	2	3	4	5	6
2	4	6	8	10	12
3	6	9	12	15	18
4	8	12	16	20	24
5	10	15	20	25	30
6	12	18	24	30	36

   a. What is the percent that the product will be greater than 20?

   > Greater than 20 does not include 20.

   > I know the numerator represents the number of outcomes with a product greater than 20, and the denominator represents the total number of outcomes.

   $$\frac{6}{36} = \frac{1}{6} = 16\frac{2}{3}\%$$

   b. In order to win the carnival game, the product can be no more than 10. What percent chance do you have of winning the game?

   > No more than 10 means the product must be 10 or less.

   $$\frac{19}{36} = 52\frac{7}{9}\%$$

   I have about a 53% chance of winning the carnival game.

EUREKA MATH

2. Calleigh loves to accessorize. She always wears three pieces of jewelry using combinations of rings, necklaces, and bracelets. The table shows the different combinations of accessories Calleigh wore with her last eight outfits.

R	B	N	R	B	N	N	B
R	N	B	B	N	R	R	B
R	R	N	B	R	B	B	B

a. What percent of Calleigh's outfits included at least one ring?

$$\frac{6}{8} = \frac{3}{4} = 75\%$$

> There are 6 outfits where Calleigh wore at least one ring and 8 total outfits.

> At least 1 ring means that Calleigh wears 1 or more rings.

b. What percent of Calleigh's outfits only included one type of accessory?

$$\frac{2}{8} = \frac{1}{4} = 25\%$$

> The first and last outfit Calleigh wore only included one type of accessory.

Homework Helpers

Grade 7
Module 5

G7-M5-Lesson 1: Chance Experiments

Probability Scale

The probability of an event will fall somewhere on the probability scale.

Probability Scale

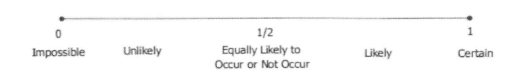

Decide whether each event is impossible, unlikely, equally likely, likely, or certain to occur.

1. It will start raining gum drops on the way home from school.

    Impossible

2. An even number will be chosen from a bag containing items numbered 1 through 20.

    Equally Likely

    > I know there are 20 numbers in the bag, and 10 of them are even. Therefore, the probability will be $\frac{10}{20} = \frac{1}{2}$.

3. I will roll a composite number on a six-sided number cube with sides numbered 1 through 6.

    Unlikely

    > There are two composite numbers (4 and 6) on a six-sided number cube. That means two out of the six possible numbers are composite, making the probability less than half.

4. A letter chosen from the alphabet is a consonant.

    Likely

    > Twenty-one of the twenty-six letters in the alphabet are consonants, which means the probability is greater than half.

EUREKA
MATH™

5. A number will be randomly drawn from the box shown below. Decide where each event would be located on the probability scale. Then, place the letter for each event on the appropriate location on the probability scale.

> There are 10 possible outcomes.

```
1
  2    4    3
4
     3     4
2
   4     2
```

Event:

> Seven of the numbers are even.

A. An even number is drawn.

B. A 1 is drawn.

> All the outcomes are numbers.

C. A number is drawn.

> There are no letters.

D. A letter is drawn.

> Three appears twice, which means the event is unlikely. However, there are more possible outcomes for event E than for event B, which means event E should be to the right of event B, but event E is still unlikely.

E. A 3 is drawn.

PROBABILITY SCALE

```
D   B   E                              A              C
•                                                     •
0                    1/2                              1

Impossible    Unlikely    Equally Likely to    Likely    Certain
                          Occur or Not Occur
```

EUREKA
MATH

G7-M5-Lesson 2: Estimating Probabilities by Collecting Data

Cole is eating candy from a bag that consists of different-colored pieces. Cole randomly picked pieces from the bag and recorded the number of each color in the table below.

Color	Number
Red	4
Brown	7
Green	4
Yellow	10
Blue	7
Orange	8

a. How many pieces of candy are in the bag?

40

> I add the number of each color of candy together to find the total amount of candy.

b. How many pieces of candy are yellow?

10

If Cole randomly selected a piece of candy from the bag:

c. What is the estimated probability of Cole eating an orange piece of candy?

$\frac{8}{40} = \frac{1}{5} = 20\%$

> The number of observed occurrences is 8, and the total number of observations is 40.

d. What is the estimated probability Cole will eat either a brown or blue piece of candy?

$\frac{14}{40} = \frac{7}{20} = 35\%$

> The number of observed occurrences is 14 because there are 7 brown pieces of candy and 7 blue pieces of candy in the bag.

e. If the bag of candy has 600 pieces of candy, how many pieces would you expect to be red?

$$\frac{4}{40} = \frac{1}{10} = 10\%$$

> I find the estimated probability of choosing a red piece of candy. I can use this percentage to estimate the total number of red pieces of candy in the bag.

An estimate for the number of red pieces of candy would be 60 because 10% of 600 is 60.

© 2015 Great Minds eureka-math.org
G7-M5-HWH-1.3.0-10.2015

G7-M5-Lesson 3: Chance Experiments with Equally Likely Outcomes

> The sample space is all the possible outcomes.

For each of the following chance experiments, list the sample space.

1. Selecting a marble from a bag of 6 green marbles, 8 yellow marbles, and 4 red marbles

    Green, yellow, and red

> When listing the sample space, I list all the letters in the word *homework*. However, the letter *o* only needs to be listed once.

2. Selecting a letter from the word *homework*

    h, o, m, e, w, r, and k

3. Spinning the spinner below

    1, 2, and 3

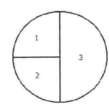

> It does not matter if the outcomes are equally likely; the sample space just focuses on the possible outcomes.

For each of the following problems, decide if the two outcomes listed are equally likely to occur. Give a reason for your answer.

> The letters *i* and *b* both occur twice in the word *probability*.

4. Selecting the letters *i* or *b* from the word *probability*

    Yes, both i and b occur the same number of times in the word probability.

5. Selecting a red or blue uniform shirt when Lincoln has 4 red uniform shirts and 5 blue uniform shirts

    No, Lincoln has a slightly higher chance of picking a blue shirt.

> Lincoln has a different number of each color shirt, which means each outcome is not equally likely.

© 2015 Great Minds eureka-math.org
G7-M5-HWH-1.3.0-10.2015

6. Landing on blue or green on the spinner below

    No, it is more likely to land on green than on blue.

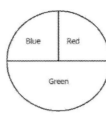

The area of green on the spinner is larger than the area of blue. Therefore, the outcomes are not equally likely.

G7-M5-Lesson 4: Calculating Probabilities for Chance Experiments with Equally Likely Outcomes

Calculate the Probability of Events when Outcomes are Not Equally Likely

1. In a middle school orchestra, there are 6 sixth graders, 11 seventh graders, and 8 eighth graders.

> There are 25 students in the orchestra because $6 + 11 + 8 = 25$. I know this represents the number of possible outcomes.

  a. If one student is randomly chosen to complete a solo, what is the probability that a seventh grader is chosen?

   $\dfrac{11}{25}$

> The number of favorable outcomes is the number of seventh graders in the orchestra.

  b. If one student is randomly chosen, is it equally likely to pick a sixth, seventh, or eighth grader? Explain.

   No, there are not the same number of sixth, seventh, or eighth graders.

> In order for outcomes to be equally likely, the number of favorable outcomes must be the same.

Calculate the Probability of Events with Equally Likely Outcomes

2. Use the spinner to the right to answer the following questions.
  a. What is the probability of landing on an even number?

> There are two even numbers (2 and 4) on the spinner.

> There are 4 possible outcomes because there are 4 sections on the spinner.

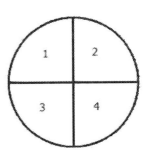

b. What is the probability of landing on a composite number?

$\frac{1}{4}$

> There is only one composite number, 4, on the spinner.

c. Is landing on each section of the spinner equally likely to occur? Explain.

Yes, each section has the same area.

3. A chance experiment consists of rolling a number cube with the numbers 1–6 on the faces of the cube and flipping a coin.

a. List the sample space of this chance experiment. List the probability of each outcome in the sample space.

Sample Space: 1t, 1h, 2t, 2h, 3t, 3h, 4t, 4h, 5t, 5h, 6t, 6h

The probability of each outcome is $\frac{1}{12}$.

> There are 12 possible outcomes, and they are all equally likely to occur.

b. What is the probability of getting the number 5 on the number cube and a tails on the coin?

$\frac{1}{12}$

> It is estimated that this outcome will occur once in 12 trials.

c. What is the probability of getting a heads on the coin and an odd number on the number cube?

$\frac{3}{12}$, *or* $\frac{1}{4}$

> It is estimated that this outcome will occur three times in 12 trials.

8   **Lesson 4:**   Calculating Probabilities for Chance Experiments with Equally Likely
                            Outcomes

© 2015 Great Minds eureka-math.org
G7-M5-HWH-1.3.0-10.2015

EUREKA
MATH

G7-M5-Lesson 5: Chance Experiments with Outcomes That Are Not Equally Likely

1. Charlie is training for a race and is supposed to run every day during the week. The table below shows the estimated probabilities of running 1, 2, 3, 4, 5, 6, or 7 days a week.

Number of Days	1	2	3	4	5	6	7
Probability	0.1	0.1	0.1	0.2	0.3	0.2	0

Find the probability that Charlie will

> In order to find the probability of an event, I add the probability of each of the desired outcomes together.

a. Run more than 4 days during the week.

> "More than 4 days" means that Charlie will run 5, 6, or 7 days.

$0.3 + 0.2 + 0 = 0.5$

The probability that Charlie will run more than 4 days a week is 0.5.

b. Run at most 3 days.

> "At most 3 days" means that Charlie will run 3 or fewer days.

$0.1 + 0.1 + 0.1 = 0.3$

The probability that Charlie will run at most 3 days is 0.3.

c. Not run exactly 1 day.

Method 1:

$0.1 + 0.1 + 0.2 + 0.3 + 0.2 + 0 = 0.9$

Method 2:

$1 - 0.1 = 0.9$

The probability that Charlie will not run exactly 1 day is 0.9.

> I can solve this problem two ways:
> 1. I can find the sum of all the probabilities, except for the probability of running 1 day.
> 2. The total probability is 1, so I can subtract $1 - P(1)$.

© 2015 Great Minds eureka-math.org
G7-M5-HWH-1.3.0-10.2015

2. Sarah surveyed her friends to determine the number of pets each friend has. The survey results are shown in the table below.

Number of Pets	0	1	2	3	4
Number of Friends	8	6	3	1	2

a. How many friends did Sarah survey?

$8 + 6 + 3 + 1 + 2 = 20$

Sarah surveyed 20 friends.

b. What is the probability that a randomly selected friend does not have any pets? Write your answer as a fraction in lowest terms.

$\dfrac{8}{20} = \dfrac{2}{5}$

> The 8 represents the number of friends who have zero pets, and the 20 represents the total number of friends surveyed.

The probability that Sarah will select a friend who does not have any pets is $\dfrac{2}{5}$.

c. The table below shows the possible number of pets and the probabilities of each number of pets. Complete the table by writing the probabilities as fractions in lowest terms.

Number of Pets	0	1	2	3	4
Probability	$\dfrac{8}{20} = \dfrac{2}{5}$	$\dfrac{6}{20} = \dfrac{3}{10}$	$\dfrac{3}{20}$	$\dfrac{1}{20}$	$\dfrac{2}{20} = \dfrac{1}{10}$

> To find each probability, I put the number of favorable outcomes in the numerator and the total number of outcomes in the denominator. If possible, I simplify the fraction.

© 2015 Great Minds eureka-math.org
G7-M5-HWH-1.3.0-10.2015

d. Writing your answers as fractions in lowest terms, find the probability that the student:

  i. Has fewer than 3 pets.

$$\frac{2}{5} + \frac{3}{10} + \frac{3}{20}$$

$$\frac{8}{20} + \frac{6}{20} + \frac{3}{20}$$

$$\frac{17}{20}$$

In order to add the probabilities of a friend having 0, 1, or 2 pets, I find a common denominator or use the fractions that are not simplified from the table.

  ii. Does not have exactly 4 pets.

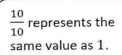
$\frac{10}{10}$ represents the same value as 1.

$$1 - \frac{1}{10}$$

$$\frac{10}{10} - \frac{1}{10}$$

$$\frac{9}{10}$$

The total probability is 1, so I would subtract the probability of a friend having four pets from 1.

NOTE: I could also add the probabilities of a friend having 0, 1, 2, or 3 pets together to get the probability of not having 4 pets.

G7-M5-Lesson 6: Using Tree Diagrams to Represent a Sample Space and to Calculate Probabilities

1. The Johnson family has decided to get two new pets, one for their son and one for their daughter. Mr. and Mrs. Johnson are allowing the kids to choose between a cat, a dog, or a bird. Each type of pet has an equally likely chance of being chosen.

    a. Using C for cat, D for dog, and B for bird, develop a tree diagram that shows the nine possible outcomes for the two different types of pets.

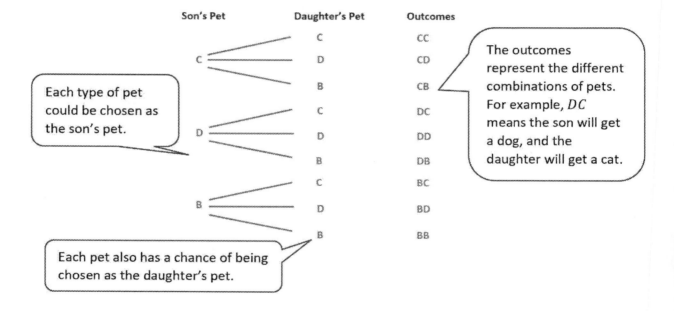

Each type of pet could be chosen as the son's pet.

Each pet also has a chance of being chosen as the daughter's pet.

The outcomes represent the different combinations of pets. For example, DC means the son will get a dog, and the daughter will get a cat.

    b. What is the probability of the son choosing a bird and the daughter choosing a cat?

$$\frac{1}{3} \cdot \frac{1}{3} = \frac{1}{9}$$

Since each pet has an equal chance to be chosen, the probability for each type of pet is $\frac{1}{3}$.

© 2015 Great Minds eureka-math.org
G7-M5-HWH-1.3.0-10.2015

EUREKA
MATH

c. Is the probability that both children will choose a dog the same as the probability that both children will choose a bird? Explain.

The probability of both children choosing a dog is $\frac{1}{3} \cdot \frac{1}{3} = \frac{1}{9}$. The probability of both children choosing a bird is also $\frac{1}{3} \cdot \frac{1}{3} = \frac{1}{9}$. Therefore, the probability of both children choosing a dog is the same as the probability of both children choosing a bird.

2. Ms. Bailey's class is playing a game where they have to spin the spinner below.
   a. Develop a tree diagram showing the nine possible outcomes of spinning the spinner twice.

First Spin	Second Spin	Outcomes
	1	1 1
1	2	1 2
	3	1 3
	1	2 1
2	2	2 2
	3	2 3
	1	3 1
3	2	3 2
	3	3 3

At this point, I just list the sample space and don't worry about the probability of each outcome.

The outcomes represent the different combinations of the two spins but does not yet indicate the probability of each outcome.

b. What is the probability that a student will spin a 2 on the first spin and a 3 on the second spin?

$(0.25)(0.5) = 0.125$

The probability of spinning a 2 is 0.25 because this section covers 25% of the spinner's area. The probability of spinning a 3 is 0.5 because this section covers 50% of the spinner's area.

c. What is the probability that the spinner will land on the 1 for both spins?

$(0.25)(0.25) = 0.0625$

The probability of spinning a 1 on either spin is 0.25 because this section covers 25% of the spinner's area.

G7-M5-Lesson 7: Calculating Probabilities of Compound Events

Kaia's four kids are arguing over the type of game they want to play. Therefore, Kaia agrees to roll a four-sided die with sides numbered $1, 2, 3,$ and 4. If the die lands on a $1, 2,$ or 3, they will play a matching game, and if the die lands on a 4, they will play a card game.

a. Kaia agrees to play three games with her kids. Create a tree diagram to show the different types of games they may play.

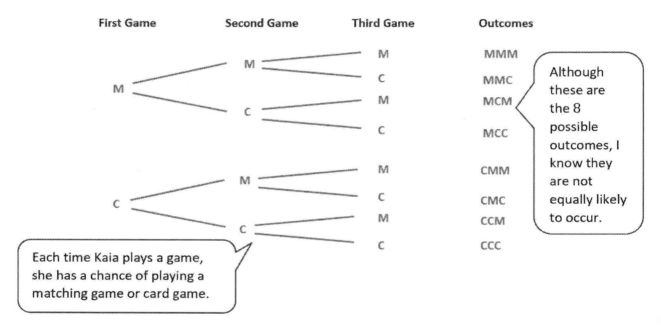

b. What is the probability that all three games will be a matching game?

$$P(MMM) = (0.75)(0.75)(0.75) = 0.421875$$

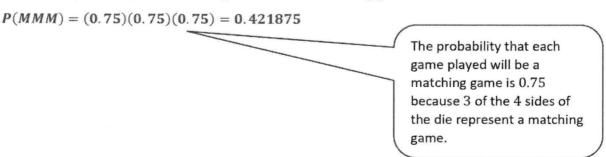

© 2015 Great Minds eureka-math.org
G7-M5-HWH-1.3.0-10.2015

EUREKA MATH

The probability that a card game will be played is 0.25 because 1 of the 4 sides of the die represents a card game.

c.   What is the probability that at least two card games will be played?

The possible outcomes and their probabilities are

$P(MCC) = (0.75)(0.25)(0.25) = 0.046875$

$P(CMC) = (0.25)(0.75)(0.25) = 0.046875$

$P(CCM) = (0.25)(0.25)(0.75) = 0.046875$

$P(CCC) = (0.25)(0.25)(0.25) = 0.015625$

In order to find the total probability of playing at least two card games, I calculate the sum of these probabilities.

The probability of playing at least two card games is

$0.046875 + 0.046875 + 0.046875 + 0.015625 = 0.15625$

d.   What is the probability that Kaia and her kids will play at least one matching game?

$$P(CCC) = (0.25)(0.25)(0.25) = 0.015625$$

The only time the family will not play at least one matching game is when they play three card games.

$P(no\ M) = 1 - P(CCC)$

$P(no\ M) = 1 - 0.015625$

$P(no\ M) = 0.984375$

The probability of playing at least one matching game is the total probability (which is 1) minus the probability of playing three card games.

EUREKA MATH™

© 2015 Great Minds eureka-math.org
G7-M5-HWH-1.3.0-10.2015

G7-M5-Lesson 8: The Difference Between Theoretical Probabilities and Estimated Probabilities

Predicting Theoretical Probability

1. Consider the data you collected in class when you taped 10 pennies in a tall stack. Would the probability of landing on a head be more likely or less likely if we taped more than 10 pennies in a stack? Explain.

    As we create a bigger stack, the probability of landing on a head becomes less likely because the larger stacks will land on their sides more often.

I can perform the experiment if I am not sure how to answer this question.

Large stacks of pennies are difficult to balance standing upright, so they will not land standing upright very often.

2. If you created a stack of pennies shorter than 10 pennies, how would the probability of landing on a head change?

    A smaller stack of pennies would increase the probablity of landing on a head because it is easier to stand small stacks upright.

As the stack of pennies gets smaller, the probability of landing on a head increases.

EUREKA MATH

© 2015 Great Minds eureka-math.org
G7-M5-HWH-1.3.0-10.2015

Estimated Probability

3. Assume we taped 3 pennies into a stack, tossed the stack 20 times, and recorded our results in the table below.

Number of Tosses	Total Number of Heads so Far	Relative Frequency of Heads so Far (to the nearest hundredth)
1	0	$\frac{0}{1} = 0.0$
5	2	$\frac{2}{5} = 0.4$
10	3	$\frac{3}{10} = 0.3$
15	5	$\frac{5}{15} = 0.\overline{3}$
20	6	$\frac{6}{20} = 0.3$

> In order to calculate the relative frequency, I set up a fraction to show the number of heads out of the total number of tosses.

a. Complete the table by calculating the relative frequencies. If necessary, round to the nearest hundredth.

b. What is your estimated probability that our stack of pennies will land heads up when tossed? Explain.

My estimated probability that our stack of pennies will land heads up is 0.3 because all of the relative frequencies are close to this number.

> Answers will vary but should be based on the relative frequencies.

© 2015 Great Minds eureka-math.org
G7-M5-HWH-1.3.0-10.2015

G7-M5-Lesson 9: Comparing Estimated Probabilities to Probabilities Predicted by a Model

Picking Green! This is a game similar to the one you played in class, where you try to pick as many green chips as possible before picking one white chip. One bag has the same number of green and white chips, and the ratio of green to white chips in the second bag is unknown.

> After experimenting, I either choose Bag A or Bag B in hopes of picking the most green chips while avoiding white chips.

Laura and Carly completed an experiment, and their results are shown in the tables below.

Laura's Results:

Bag	Number of Green Chips Picked	Number of White Chips Picked
A	35	15
B	22	28

Carly's Results:

Bag	Number of Green Chips Picked	Number of White Chips Picked
A	7	8
B	9	6

1. If all you know about the bags are the results from Laura's research, which bag would you select for the game? Explain.

   I would choose Bag A because Laura's results show that she picked a lot more green chips than white chips from Bag A.

> In order to win, I want to pick the bag that I think has the most green chips.

2. If all you know about the bags are the results from Carly's research, which bag would you select for the game? Explain.

   I would choose Bag B because Carly's results show that she picked a few more green chips than white chips from Bag B.

> Both Bag A and Bag B had similar results, but Carly picked a few more green chips from Bag B.

EUREKA MATH

3. Whose research gives you a better indication of the makeup of green and white chips in each bag? Explain.

Laura's results would be a better indication of the makeup of green and white chips in each bag because she collected more data than Carly.

The more data we collect, the closer the outcome is to the theoretical probability.

> I know that the more outcomes carried out, the closer the relative frequency is to the theoretical probability.

4. If there were three colors of chips in each bag, how would you collect data in order to choose a bag?

My data collection would be the same. I would just have to extend my table to include a third color.

G7-M5-Lesson 10: Conducting a Simulation to Estimate the Probability of an Event

Predicting a Mouse's Path

1. Samantha bought her hamster a new maze for his cage, which is shown below. The hamster can only exit the maze at one point. At each point where the hamster has to decide which direction to go, assume that it is equally likely to go in either direction. At each decision point, A, B, and C, it must decide whether to go left (L) or right (R).

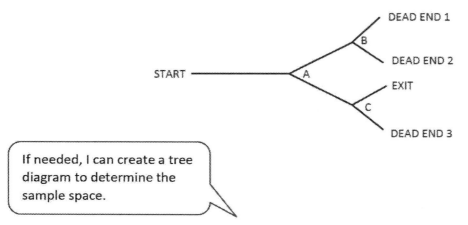

> If needed, I can create a tree diagram to determine the sample space.

a. List the possible paths of a sample space for the paths the hamster can take. For example, if the hamster goes left at decision point A and then right at decision point B, then the path would be denoted LR.

   The sample space is LL, LR, RL, RR.

b. Are the paths in the sample space equally likely? Explain.

   At each decision point there are two choices, which are equally likely. Therefore, each path in the sample space is equally likely as the other paths.

c. What is the theoretical probability of the hamster finding the exit?

   Only one of the four possible paths will lead the hamster to the exit.

   Therefore, the probability of the hamster reaching the exit is $\frac{1}{4}$.

> The only path that leads to the exit is RL.

d.   What is the theoretical probability of the hamster reaching a dead end?

Three of the four possible paths will lead to a dead end, which means the probability is $\frac{3}{4}$.

e.   Based on the set of simulated paths, estimate the probabilities that the hamster arrives at the exit and any of the dead ends. Explain.

RR	RL	LR	LL	LR	LL	RR	LL	RR	RL
LL	LR	LR	RL	RR	RL	LR	RL	RL	LL
RL	LR	LL	RR	RL	RL	LR	RR	LL	RR

> There are 30 trials listed here.

The probability of the hamster reaching the exit is $\frac{9}{30}$ because 9 of the outcomes resulted in the hamster going RL, which is the only path that leads to the exit.

The probability of the hamster reaching a dead end is $1 - \frac{9}{30} = \frac{21}{30}$ because all the other paths lead toward a dead end.

Using Simulation with a Dart Board

2.   Suppose a dart board is made up of the 6×6 grid of squares shown below. Also, suppose that when a dart is thrown, it is equally likely to land on any one of the 36 squares. A point is won if the dart lands on one of the 12 red squares. Zero points are earned if the dart lands in a white square.

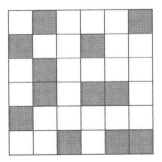

a.   For one throw of a dart, what is the probability of winning a point?

$$\frac{12}{36} = \frac{1}{3}$$

> I win a point if I land on one of the 12 red squares. I also know there are 36 total squares.

b. Dylan wants to use a six-sided number cube with the sides numbered 1 through 6 to simulate the results of one dart. How could he assign the six numbers on the number cube to create an appropriate simulation?

Dylan can assign 1 and 2 to simulate winning a point and the numbers 3, 4, 5, and 6 to simulate not winning a point.

> Since there are six different numbers on a number cube, I know that 2 of the numbers must represent winning a point because $\frac{2}{6} = \frac{1}{3}$. The other four numbers will represent not winning a point.

Suppose a game consists of throwing four darts. A trial consists of four rolls of the number cube. Based on your suggestion in part (b) and the following simulated rolls,

1234	3321	5624	2451	6253
1625	3452	6115	2511	2361
5436	2251	5461	1253	6344
5513	6634	5112	3426	5534

c. What is the probability that none of the four darts will score a point?

Note: These four trials are circled above.

$$\frac{4}{20} = \frac{1}{5}$$

> I determine how many of the 20 trials do not include a 1 or 2 because these numbers represent winning a point.

d. What is the probability that three of the darts will score a point?

Note: These three trials are boxed above.

$$\frac{3}{20}$$

> I determine how many of the 20 trials have three rolls that are either a 1 or 2.

© 2015 Great Minds eureka-math.org
G7-M5-HWH-1.3.0-10.2015

EUREKA MATH

G7-M5-Lesson 11: Conducting a Simulation to Estimate the Probability of an Event

1. George typically takes 6 free throws during one basketball game. Usually, George makes 80% of his free throw shots. Design a simulation to estimate the probability that George will make at least 4 free throws during his next game.

   a. How would you simulate the number of free throws George makes and misses?

      I could put 10 slips of paper in a bag, 8 of them labeled M, for a made shot, and 2 of them labeled L, for a missed shot.

      > I can do this in more than one way but would have to have either 5 or 10 possible outcomes since 80% represents $\frac{8}{10}$ or $\frac{4}{5}$.

   b. What constitutes a trial for this simulation?

      A trial for this simulation would be picking 6 pieces of paper from the bag, replacing each piece of paper before picking again.

      > Each piece of paper represents one shot.

   c. What constitutes a success in a trial in this problem?

      A success would be looking at the 6 pieces of paper that were picked and seeing 4 or more papers that say "made."

      > A success is a simulation where the results show George making 4 or more free throws.

   d. Carry out 12 trials, list your results, and compute an estimate of the probability that George will make at least 4 of his free throw shots.

      > I will refer back to part (b) to remember what a trial consists of and repeat this 12 times.

MMMLML	LMLLMM	MMLMMM
LMLLMM	LMMMMM	LMLMMM
MLLMMM	MMLMLL	MMMMMM
MMLMMM	LLMLMM	MMMLMM

      > 8 of the 12 trials show at least four made (M) shots.

      $$\frac{8}{12} = \frac{2}{3}$$

G7-M5-Lesson 12: Applying Probability to Make Informed Decisions

A recall has been issued for one type of small toy car and one type of large toy car because so many of the cars have small pieces breaking off.

Brett believed that the probability of having a large toy car that was recalled is bigger than the probability of having a small toy car that was recalled because the large toy car would have more parts that could break. However, Rachel believed that the probability of having a recalled large toy car is the same as having a recalled small toy car.

a. Simulate inspecting a small toy car by pulling a single card from a standard 52-card deck of cards. Let a heart simulate a recalled small toy car and all other cards simulate a safe small toy car. Do 50 trials, and compute an estimate of the probability that a small toy car is recalled.

> In order to have an accurate estimated probability, I replace each card before picking a new one.

Students pick 50 cards (replacing them each time) and record the results. Students then identify the number of hearts chosen out of the 50 trials. Since hearts represent $\frac{1}{4}$ of a standard 52-card deck, the estimated probability should be close to $\frac{1}{4}$.

b. Simulate inspecting a large toy car by pulling a single card from a standard 52-card deck of cards. Let a black face card simulate a recalled large toy car and all other cards simulate a safe large toy car. Do 50 trials, and compute an estimate of the probability that a large toy car is recalled.

> I know a face card is a Jack, Queen, or King.

Students again pick 50 cards (replacing them each time) and record the results. Students then identify the number of black face cards chosen out of the 50 trials. Since black face cards represent $\frac{6}{52}$ or $\frac{3}{26}$ of the deck of cards, the estimated probability should be close to $\frac{3}{26}$.

EUREKA MATH

c. For this problem, suppose that the two simulations provide accurate estimates of the probability of a recalled small toy car and a recalled large toy car. Compare your two probability estimates, and decide whether Brett's or Rachel's belief was more reasonable than the other. Explain your reasoning.

Neither person had the correct idea. The probability of having a recalled small toy car was greater than the probability of having a recalled large toy car.

> Although the estimates will be different, there is a greater chance of picking a heart than a black face card from a deck of cards. Therefore, I know that it is more likely to have a greater probability in part (a) than in part (b).

G7-M5-Lesson 13: Populations, Samples, and Generalizing from a Sample to a Population

1. For each of the following questions: (1) Describe how you would collect data to answer the question, and (2) decide whether it would result in a sample statistic or a population characteristic.

    a. How many pets do people own in my class?

        (1) I can provide all students in my class a slip of paper and have them write the number of pets they have on the piece of paper.

        (2) The result would be a population characteristic because I would be gathering data from the entire population (my class).

        > I am able to collect data from the entire population because the population size is small.

        > There are too many people in my city to collect data from everyone, so I only collect data from a sample.

    b. How many pets do people own in my city?

        (1) I can stand outside a grocery store and ask customers as they enter the store how many pets they own.

        (2) The result would be a sample statistic because I would be gathering information from only a small subset of the entire population (my city).

2. Identify a question that would lead to collecting data from the given set as a population and one where the data could be a sample from a larger population.

    a. The entire seventh grade

        The entire seventh grade could be a population when determining the number of seventh grade student absences on a given day.

        > Data that could be collected easily, maybe from a computer, can be collected from an entire population.

        The entire seventh grade could be a sample when determining the number of hours a middle school student sleeps on a school night.

        > I would want to collect data that can be summarized from a sample to generalize to the population.

Lesson 13:   Populations, Samples, and Generalizing from a Sample to a Population

EUREKA MATH™

b.   The entire school district

I know answers will vary for this type of problem.

The entire school district might be a population when determining math scores on the state assessment for the district.

The entire school district might be a sample when determining the median family income in the state.

G7-M5-Lesson 14: Selecting a Sample

1. Would any of the following provide a random sample of the length of words in a children's book? If not, explain.

    a. Placing all the words in a bag and picking a sample of words from the bag

       This method would provide a random sample.

       > If I use a method to find a sample, it eliminates the randomness and is not a random sample.

    b. Finding the length of the last word on each page of the book

       This would not be a random sample because the book may be a rhyming book, which would make the last words on each page similar to each other and maybe not a good representation of the other words in the book.

2. Indicate whether the following are random samples from the given population, and explain why or why not.

    a. Population: All families in the city; sample includes people sitting at one bus stop.

       No, because the sample only includes people in one part of the city and only people who ride the bus.

       > This sample only includes a specific group of people from my city.

    b. Population: Teachers at a school; sample selected by putting names into a bowl and drawing the sample from the bowl.

       Yes, all the teachers have the same opportunity to be chosen.

3. What questions about the samples and populations might you want to ask if you saw the following headlines in a newspaper?

    a. Soccer is the new favorite sport of children!

       > Answers may vary.

       How many people were interviewed? Was the survey conducted at a soccer field?

       > I have to think of ways that a biased sample may have been chosen.

    b. Spicy Mint Gum is favored by 80% of consumers.

       What were the other choices? How many people were surveyed?

EUREKA MATH

G7-M5-Lesson 15: Random Sampling

Consider the distribution below:

1. What would you expect the distribution of a random sample size of 10 from the population look like?

   I would expect that a majority of the 10 data values will be between 56 and 64, with maybe one data point smaller than 56 and two data points larger than 64.

   > I know the sample should resemble the population, but there is more than one correct answer.

2. Random samples of different sizes that were selected from the population in Problem 1 are displayed below. How did your answer to Problem 1 compare to this sample of 10?

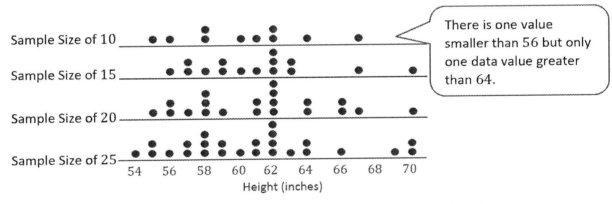

   > There is one value smaller than 56 but only one data value greater than 64.

   My expectation from Problem 1 closely matches the sample given in the first dot plot here.

> I notice that the dot plots are all similarly shaped. As the sample size gets larger, the dot plot looks even more like the dot plot of the population.

3. Why is it reasonable to think that these samples could have come from the above population?

    Each of the dot plots has a similar shape to the dot plot that represents the population.

4. Which of the box plots could represent a random sample from the distribution? Explain your thinking.

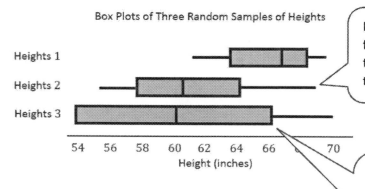

Box Plots of Three Random Samples of Heights

> I know the lines extending from the boxes extend to the smallest data value and the largest data value.

> The box part of the box plot represents the middle half of the data. The line separating the box into two represents the median of the data.

The first sample is probably not from the distribution because the middle half of the data is too high for the data provided.

The second sample could be a sample of the distribution because the middle half of the data seems to represent the same heights as the middle half of the data in the original distribution.

The third sample is not from the distribution because the range for the middle half of the data is too big.

EUREKA
MATH

G7-M5-Lesson 16: Methods for Selecting a Random Sample

> The population is all the teachers in my school.

1. The suggestions below describe ways to choose a random sample of teachers in your school that were made and vetoed. Explain why you think each was vetoed.

   a. Stand in the teachers' lounge, and use every teacher that enters before school.

      Teachers who do not enter the teachers' lounge in the morning do not have a chance to be selected, so the sample would not be random.

      > In order for a sample to be random, everyone in the population must have an equal chance of being selected.

   b. Use all the science teachers in the school.

      The teachers who do not teach science do not have a chance to be selected, so the sample would not be random.

2. The school wanted random seventh graders to complete a survey every week in order to gain information about students' thoughts about the school.

   a. Describe how the school might choose a random sample of 25 seventh graders from the total of 120 seventh graders in the school.

      Each seventh grade student could be assigned a number, and then the numbers could be placed in a bag. Every week, 25 numbers could be pulled from the bag to have students complete the survey.

      > I could also put all 120 names into a bag and pick 25 names every week.

   b. There are 40 weeks during the school year. If a random sample of 25 seventh graders is picked every week, would every student be chosen at least once? Why or why not?

      The probability of being chosen each week is $\frac{25}{120}$ or approximately 21%. Although the number of chances to get picked is high, the probability is low.

      > I could carry out the investigation to determine if it is likely for every student to be chosen.

G7-M5-Lesson 17: Sampling Variability

1. Holly is trying to convince her mom that she needs a fancy dress for prom. She wants to estimate the mean price girls at her school pay (in dollars) for prom dresses at this time. Holly selects a random sample of 12 girls from her school and asks what they paid for their prom dress. The results are shown below.

$$100 \quad 54 \quad 32 \quad 97 \quad 68 \quad 89 \quad 142 \quad 61 \quad 77 \quad 106 \quad 96 \quad 49$$

a. Holly will estimate the mean dress cost of all dresses bought by girls at her school by calculating the mean for her sample. Calculate the sample mean, and record your answer below.

$$\frac{100 + 54 + 32 + 97 + 68 + 89 + 142 + 61 + 77 + 106 + 96 + 49}{12} = \frac{971}{12} \approx 80.9$$

> To calculate the mean, I add all the data values together and then divide by the number of data values, 12.

The mean cost of a prom dress is approximately $81.00.

b. If Holly collected another sample of dress prices, would the result be the same?

It is not likely that another sample would have the same mean as this one.

> It is very rare that two samples will result in the exact same mean.

c. Explain why the means of a variety of samples will be different.

Sample variability explains that there will be differences between samples of the same population, which would result in different means.

2. Think about the mean number of pets for all students at your school.

a. What do you think is the approximate value of the mean number of pets for the population of students at your school?

The mean number of pets is 2.

> Answers will vary but should be realistic.

EUREKA
MATH™

b. How could you find a better estimate of this population mean?

I could ask a random sample of students how many pets they have and then calculate the sample mean.

I calculate the mean by calculating the sum of all the data values and dividing by the number of data values. Due to sampling variability, I know each sample could have a different mean.

G7-M5-Lesson 18: Sampling Variability and the Effect of Sample Size

The distances, in miles, that 200 people have to travel to the airport are recorded in the table below.

	0	1	2	3	4	5	6	7	8	9
00	45	58	49	78	59	36	52	39	70	51
01	50	45	45		71	55	65	33	60	51
02	53	83	40	51	83	57	75	38	43	77
03	49	49	81	57	42	36	22	66	68	52
04	60	67	43	60	55	63	56	44	50	58
05	64	41	67	73	55	69	63	46	50	65
06	54	58	53	55	51	74	53	55	64	16
07	28	48	62	24	82	51	64	45	41	47
08	70	50	38	16	39	83	62	50	37	58
09	79	62	45	48	42	51	67	68	56	78
10	61	56	71	55	57	77	48	65	61	62
11	65	40	56	47	44	51	38	68	64	40
12	53	22	73	62	82	78	84	50	43	43
13	81	42	72	49	55	65	41	92	50	60
14	56	44	40	70	52	47	30	9	58	53
15	84	64	64	34	37	69	57	75	62	67
16	45	58	49	78	59	36	52	39	70	51
17	50	45	45	66	71	55	65	33	60	51
18	53	83	40	51	83	57	75	38	43	77
19	49	49	81	57	42	36	22	66	68	52

1. Using the random digit table, the following 15 values were chosen.

$$82, 64, 40, 64, 33, 81, 22, 50, 66, 51, 78, 49, 70, 58, 84$$

> I add the data values together and divide by the number of data values.

Calculate the mean of the sample.

$$\frac{82 + 64 + 40 + 64 + 33 + 81 + 22 + 50 + 66 + 51 + 78 + 49 + 70 + 58 + 84}{15} = \frac{892}{15} \approx 59.5$$

The average distance people travel to the airport is approximately 59.5 miles.

EUREKA MATH

2. Using the random digit table, the following 25 values were chosen.

$$45, 67, 71, 49, 50, 38, 67, 77, 55, 45, 64, 22, 36, 9, 49, 30, 51, 70, 75, 36, 73, 62, 79, 50, 40$$

Calculate the mean of the sample.

$$\frac{1310}{25} = 52.4$$

The average distance people travel to the airport is approximately 52.4 miles.

3. Which sample mean would you expect to be closer to the population mean? Explain your reasoning.

The sample mean from Problem 2 would be closer the population mean because the sample size is greater.

> The sample variability is smaller with a larger sample and larger with a smaller sample.

© 2015 Great Minds eureka-math.org
G7-M5-HWH-1.3.0-10.2015

G7-M5-Lesson 19: Understanding Variability When Estimating a Population Proportion

A group of friends want to determine the number of chocolate pieces of candy in a bag of mixed candy. Each friend took a random sample of 10 pieces of candy. The table below shows the proportion of chocolate pieces of candy each friend found.

0.2	0.7	0.5	0.7	0.6
0.5	0.4	0.7	0.6	0.5
0.2	0.8	0.6	0.6	0.5

1. Construct a dot plot of the sample proportions.

Dot Plot of Proportions of Chocolate Pieces

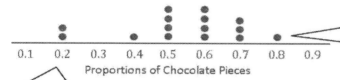

Proportions of Chocolate Pieces

> Each dot represents one data value. If a value is represented more than once in the distribution, I place the additional dots above the original dot.

> The number line of a dot plot must have a constant scale. I cannot skip numbers, even if a number is not represented in the distribution.

2. Describe the variability of the distribution.

    The spread of the data is 0.2 to 0.8; however, most of the data is between 0.5 and 0.7.

> The spread explains the location of the data values using the minimum and maximum.

> I know the sampling variability decreases when my sample size increases.

3. Suppose each friend picked 40 pieces of candy from the bag. Describe how the sampling distribution would change from the one you constructed in Problem 1.

    The sampling variability would decrease.

EUREKA MATH

G7-M5-Lesson 20: Estimating a Population Proportion

A group of 20 seventh graders wanted to estimate the proportion of middle school students who buy school lunch every day. Each seventh grader took a random sample of 20 middle school students and asked each student whether or not he or she bought lunch. Following are the sample proportions the seventh graders found in 20 samples.

0.15	0.10	0.20	0.00	0.05
0.25	0.30	0.00	0.10	0.15
0.10	0.05	0.20	0.10	0.10
0.15	0.15	0.20	0.00	0.10

> I can write this number as a fraction, $\frac{25}{100}$. To determine how many students in the sample buy school lunch every day, I find an equivalent fraction where the denominator is the sample size.

1. One of the seventh graders reported a sample proportion of 0.25. What does this value mean in terms of the scenario?

$$\frac{25}{100} = \frac{5}{20}$$

A sample proportion of 0.25 means that 5 out of 20 students in the sample buy school lunch every day.

2. Construct a dot plot of the 20 sample proportions.

3. Describe the shape of the distribution.

    The shape of the distribution is symmetric.
    It centers at approximately 0.10.

    > A majority of the data values center around the
    > same number. I notice the dot plot looks like a
    > mound, so it would have a symmetric shape.

4. Using the 20 sample proportions listed above, what is your estimate for the proportion of all the middle
    school students who bought school lunch every day?

    My estimate for the proportion of all middle school students who bought school lunch every day is 0.12
    because I think the proportion will be between 0.10 *and* 0.15.

    > Answers will vary but
    > should be close to the
    > actual mean of 0.1225.

© 2015 Great Minds eureka-math.org
G7-M5-HWH-1.3.0-10.2015

EUREKA
MATH

G7-M5-Lesson 21: Why Worry About Sampling Variability?

Below are two dot plots. Each dot plot represents the differences in sample means for random samples selected from two populations (Bag A and Bag B). For each distribution, the differences were found by subtracting the sample means of Bag B from the sample means of Bag A (sample mean A – sample mean B).

1. Examine the dot plot below.

Sample Mean A – Sample Mean B

> I notice that a majority of the differences are a positive value.

a. Does the dot plot above indicate that the population mean of Bag A is larger than the population mean of Bag B? Why or why not?

The population mean of Bag A is larger than the population mean of Bag B because a majority of the differences are positive, which means the sample means for Bag A were larger than the sample means for Bag B.

> Due to the order of the subtraction, if the population mean of Bag B were bigger than Bag A, a majority of the differences would be negative.

b. In the above graph, how many differences are greater than 0? How many differences are less than 0? What might this tell you?

There are 17 differences that are greater than 0 and only 6 differences that are less than 0. This would tell me that the population mean for Bag A is most likely larger than the population mean for Bag B because a larger number minus a smaller number results in a positive number.

> It is possible that the population mean of Bag B is larger than the population mean of Bag A, but it is not very likely since there are a lot more positive differences than negative differences.

2. Examine the dot plot below.

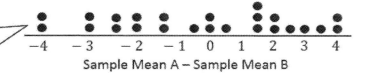

> The dot plot is centered around 0, so I expect that the difference of the two population means is also close to 0.

Sample Mean A – Sample Mean B

Does the dot plot above indicate that the population mean of Bag A is larger than the population mean of Bag B? Why or why not?

The dot plot indicates that the population means of both bags are about the same because there are the same number of positive and negative values on the dot plot.

EUREKA MATH

G7-M5-Lesson 22: Using Sample Data to Compare the Means of Two or More Populations

Measure of Variability

1. A school is trying to decide which math program to purchase.

   a. How many mean absolute deviations (MADs) separate the mean mathematics score for the Math Facts program (mean $= 42.7$, MAD $= 3.7$, $n = 32$) and the Math Genius program (mean $= 38.6$, MAD $= 4.0$, $n = 28$)?

$$\frac{47.7 - 38.6}{4.0} = 2.275$$

> I subtract the two sample means and then divide by the MAD. If the two MADs are different, I use the larger of the two MADs.

> This value indicates that the data are separated by a little more than 2 MADs.

   The number of MADs that separate the sample mean mathematics score for the Math Facts program and the Math Genius program is 2.275, a little more than two MADs.

   b. What recommendation would you make based on the result?

   The number of MADs that separate the two programs is significant, so I would recommend the Math Facts program because it produces higher scores.

> I know Math Facts produces significantly higher scores because the mean is higher than the Math Genius mean.

> In general, if the MADs are separated by 2 or more, then this is significant.

2. Does a pickup truck or an SUV get better gas mileage? A sample of 10 different cars and pickup trucks and their gas mileage (miles per gallon) is provided in the table below.

Trucks	16	15	19	18	18	21	17	19	20	20
SUVs	20	20	20	23	25	23	24	22	30	26

a. Calculate the difference between the sample mean gas mileage for the trucks and for SUVs.

Sample mean gas mileage (in miles per gallon) for trucks:

$$\frac{16 + 15 + 19 + 18 + 18 + 21 + 17 + 19 + 20 + 20}{10} = 18.3$$

> To calculate the mean, I add my data values together and divide by the number of data values.

Sample mean gas mileage (in miles per gallon) for SUVs:

$$\frac{20 + 20 + 20 + 23 + 25 + 23 + 24 + 22 + 30 + 26}{10} = 23.3$$

$23.3 - 18.3 = 5$

The difference between the two sample means is 5.

b. On the same scale, draw dot plots of the two distributions, and discuss the variability in each distribution.

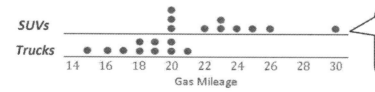

> The dots on the SUVs dot plot are a little more spread out than the dots on the trucks dot plot.

The SUVs have a little larger variability than the trucks.

Lesson 22:   Using Sample Data to Compare the Means of Two or More Populations

© 2015 Great Minds eureka-math.org
G7-M5-HWH-1.3.0-10.2015

EUREKA MATH™

To calculate the MAD, I first need to determine the deviations or the distance each point is from the mean.

c. Calculate the MAD for each distribution. Based on the MADs, compare the variability in each distribution. Is the variability about the same? Interpret the MADs in the context of the problem.

Deviations of Trucks:

$18.3 - 16 = 2.3$

$18.3 - 15 = 3.3$

$19 - 18.3 = 0.7$

$18.3 - 18 = 0.3$

Now that I know the deviations, I find the sum of the deviations and divide the sum by the number of data values.

$18.3 - 18 = 0.3$

$\dfrac{2.3 + 3.3 + 0.7 + 0.3 + 0.3 + 2.7 + 1.3 + 0.7 + 1.7 + 1.7}{10} = \dfrac{15}{10} = 1.5$

$18.3 - 18 = 0.3$

$21 - 18.3 = 2.7$

$18.3 - 17 = 1.3$

$19 - 18.3 = 0.7$

$20 - 18.3 = 1.7$

$20 - 18.3 = 1.7$

I follow the same process to calculate the MAD for SUVs.

SUVs:

$$\dfrac{3.3 + 3.3 + 3.3 + 0.3 + 1.7 + 0.3 + 0.7 + 1.3 + 6.7 + 2.7}{10} = \dfrac{23.6}{10} = 2.36$$

The MAD for trucks is 1.5, which means the typical deviation from the mean of 18.3 is 1.5.

The MAD for SUVs is 2.36, which means the typical deviation from the mean of 23.3 is 2.36.

d. Based on your calculations, is the difference in mean distance meaningful?

$\dfrac{5}{2.36} = 2.11$

There is a separation of 2.11 MADs. There is a meaningful distance between the means.

I know a meaningful distance is similar to a significant difference.

G7-M5-Lesson 23: Using Sample Data to Compare the Means of Two or More Populations

Principal MacDonald wanted to determine if sixth graders or eighth graders were absent more often. The table below shows the number of absences 12 students in each grade had throughout the year.

Sixth Grade	4	0	6	10	8	7	3	2	4	7	6	5
Eighth Grade	0	8	12	4	7	6	9	10	1	3	2	2

1. On the same scale, draw dot plots for the two sample data sets.

2. Looking at the dot plots, list some observations comparing the number of absences for sixth graders and the number of absences for eighth graders.

   The dot plots look similar. The variability is slightly larger for eighth grade students than for sixth grade students. However, both data distributions look like they have means close to each other.

   Although answers may vary a little, it is important for students to notice the dot plots are similar.

EUREKA MATH

> An additional explanation for how to calculate this information can be found in Lesson 22.

3. Calculate the mean and MAD for each of the data sets. Round to the nearest hundredth if necessary.

	Mean (days)	MAD (days)
Sixth Grade	5.17	2.17
Eighth Grade	5.33	3.33

> I add all the data values and divide by the number of data values.

> I remember from Lesson 22 that I calculate the sum of the deviations and divide by the number of data values.

4. How many MADs separate the two sample means?

$$\frac{5.33 - 5.17}{3.33} \approx 0.05$$

> I calculate the difference between the means and divide by the largest MAD.

5. What can you say about the average number of absences for all sixth graders in the population compared to the average number of absences for all eighth graders in the population?

Since the number of MADs that separate the means is approximately 0.05, we can assume sixth graders and eighth graders miss about the same amount of school.

> In order to conclude that students in one grade miss more school than another grade, the separation between the means needs to be significant.

Homework Helpers

Grade 7
Module 6

G7-M6-Lesson 1: Complementary and Supplementary Angles

1. Two lines meet at the endpoint of a ray. Set up and solve the appropriate equations to determine a and b.

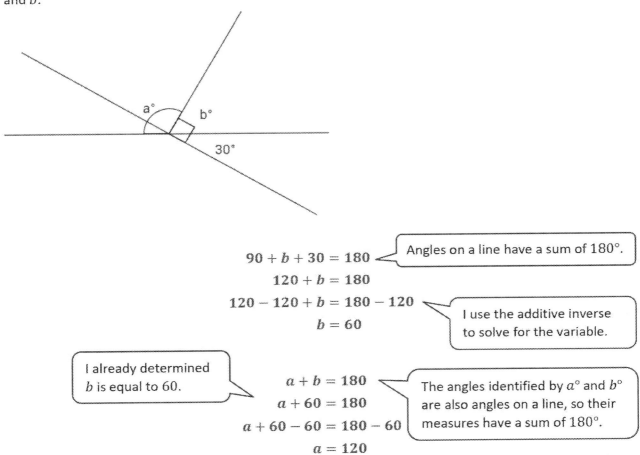

$$90 + b + 30 = 180$$

Angles on a line have a sum of $180°$.

$$120 + b = 180$$
$$120 - 120 + b = 180 - 120$$
$$b = 60$$

I use the additive inverse to solve for the variable.

I already determined b is equal to 60.

$$a + b = 180$$
$$a + 60 = 180$$
$$a + 60 - 60 = 180 - 60$$
$$a = 120$$

The angles identified by $a°$ and $b°$ are also angles on a line, so their measures have a sum of $180°$.

Therefore, the angles identified by $a°$ and $b°$ have measures of $120°$ and $60°$, respectively.

2. Two lines meet at the common endpoint of two rays. Set up and solve the appropriate equations to determine c and d.

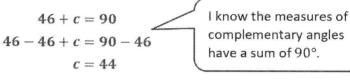

$$46 + c = 90$$
$$46 - 46 + c = 90 - 46$$
$$c = 44$$

I know the measures of complementary angles have a sum of 90°.

$$46 + d = 90$$
$$46 - 46 + d = 90 - 46$$
$$d = 44$$

Therefore, the angles identified by $c°$ and $d°$ both have measures of 44°.

I could also recognize that c and d have equal values because the angles they are identified with are both complements to the same angle.

3. Set up and solve appropriate equations for e and f.

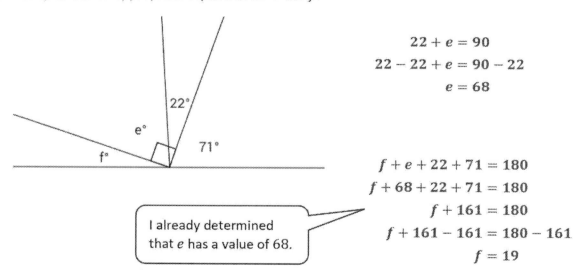

$$22 + e = 90$$
$$22 - 22 + e = 90 - 22$$
$$e = 68$$

$$f + e + 22 + 71 = 180$$
$$f + 68 + 22 + 71 = 180$$
$$f + 161 = 180$$
$$f + 161 - 161 = 180 - 161$$
$$f = 19$$

I already determined that e has a value of 68.

Therefore, the angles identified by $e°$ and $f°$ have measures of 68° and 19°, respectively.

Lesson 1:   Complementary and Supplementary Angles

EUREKA MATH

4. The measurement of the supplement of an angle is $30°$ more than double the measurement of the angle. Find the measurements of the angle and its supplement.

Let $x°$ represent the measurement of the angle.

$$x + (2x + 30) = 180$$
$$3x + 30 = 180$$
$$3x + 30 - 30 = 180 - 30$$
$$3x = 150$$
$$\left(\frac{1}{3}\right)3x = \left(\frac{1}{3}\right)150$$
$$x = 50$$

> I know the measures of supplementary angles have a sum of $180°$.

> I use my knowledge of solving equations to determine the value of x.

Let $(2x + 30)°$ represent the measurement of the supplement of the angle.

$$2x + 30$$
$$= 2(50) + 30$$
$$= 100 + 30$$
$$= 130$$

> To find the measure of the supplement, I can either subtract the measure of the angle from $180°$, or I can substitute the value of x into the expression $2x + 30$.

The angle measures $50°$, and its supplement measures $130°$.

5. The measurement of the complement of an angle exceeds the measurement of the angle by 50%. Find the measurements of the angle and its complement.

Let $x°$ represent the measurement of the angle and let $(x + 0.5x)°$ represent the measurement of its complement.

$$x + (x + 0.5x) = 90$$
$$2.5x = 90$$
$$\left(\frac{1}{2.5}\right)2.5x = \left(\frac{1}{2.5}\right)90$$
$$x = 36$$

> The measure of the complement of the angle is the sum of the measure of the angle plus another 50% of its measure.

$$90 - 36 = 54$$

> We could also substitute 36 into the expression $x + 0.50x$ to determine the measure of the complement.

The angle measures $36°$ and its complement measures $54°$.

6. The ratio of the measurement of an angle to the measurement of its supplement is $2\colon 7$. Find the measurements of the angle and its supplement.

Let $2x°$ represent the measurement of the angle and let $7x°$ represent the measurement of its supplement.

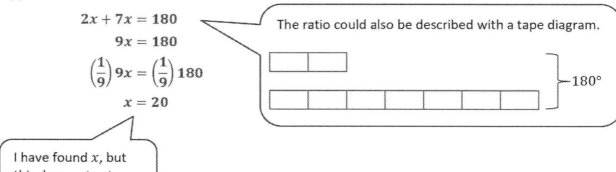

$$2x + 7x = 180$$
$$9x = 180$$
$$\left(\frac{1}{9}\right) 9x = \left(\frac{1}{9}\right) 180$$
$$x = 20$$

The ratio could also be described with a tape diagram.

180°

I have found x, but this does not yet answer the question.

Angle: $2(20)° = 40°$ *Supplement:* $7(20)° = 140°$

Therefore, the angle measures $40°$ and its supplement measures $140°$.

EUREKA MATH

G7-M6-Lesson 2: Solving for Unknown Angles Using Equations

1. Two lines meet at the endpoint of a ray. Set up and solve an equation to find the values of h and j.

> I know that vertical angles have the same angle measure.

$$110 = 90 + h$$
$$110 - 90 = 90 - 90 + h$$
$$20 = h$$

> I know that the measures of angles on a line have a sum of $180°$.

$$110 + j = 180$$
$$110 - 110 + j = 180 - 110$$
$$j = 70$$

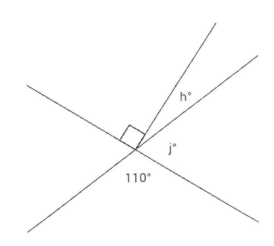

The value of h is 20 and the value of j is 70.

2. Two lines meet at the vertex of an angle formed by two rays. Set up and solve an equation to find the value of k.

> I know that the measures of complementary angles have a sum of $90°$.

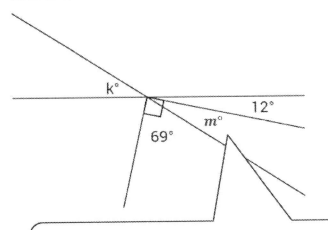

$$69 + m = 90$$
$$69 - 69 + m = 90 - 69$$
$$m = 21$$

$$21 + 12 = k$$
$$33 = k$$

> I know the measures of two adjacent angles that form a vertical angle to the angle $k°$.

> I need to determine the measure of this unknown angle in order to determine the value of k. I'll let this angle have a measure of $m°$.

The value of k is 33.

3. Three lines meet at the endpoint of a ray. Set up and solve an equation to find the value of each variable in the diagram.

$62 + 44 = c$

$106 = c$

I can use my knowledge of vertical angles and complementary angles to determine the values of c and a.

$a + 62 = 90$

$a + 62 - 62 = 90 - 62$

$a = 28$

$b + a + 62 + 44 = 180$

$b + 28 + 62 + 44 = 180$

$b + 134 = 180$

$b + 134 - 134 = 180 - 134$

$b = 46$

Now that I know the value of a, I can calculate the value of b because I know that the measures of angles on a line have a sum of 180°.

$b = e$

$46 = e$

Now, I can use my knowledge of vertical angles to determine the values of e and d.

$a = d$

$28 = d$

4. Set up and solve an equation to find the value of x. Find the measurements of $\angle MOP$ and $\angle NOP$.

$5x + 15x = 180$

$20x = 180$

$\left(\dfrac{1}{20}\right) 20x = \left(\dfrac{1}{20}\right) 180$

$x = 9$

I can use the value of x to determine the measure of the two unknown angles.

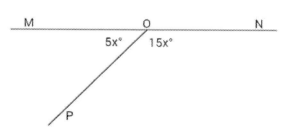

$\angle MOP = 5x° = 5(9)° = 45°$

$\angle NOP = 15x° = 15(9)° = 135°$

I can check my answers by making sure the measures of the two angles have a sum of 180°.

EUREKA
MATH

5. Set up and solve an equation to find the value of y. Find the measurements of $\angle AOB$ and $\angle BOC$.

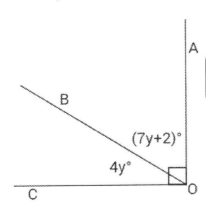

$(7y+2)°$

$4y°$

$$4y + 7y + 2 = 90$$
$$11y + 2 = 90$$
$$11y + 2 - 2 = 90 - 2$$
$$11y = 88$$
$$\left(\frac{1}{11}\right)11y = \left(\frac{1}{11}\right)88$$
$$y = 8$$

> I need to collect like terms before solving the equation.

$$\angle BOC = 4y° = 4(8)° = 32°$$
$$\angle AOB = (7y + 2)° = (7(8) + 2)° = 58°$$

> I can check my answers by making sure the measures of the two angles have a sum of 90°.

G7-M6-Lesson 3: Solving for Unknown Angles Using Equations

1. Two lines meet at a point. Find the measurement of a vertical angle. Is your answer reasonable? Explain how you know.

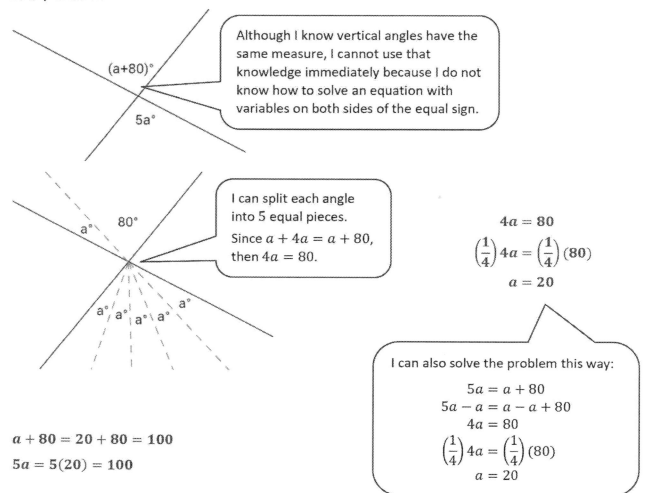

> Although I know vertical angles have the same measure, I cannot use that knowledge immediately because I do not know how to solve an equation with variables on both sides of the equal sign.

> I can split each angle into 5 equal pieces. Since $a + 4a = a + 80$, then $4a = 80$.

$$4a = 80$$
$$\left(\frac{1}{4}\right)4a = \left(\frac{1}{4}\right)(80)$$
$$a = 20$$

> I can also solve the problem this way:
> $$5a = a + 80$$
> $$5a - a = a - a + 80$$
> $$4a = 80$$
> $$\left(\frac{1}{4}\right)4a = \left(\frac{1}{4}\right)(80)$$
> $$a = 20$$

$a + 80 = 20 + 80 = 100$

$5a = 5(20) = 100$

Therefore, each vertical angle has a measure of $100°$.

My answer is reasonable because the vertical angle looks to be close to the measure of a right angle.

2. Three lines meet at the endpoint of a ray. Set up and solve an equation to find the value of b.

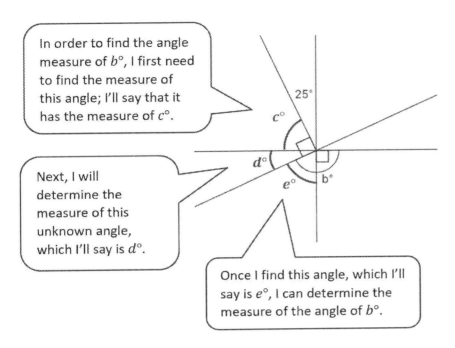

In order to find the angle measure of $b°$, I first need to find the measure of this angle; I'll say that it has the measure of $c°$.

Next, I will determine the measure of this unknown angle, which I'll say is $d°$.

Once I find this angle, which I'll say is $e°$, I can determine the measure of the angle of $b°$.

$$c + 25 = 90$$
$$c + 25 - 25 = 90 - 25$$
$$c = 65$$

$$c + d = 90$$
$$65 + d = 90$$
$$65 - 65 + d = 90 - 65$$
$$d = 25$$

$$d + e = 90$$
$$25 + e = 90$$
$$25 - 25 + e = 90 - 25$$
$$e = 65$$

Looking at the diagram, I see that the angle of measure $b°$ consists of a right angle and the angle of measure $e°$.

$$90 + 65 = 155$$

Therefore, the value of b is 155.

3. Four angles meet at a point. The second angle measures 10° more than the first angle, the third angle measures 15° more than the second angle, and the fourth angle measures 20° more than the third angle. Find the measurements of all four angles.

> I know that the measures of angles that meet at a point have a sum of 360°.

Let x represent the value of the first angle measurement.

$$(x) + (x + 10) + (x + 10 + 15) + (x + 10 + 15 + 20) = 360$$
$$4x + 80 = 360$$
$$4x + 80 - 80 = 360 - 80$$
$$4x = 280$$
$$\left(\frac{1}{4}\right) 4x = \left(\frac{1}{4}\right) 280$$
$$x = 70$$

> Each set of parentheses represents the measure of each of the angles.

The following are the measures of each of the angles:

Angle 1: $70°$

Angle 2: $(70)° + 10° = 80°$

Angle 3: $(70)° + 10° + 15° = 95°$

Angle 3: $(70)° + 10° + 15° + 20° = 115°$

> To check my answers, I could add the measures of the four angles together to determine if they have a sum of 360°.

EUREKA
MATH

G7-M6-Lesson 4: Solving for Unknown Angles Using Equations

1. $\overleftrightarrow{BE}$ and $\overleftrightarrow{AD}$ meet at G. Set up and solve an equation to find the value of y. Find the measurements of $\angle BGC$ and $\angle CGD$.

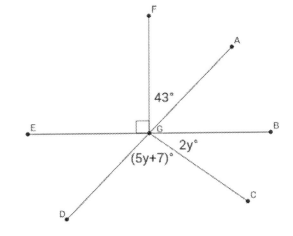

$$43 + \angle AGB = 90$$
$$43 - 43 + \angle AGB = 90 - 43$$
$$\angle AGB = 47$$

> I need to determine the measurement of $\angle AGB$ before finding the measurements of $\angle BGC$ and $\angle CGD$.

$$\angle AGB + 2y + 5y + 7 = 180$$
$$47 + 2y + 5y + 7 = 180$$
$$54 + 7y = 180$$
$$54 - 54 + 7y = 180 - 54$$
$$7y = 126$$
$$y = 18$$

> Now that I know the value of y, I can calculate the measurements of $\angle BGC$ and $\angle CGD$.

The measurement of $\angle BGC$: $2(18)° = 36°$

The measurement of $\angle CGD$: $(5(18) + 7)° = (90 + 7)° = 97°$

2. Five rays meet at a point. Set up and solve an equation to find the value of m. Find the measurements of $\angle EDF$ and $\angle HDG$.

$$7m + 4m + 5m + 4m + 100 = 360$$
$$20m + 100 = 360$$
$$20m + 100 - 100 = 360 - 100$$
$$20m = 260$$

I can use the value of m to determine the measures of the unknown angles.

$$\left(\frac{1}{20}\right)20m = \left(\frac{1}{20}\right)260$$
$$m = 13$$

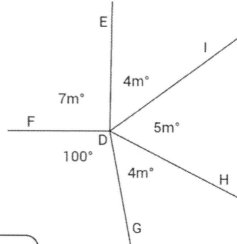

$$\angle EDF = 7m° = 7(13)° = 91°$$
$$\angle HDG = 4m° = 4(13)° = 52°$$

I only need to determine the measures of the two angles presented in the question.

3. Three adjacent angles form a line. The measurement of each angle is one of three consecutive, positive whole numbers. Determine the measurements of all three angles.

Consecutive numbers are ones that directly follow each other. For example, 2, 3, 4.

Let $x°$ represent the smallest angle measure.

Since $x°$ represents the measure of the smallest angle, then the measure of the second angle is 1° larger than $x°$, and the measure of the third angle is 2° larger than $x°$.

$$x + (x + 1) + (x + 2) = 180$$
$$3x + 3 = 180$$
$$3x + 3 - 3 = 180 - 3$$
$$3x = 177$$
$$\left(\frac{1}{3}\right)3x = \left(\frac{1}{3}\right)177$$
$$x = 59$$

The three angles measure 59°, 60°, and 61° because I determined the smallest angle measures 59°, and the measures of the other two angles are consecutive numbers.

EUREKA
MATH™

4. The ratio of measurement of an angle to the measurement of its supplement is $1:4$.

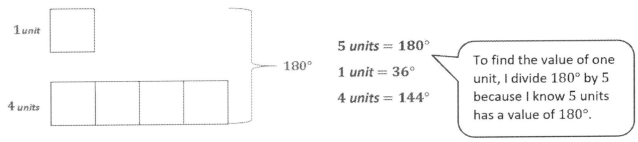

$5\ units = 180°$

$1\ unit = 36°$

$4\ units = 144°$

> To find the value of one unit, I divide $180°$ by 5 because I know 5 units has a value of $180°$.

The measure of the angle that satisfies these criteria is $36°$.

5. The sum of four times the measurement of the complement of an angle and the measurement of the supplement of that angle is $240°$. What is the measurement of the angle?

Let $a°$ represent the measurement of the angle.

> I use my knowledge of complements and supplements to write an equation.

$$4(90 - a) + (180 - a) = 240$$
$$360 - 4a + 180 - a = 240$$
$$540 - 5a = 240$$
$$540 - 540 - 5a = 240 - 540$$
$$-5a = -300$$
$$\left(-\frac{1}{5}\right)(-5a) = \left(-\frac{1}{5}\right)(-300)$$
$$a = 60$$

> I need to be careful when collecting like terms. I remember that subtracting is the same as adding the opposite, so I could rewrite the equation as follows:
> $360 + (-4a) + 180 + (-a) = 240$.

The measurement of the angle is $60°$.

G7-M6-Lesson 5: Identical Triangles

1. Given the following triangles' correspondences, use double arrows to show the correspondence between vertices, angles, and sides.

The order in which the vertices are listed for each triangle is important. The correspondence of vertices, angles, and sides are determined by the order of the label.

The first vertex labeled in the first triangle corresponds with the first vertex labeled in the second triangle. The same is true for the other two vertices.

The same correspondence rule for vertices is true for angle correspondence.

Triangle Correspondence	$\triangle MNP \leftrightarrow \triangle XYZ$
Correspondence of Vertices	$M \longleftrightarrow X$ $N \longleftrightarrow Y$ $P \longleftrightarrow Z$
Correspondence of Angles	$\angle M \longleftrightarrow \angle X$ $\angle N \longleftrightarrow \angle Y$ $\angle P \longleftrightarrow \angle Z$
Correspondence of Sides	$\overline{MN} \longleftrightarrow \overline{XY}$ $\overline{NP} \longleftrightarrow \overline{YZ}$ $\overline{MP} \longleftrightarrow \overline{XZ}$

The sides of triangles are line segments and are defined by two vertices. The corresponding sides also depend on the order of the triangle labels.

EUREKA MATH

2. Name the angle pairs and side pairs to find a triangle correspondence that matches sides of equal length and angles of equal measurement.

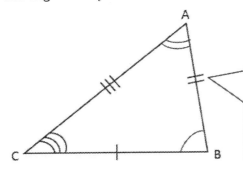

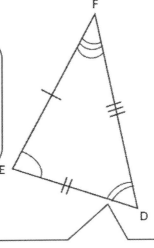

The tick marks on the triangles' sides indicate correspondence. Corresponding sides have the same number of tick marks.

The arcs in the triangles' angles indicate correspondence. Corresponding angles have the same number of arcs.

$AB = DE$ $BC = EF$ $AC = DF$

$\angle A = \angle D$ $\angle B = \angle E$ $\angle C = \angle F$

$\triangle ABC \leftrightarrow \triangle DEF$

I know the order that I use to name the triangles is important. The letters of the corresponding angles must be in the same position for both triangles.

G7-M6-Lesson 6: Drawing Geometric Shapes

Necessary Tools

Students need a ruler, protractor, and compass to complete the homework assignment.

> I use rulers to measure and draw line segments, protractors to construct angles, and compasses to draw circles.

Use a ruler, protractor, and compass to complete the following problems.

1. Draw a segment BC that is 4 cm in length, perpendicular to segment DE, which is 7 cm in length.

> I know that perpendicular tells me that the two segments will create a right angle.

> I first use my ruler to draw segment BC.

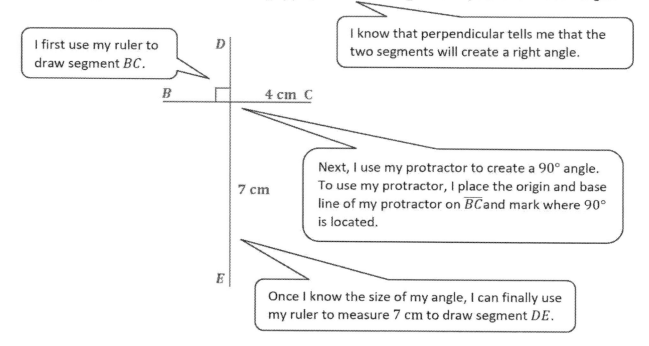

> Next, I use my protractor to create a 90° angle. To use my protractor, I place the origin and base line of my protractor on $\overline{BC}$ and mark where 90° is located.

> Once I know the size of my angle, I can finally use my ruler to measure 7 cm to draw segment DE.

EUREKA MATH

2. Draw △ XYZ so that ∠Y has a measurement of 75°.

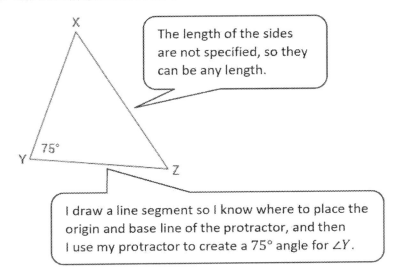

The length of the sides are not specified, so they can be any length.

I draw a line segment so I know where to place the origin and base line of the protractor, and then I use my protractor to create a 75° angle for ∠Y.

3. Draw a segment BC that is 2 cm in length. Draw a circle with center B and radius BC. Draw a second circle with diameter BC.

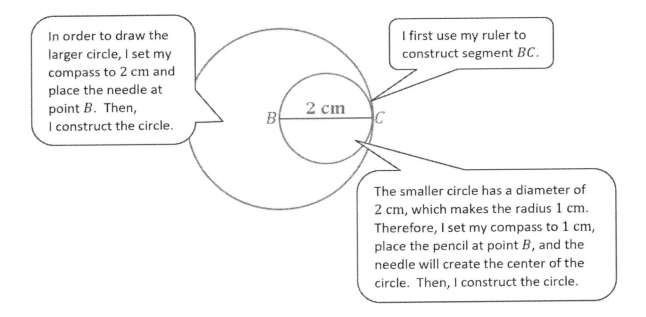

In order to draw the larger circle, I set my compass to 2 cm and place the needle at point B. Then, I construct the circle.

I first use my ruler to construct segment BC.

The smaller circle has a diameter of 2 cm, which makes the radius 1 cm. Therefore, I set my compass to 1 cm, place the pencil at point B, and the needle will create the center of the circle. Then, I construct the circle.

G7-M6-Lesson 7: Drawing Parallelograms

Necessary Tools

Students need a ruler, protractor, and setsquare to complete this homework assignment. Students created setsquares at school, but, if necessary, students can follow the diagrams below to make a new one.

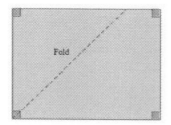 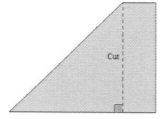 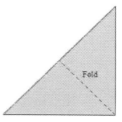 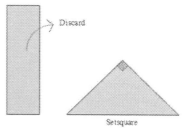

1.   Use a setsquare and a ruler to construct rectangle $WXYZ$ with $WX = 4$ cm and $XY = 5$ cm.

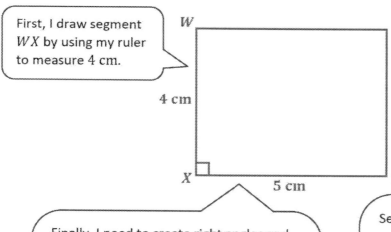

First, I draw segment WX by using my ruler to measure 4 cm.

Finally, I need to create right angles and connect the two parallel segments. To do this, I align one leg of my setsquare with $\overline{WX}$, line up my ruler so the outer portion goes through point X, and then I draw a segment. I mark the point that intersects the segment parallel to $\overline{WX}$ as Y. I repeat this process to find point Z.

Second, I use the setsquare to create a segment that is parallel to $\overline{WX}$. To do this, I align one leg of the setsquare with $\overline{WX}$ and place the ruler along the other leg of the setsquare. I make a mark 5 cm away from $\overline{WX}$. I slide the setsquare along the ruler until I reach the mark and use the leg of the setsquare to draw a segment through the mark that is parallel to $\overline{WX}$.

EUREKA MATH

2. Use a setsquare, ruler, and protractor to draw parallelogram $ABCD$ so that $\angle A = 60°$, $AB = 4$ cm, $\angle B = 120°$, and the altitude to $\overline{AB}$ is 7 cm.

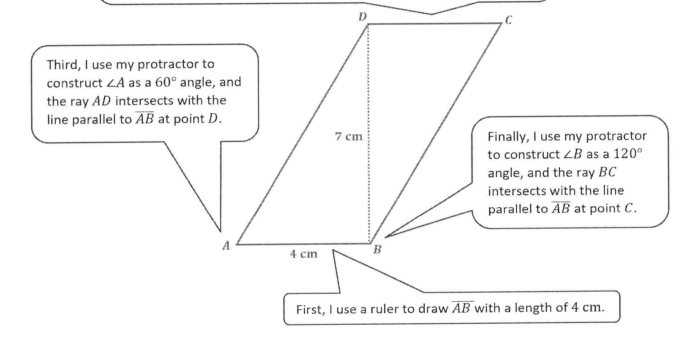

Second, I align the setsquare and ruler so that one leg of the setsquare aligns with $\overline{AB}$, and I mark a point, X, 7 cm from $\overline{AB}$. Then, I slide the setsquare along the ruler so that one side of the setsquare passes through X, and I draw a line through X; this line is parallel to $\overline{AB}$.

Third, I use my protractor to construct $\angle A$ as a 60° angle, and the ray AD intersects with the line parallel to $\overline{AB}$ at point D.

Finally, I use my protractor to construct $\angle B$ as a 120° angle, and the ray BC intersects with the line parallel to $\overline{AB}$ at point C.

First, I use a ruler to draw $\overline{AB}$ with a length of 4 cm.

7 cm

4 cm

EUREKA MATH™

© 2015 Great Minds eureka-math.org
G7-M6-HWH-1.3.0-10.2015

G7-M6-Lesson 8: Drawing Triangles

Necessary Tools

Students need a ruler and protractor to complete the homework assignment.

1. Draw two different equilateral triangles, △ ABC and △ $A'B'C'$. A side length of △ ABC is 2 cm. A side length of △ $A'B'C'$ is 4 cm. Label all sides and angle measurements. Why are your triangles not identical?

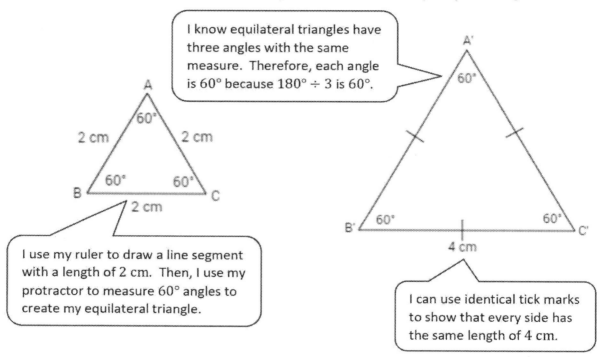

I know equilateral triangles have three angles with the same measure. Therefore, each angle is 60° because 180° ÷ 3 is 60°.

I use my ruler to draw a line segment with a length of 2 cm. Then, I use my protractor to measure 60° angles to create my equilateral triangle.

I can use identical tick marks to show that every side has the same length of 4 cm.

Even though the angles are identical in both triangles, the triangles are not identical because there is no correspondence that matches equal sides to equal sides.

I know that identical triangles must have three identical angles *and* three identical sides.

2. Draw all the isosceles triangles that satisfy the following conditions: one angle measure is 100° and one side has a length of 5 cm. Label all angle and side measurements. How many triangles can be drawn under these conditions?

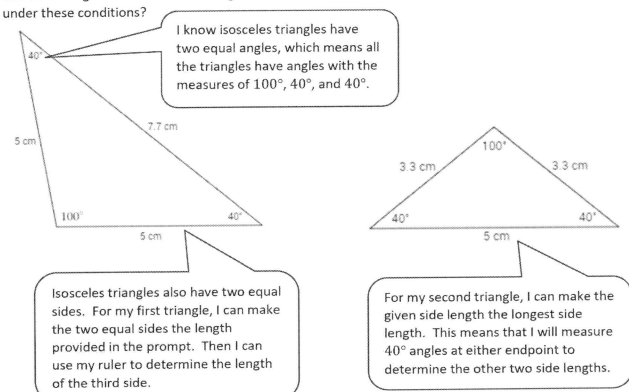

I know isosceles triangles have two equal angles, which means all the triangles have angles with the measures of 100°, 40°, and 40°.

Isosceles triangles also have two equal sides. For my first triangle, I can make the two equal sides the length provided in the prompt. Then I can use my ruler to determine the length of the third side.

For my second triangle, I can make the given side length the longest side length. This means that I will measure 40° angles at either endpoint to determine the other two side lengths.

Only two triangles can be created under these conditions.

3. Draw three non-identical triangles so that two angles measure 60° and 80° and one side measures 6 cm. Why are these triangles not identical?

    Even though there is a correspondence that will match equal angles to equal angles, these triangles are not identical because there is no correspondence that will match equal sides to equal sides.

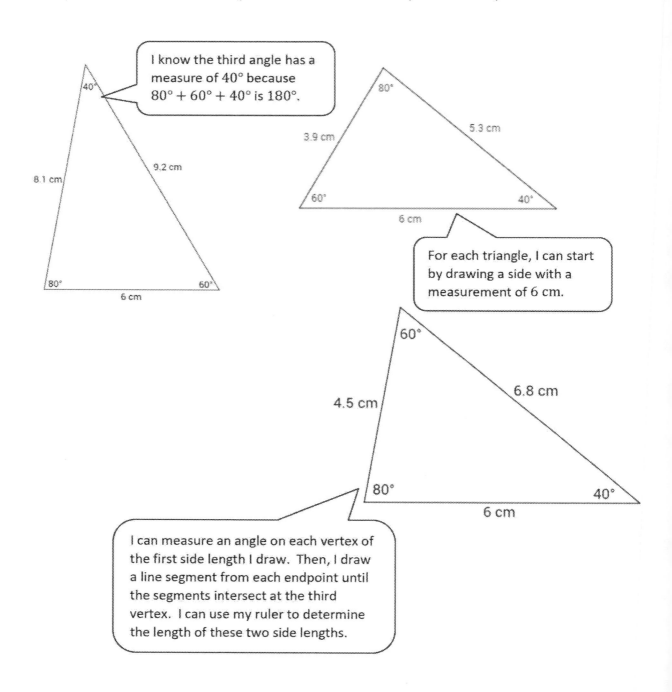

I know the third angle has a measure of 40° because 80° + 60° + 40° is 180°.

For each triangle, I can start by drawing a side with a measurement of 6 cm.

I can measure an angle on each vertex of the first side length I draw. Then, I draw a line segment from each endpoint until the segments intersect at the third vertex. I can use my ruler to determine the length of these two side lengths.

EUREKA MATH™

G7-M6-Lesson 9: Conditions for a Unique Triangle—Three Sides and Two Sides and the Included Angle

Necessary Tools

Students need a ruler, protractor, and compass to complete this homework assignment.

1. A triangle with side lengths 5 cm, 12 cm, and 13 cm is shown below. Use your compass and ruler to draw a triangle with the same side lengths. Leave all construction marks as evidence of your work, and label all side and angle measurements.

   Under what condition is the triangle drawn? Compare the triangle you drew to the triangle shown below. Are the triangles identical? Did the condition determine a unique triangle? Use your construction to explain why.

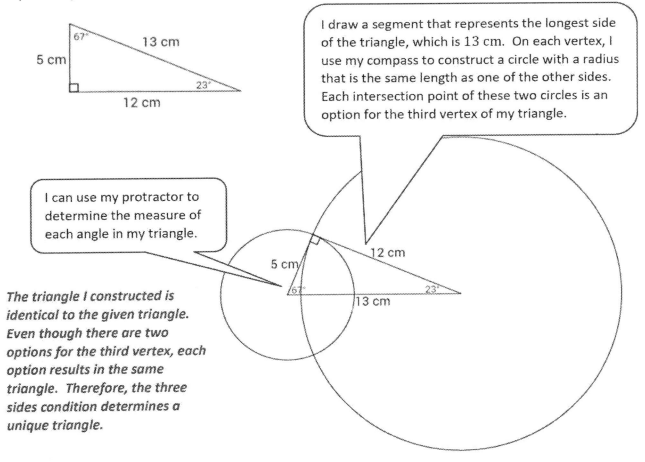

I draw a segment that represents the longest side of the triangle, which is 13 cm. On each vertex, I use my compass to construct a circle with a radius that is the same length as one of the other sides. Each intersection point of these two circles is an option for the third vertex of my triangle.

I can use my protractor to determine the measure of each angle in my triangle.

The triangle I constructed is identical to the given triangle. Even though there are two options for the third vertex, each option results in the same triangle. Therefore, the three sides condition determines a unique triangle.

2. Diagonals $\overline{WY}$ and $\overline{XZ}$ are drawn in square $WXYZ$. Show that $\triangle XYZ$ is identical to $\triangle YZW$, and then use this information to show that the diagonals are equal in length.

I can use the two sides and an included angle condition to show that $\triangle XYZ$ is identical to $\triangle YZW$. I know corresponding sides $\overline{XY}$ and $\overline{YZ}$ are the same length because they are both sides of the same square. For the same reason, corresponding sides $\overline{YZ}$ and $\overline{ZW}$ are also the same length. $\angle XYZ$ and $\angle YZW$ are both right angles, so they have the same measure.

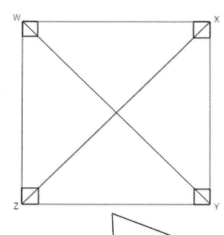

Since these two triangles are identical, I know each pair of corresponding sides must be the same length. Therefore, the diagonals (the third side of each triangle) must be the same length.

> I know that the four sides of a square are all the same length. I also know that all four angles are right angles.

3. Diagonal $\overline{BD}$ is drawn in rhombus $ABCD$. Describe the condition that can be used to justify that $\triangle ABD$ is identical to $\triangle CBD$. Can you conclude that the measures of $\angle ABD$ and $\angle CBD$ are the same? Support your answer with a diagram and an explanation of the correspondence(s) that exists.

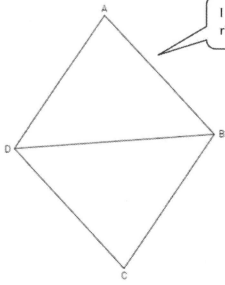

> I know all four sides of a rhombus have the same length.

I can use the three sides condition to show that $\triangle ABD$ is identical to $\triangle CBD$. I know that corresponding sides $\overline{AB}$ and $\overline{CB}$ are the same length because they are both sides of the same rhombus. For the same reason, the corresponding sides $\overline{AD}$ and $\overline{CD}$ are also the same length. The third sides of each triangle ($\overline{BD}$) are the same length because they are the same line segment.

$\angle ABD$ and $\angle CBD$ have the same measure because they are corresponding angles of two identical triangles.

> If two triangles are identical, I know there are corresponding angles that have the same measure.

Lesson 9:   Conditions for a Unique Triangle—Three Sides and Two Sides and the Included Angle

EUREKA MATH™

G7-M6-Lesson 10: Conditions for a Unique Triangle—Two Angles and a Given Side

1. In △ ABC, ∠$A = 48°$, ∠$B = 75°$, and $AB = 4$ cm. Draw △ $A'B'C'$ under the same condition as △ ABC. Label all side and angle measurements.

    What can you conclude about △ ABC and △ $A'B'C'$? Justify your response.

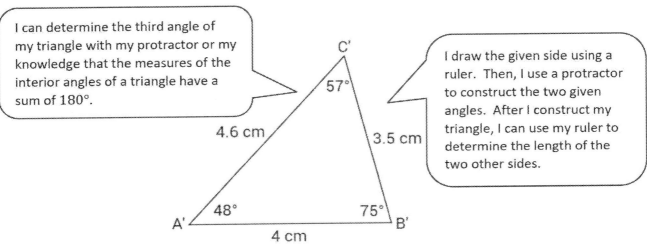

> I can determine the third angle of my triangle with my protractor or my knowledge that the measures of the interior angles of a triangle have a sum of 180°.

> I draw the given side using a ruler. Then, I use a protractor to construct the two given angles. After I construct my triangle, I can use my ruler to determine the length of the two other sides.

Since both triangles are drawn under the same condition, and the two angles and included side condition determines a unique triangle, then both triangles determine the same unique triangle. Therefore, △ ABC and △ $A'B'C'$ are identical.

2. In △ TUV, ∠$V = 42°$, ∠$T = 98°$, and $UV = 5.5$ cm. Draw △ $T'U'V'$ under the same condition as △ TUV. Label all side and angle measurements.

    What can you conclude about △ TUV and △ $T'U'V'$? Justify your response.

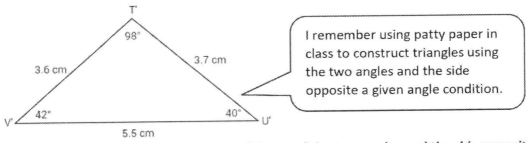

> I remember using patty paper in class to construct triangles using the two angles and the side opposite a given angle condition.

Since both triangles are drawn under the same condition, and the two angles and the side opposite a given angle condition determines a unique triangle, then both triangles determine the same unique triangle. Therefore, △ TUV and △ $T'U'V'$ are identical.

EUREKA MATH™

Lesson 10:   Conditions for a Unique Triangle—Two Angles and a Given Side   **25**

3. In the figure below, points $M, N,$ and P are collinear, and $\angle Q = \angle R$. What can be concluded about $\triangle MQN$ and $\triangle PRN$? Justify your response.

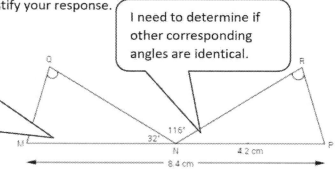

> I know I can subtract the length of $\overline{NP}$ from the total length of both segments to determine the length of $\overline{MN}$.

> I need to determine if other corresponding angles are identical.

Let x represent the measure of $\angle RNP$.

> I know from previous lessons that the measures of angles on a line have a sum of 180°.

$$32° + 116° + x = 180°$$
$$148° + x = 180°$$
$$148° - 148° + x = 180° - 148°$$
$$x = 32°$$

The measure of $\angle RNP$ is 32°. This means corresponding angles $\angle RNP$ and $\angle QNM$ have the same measure.

Let y represent the measure of $\overline{MN}$.

$$y + 4.2 \text{ cm} = 8.4 \text{ cm}$$
$$y + 4.2 \text{ cm} - 4.2 \text{ cm} = 8.4 \text{ cm} - 4.2 \text{ cm}$$
$$y = 4.2 \text{ cm}$$

The measure of $\overline{MN}$ is 4.2 cm. This means the corresponding sides $\overline{MN}$ and $\overline{PN}$ are the same length.

The diagram indicates $\angle Q$ has the same measure as $\angle R$.

Therefore, $\triangle MQN$ and $\triangle PRN$ are identical because the same measurements in both triangles satisfy the two angles and the side opposite a given angle condition, which means they both determine the same unique triangle.

EUREKA MATH

G7-M6-Lesson 11: Conditions on Measurements That Determine a Triangle

Necessary Tools

Students need a ruler and compass to complete the homework assignment.

1. Decide whether each set of three given lengths determines a triangle. For any set of lengths that does determine a triangle, use a ruler and compass to draw the triangle. Label all side lengths. For sets of lengths that do not determine a triangle, write "Does not determine a triangle," and justify your response.

   a.   3 cm, 5 cm, 7 cm

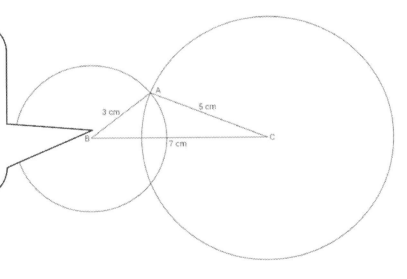

   I use my ruler to draw the longest side. On one endpoint, I use my compass to draw a circle with a radius of 3 cm. I construct a circle with a radius of 5 cm on the other endpoint. One of the intersection points of these two circles is the third vertex of my triangle.

   b.   6 cm, 13 cm, 5 cm

   These side lengths do not determine a triangle because the two shortest side lengths are too short to create a triangle with a side length of 13 cm.

   I know that three lengths determine a triangle if the largest length is less than the sum of the other two lengths.

   $$6 \text{ cm} + 5 \text{ cm} \not> 13 \text{ cm}$$

   Therefore, these sides lengths will not form a triangle.

2. For each angle measurement below, provide one angle measurement that will determine a triangle and one that will not determine a triangle. Assume that the angles are being drawn to a horizontal segment XY; describe the position of the non-horizontal rays of $\angle X$ and $\angle Y$.

$\angle X$	$\angle Y$: A Measurement That Determines a Triangle	$\angle Y$: A Measurement That Does Not Determine a Triangle
50°	40°	130°
120°	59°	61°

In order for the angles to determine a triangle, the sum of the measures of the two given angles must be less than 180°.

If the sum of the measures of two angles is greater than or equal to 180°, the angles do not determine a triangle because the non-horizontal rays do not intersect.

3. For the given lengths, provide the minimum and maximum whole number side lengths that determine a triangle.

Given Side Lengths	Minimum Whole Number Third Side Length	Maximum Whole Number Third Side Length
4 cm, 5 cm	2 cm	8 cm
2 cm, 14 cm	13 cm	15 cm

I can calculate the minimum possible third length by making the sum of the lengths of the third side and the shorter given side one whole number more than the length of the longest side.

I can calculate the maximum possible third length by calculating the sum of the two given side lengths. I know the length of the third side must be one whole number less than this sum.

EUREKA MATH™

G7-M6-Lesson 12: Unique Triangles—Two Sides and a Non-Included Angle

Necessary Tools

Students need a compass to complete the homework assignment.

1. In the triangle below, two sides and a non-included angle are marked. Use a compass to draw a non-identical triangle that has the same measurements as the marked angle and marked sides. Draw the new triangle on top of the old triangle. What is true about the marked angle in each triangle that results in two non-identical triangles under this condition?

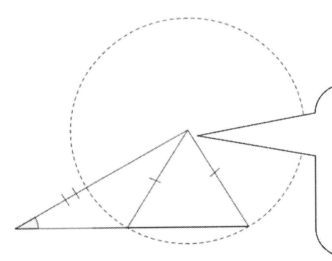

> I place the needle of my compass on the top vertex and make the radius the same length as the shortest side of the triangle. The circle intersects with the triangle in another location, which describes where an endpoint of the new triangle is located.

I was able to create a non-identical triangle with the same measurements as the marked angle and marked sides because the non-included angle is an acute angle.

> I know that if the non-included angle is smaller than 90°, the two sides and non-included angle condition does not determine a unique triangle.

2. A sub-condition of the two sides and non-included angle condition is provided in each row of the following table. Decide whether the information determines a unique triangle. Answer with a *yes, no,* or *maybe* (for a case that may or may not determine a unique triangle).

> I know that the two sides and non-included angle condition always determines a unique triangle when the non-included angle is 90° or larger.

	Condition	Determines a Unique Triangle?
1	Two sides and a non-included 100° angle	Yes
2	Two sides and a non-included 85° angle	Maybe
3	Two sides and a non-included 45° angle, where the side adjacent to the angle is longer than the side opposite the angle	No

> I know that the two sides and non-included angle condition sometimes determines a unique triangle when the non-included angle is acute.

> In order for the two sides and non-included angle condition to determine a unique triangle when the non-included angle is acute, the side adjacent to the angle must be shorter than the side opposite the angle.

EUREKA MATH

G7-M6-Lesson 13: Checking for Identical Triangles

In each of the following problems, two triangles are given. State whether the triangles are *identical, not identical,* or *not necessarily identical*. If the triangles are identical, give the triangle conditions that explain why, and write a triangle correspondence that matches the sides and angles. If the triangles are not identical, explain why. If it is not possible to definitively determine whether the triangles are identical, write "the triangles are not necessarily identical," and explain your reasoning.

1.

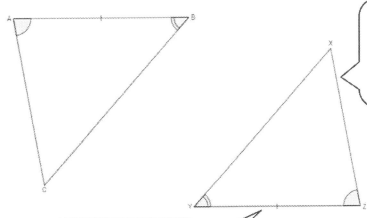

> I see two sets of identical angles and one set of identical sides. The location of the angles and sides follow the two angles and included side condition.

> I know that $\angle A$ corresponds to $\angle Z$, and $\angle B$ corresponds to $\angle Y$. I also know that side $\overline{AB}$ corresponds to $\overline{ZY}$. I can use this information to write the correspondence.

The triangles are identical by the two angles and included side condition. The correspondence $\triangle ABC \leftrightarrow \triangle ZYX$ matches two equal pairs of angles and one equal pair of included sides. Since both triangles have parts under the condition of the same measurement, the triangles must be identical.

2.

I know that the non-included angle is acute, so the two sides and non-included angle condition does not always determine a unique triangle.

The triangles are not necessarily identical by the two sides and a non-included angle condition. I would need more information about the given sides in order to determine whether or not the two triangles are identical.

I know that the side adjacent to the given angle must be shorter than the side opposite the given angle in order for these triangles to be identical. However, I cannot determine which side is longer with the information given.

In the following problems, three pieces of information are given for △ ABC and △ XYZ. Draw, freehand, the two triangles (do not worry about scale), and mark the given information. If the triangles are identical, give a triangle correspondence that matches equal angles and equal sides. Explain your reasoning.

© 2015 Great Minds eureka-math.org
G7-M6-HWH-1.3.0-10.2015

EUREKA MATH

3. $\angle A = \angle Z$, $\angle B = \angle X$, and $AB = ZX$

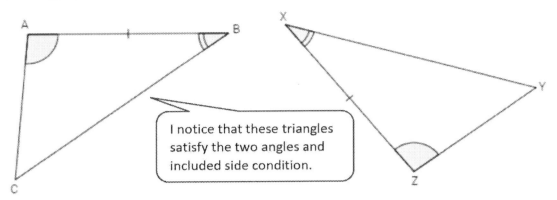

I notice that these triangles satisfy the two angles and included side condition.

These triangles are identical by the two angles and included side condition. The triangle correspondence $\triangle ABC \leftrightarrow \triangle ZXY$ matches the two pairs of equal angles and one pair of equal sides. Since both triangles have parts under the condition of the same measurement, the triangles must be identical.

When I write the correspondence, I need to make sure the equal angles and equal sides are in the same location for each triangle.

4. $AB = XY$, $BC = XZ$, and $\angle C = \angle Y$

Originally I thought these triangles satisfied the two sides and non-included angle condition. However, I notice that the side adjacent to $\angle C$ is not equal to the side that is adjacent to $\angle Y$.

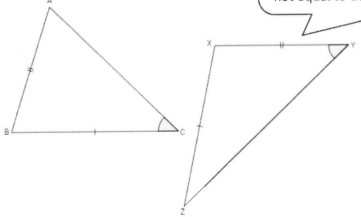

These triangles are not necessarily identical. In $\triangle ABC$, the marked angle is adjacent to the side marked with one tick mark. In $\triangle XYZ$, the marked angle is adjacent to the side marked with two tick marks. Since the sides adjacent to the equal angles are not equal in length, the triangles do not fit any of the conditions that determine a unique triangle.

G7-M6-Lesson 14: Checking for Identical Triangles

In the following problems, determine whether the triangles are *identical, not identical,* or *not necessarily identical*; justify your reasoning. If the relationship between the two triangles yields information that establishes a condition, describe the information. If the triangles are identical, write a triangle correspondence that matches the sides and angles.

1.

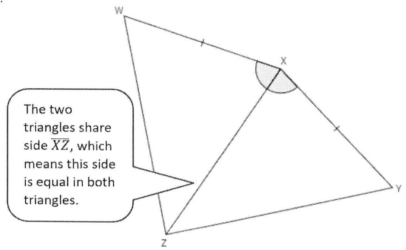

The two triangles share side $\overline{XZ}$, which means this side is equal in both triangles.

These triangles are identical by the two sides and the included angle condition. The triangle correspondence $\triangle WXZ \leftrightarrow \triangle YXZ$ matches two pairs of equal sides and one pair of equal angles.

One of the equal pairs of sides is shared side $\overline{XZ}$.

2.

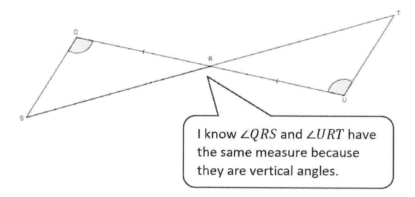

I know $\angle QRS$ and $\angle URT$ have the same measure because they are vertical angles.

The two triangles are identical by the two angles and the included side condition. The triangle correspondence $\triangle QRS \leftrightarrow \triangle URT$ matches the two pairs of equal angles and one pair of equal sides.

One of the pairs of equal angles are vertical angles.

3.

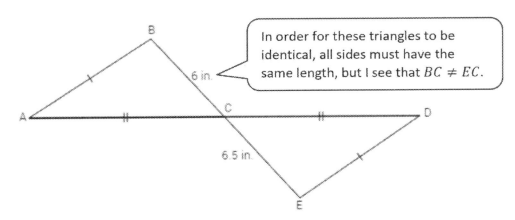

In order for these triangles to be identical, all sides must have the same length, but I see that $BC \neq EC$.

The two triangles are not identical because the correspondence that matches the two marked equal pairs of sides also matches sides $\overline{BC}$ and $\overline{EC}$, which are not equal in length.

The triangles are not identical, so I cannot write a triangle correspondence.

4.

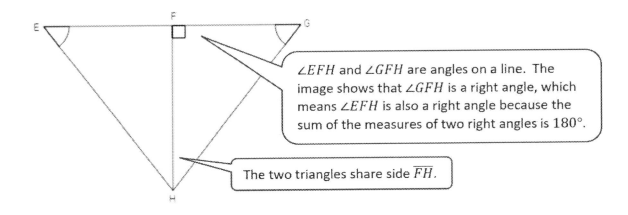

$\angle EFH$ and $\angle GFH$ are angles on a line. The image shows that $\angle GFH$ is a right angle, which means $\angle EFH$ is also a right angle because the sum of the measures of two right angles is $180°$.

The two triangles share side $\overline{FH}$.

These two triangles are identical by the two angles and side opposite a given angle condition. The correspondence $\triangle EFH \leftrightarrow \triangle GFH$ matches the two pairs of equal angles and the one pair of equal sides.

One of the pairs of equal angles is $\angle EFH$ and $\angle GFH$ because they are both right angles.

G7-M6-Lesson 15: Using Unique Triangles to Solve Real-World and Mathematical Problems

1. Ms. Thompson wants to cut different sheets of paper into four equal triangles for a class activity. She first cuts the paper into equal halves in the shape of rectangles, and then she cuts each rectangle along a diagonal.

   Did Ms. Thompson cut the paper into 4 equal pieces? Explain.

   > Each of the four triangles have two sides and one right angle from the rectangles from the first cut. Due to properties of rectangles, I know there is a correspondence between all four triangles that matches two pairs of equal sides and one pair of equal angles.

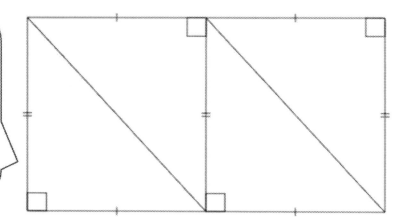

Ms. Thompson did cut the piece of paper into four identical triangles. The first cut Ms. Thompson made resulted in two equal rectangles, which means the corresponding sides have the same length. I also know that all four angles in a rectangle are right angles. Therefore, the four triangles are identical due to the two sides and an included angle condition.

EUREKA MATH

2. The bridge below, which crosses a road, is built out of two triangular supports. The point W lies on $\overline{VX}$. The beams represented by $\overline{YW}$ and $\overline{ZW}$ are equal in length, and the beams represented by $\overline{YV}$ and $\overline{ZX}$ are equal in length. If the supports were constructed so that $\angle Y$ and $\angle Z$ are equal in measurement, is point W the midpoint of $\overline{VX}$? Explain.

> If W is the midpoint of $\overline{VX}$, then $\overline{VW}$ and $\overline{XW}$ must have the same length.

> I add marks on the image from the information provided in the prompt.

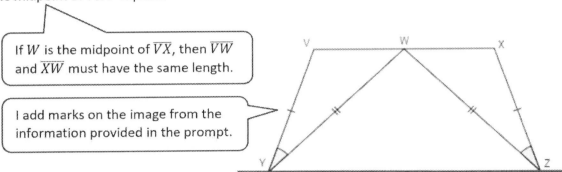

Yes, W is the midpoint of $\overline{VX}$. I know $\triangle WVY$ and $\triangle WXZ$ are identical triangles due to the two sides and included angle condition. If these two triangles are identical, that means the corresponding sides have the same length. Therefore, $\overline{VW}$ and $\overline{XW}$ are the same length.

G7-M6-Lesson 16: Slicing a Right Rectangular Prism with a Plane

A right rectangular prism is shown along with line segments that lie in a face. For segments a and b, draw and give the approximate dimensions of the slice that results when the slicing plane contains the given line segment and is perpendicular to the face that contains the line segment.

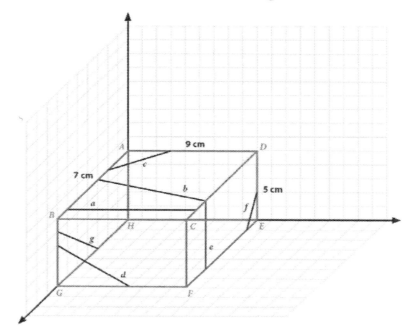

a.

I see that the line segment a is perpendicular to $DCFE$ and $ABGH$. This means that a rectangular slice will be created. I know the dimensions will match the dimensions of different lengths of the prism, in this case 9 cm by 5 cm.

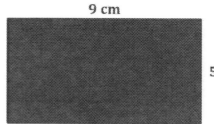

© 2015 Great Minds eureka-math.org
G7-M6-HWH-1.3.0-10.2015

EUREKA
MATH™

b.

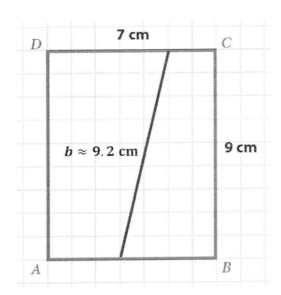

Although the result of slice *b* is still a rectangle, I need to calculate one of the side lengths.

EUREKA
MATH™

© 2015 Great Minds eureka-math.org
G7-M6-HWH-1.3.0-10.2015

G7-M6-Lesson 17: Slicing a Right Rectangular Pyramid with a Plane

A side view of a right rectangular pyramid is given. The line segments lie in the lateral faces.

a. For segment a, sketch the resulting slice from slicing the right rectangular pyramid with a slicing plane that contains the segment and is parallel to the base.

b. For segments b and c, sketch the resulting slice from slicing the right rectangular pyramid with a slicing plane that contains the line segment and is perpendicular to the base.

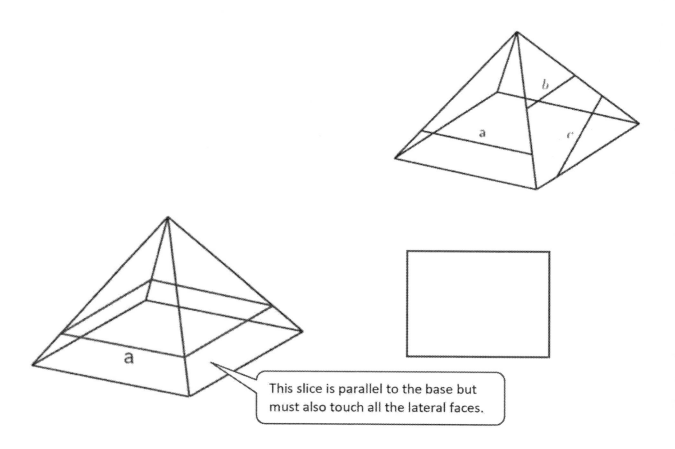

This slice is parallel to the base but must also touch all the lateral faces.

© 2015 Great Minds eureka-math.org
G7-M6-HWH-1.3.0-10.2015

EUREKA
MATH

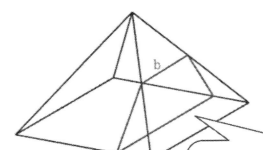

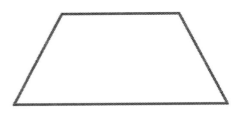

The slice must touch the lateral faces and be perpendicular to the base. I can also attempt to draw the slice within the prism for a challenge.

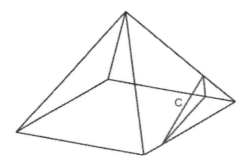

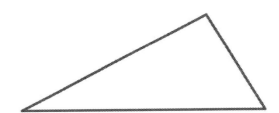

EUREKA MATH™

© 2015 Great Minds eureka-math.org
G7-M6-HWH-1.3.0-10.2015

G7-M6-Lesson 18: Slicing on an Angle

1. Draw a slice into a right rectangular prism at an angle in the form of the provided shape, and draw each slice as a 2D shape.

    a.   A quadrilateral

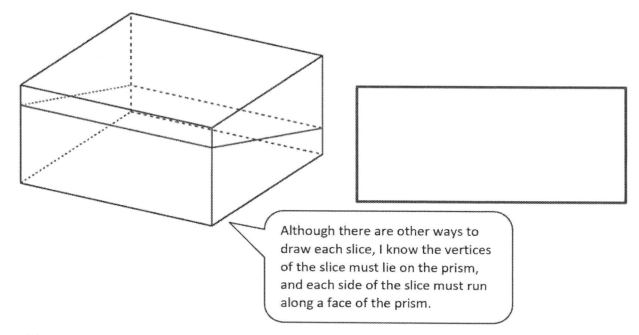

Although there are other ways to draw each slice, I know the vertices of the slice must lie on the prism, and each side of the slice must run along a face of the prism.

    b.   A hexagon

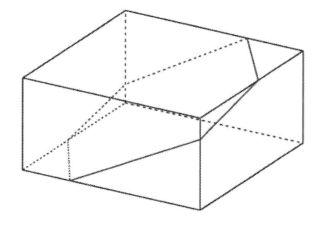

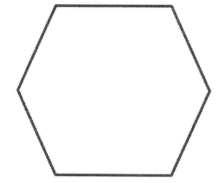

EUREKA MATH

© 2015 Great Minds eureka-math.org
G7-M6-HWH-1.3.0-10.2015

2. Draw a slice on an angle into the right rectangular pyramid below in the form of a triangle, then draw the slice as a 2D shape.

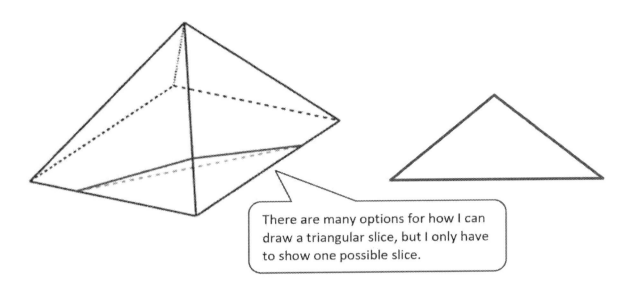

There are many options for how I can draw a triangular slice, but I only have to show one possible slice.

3. What other types of shapes can be drawn as a slice in a pyramid?

I can draw quadrilateral and pentagonal slices in a pyramid. I cannot draw a slice with more than five sides because there are only five faces on a pyramid.

G7-M6-Lesson 19: Understanding Three-Dimensional Figures

In the given three-dimensional figures, unit cubes are stacked exactly on top of each other on a tabletop. Each block is either visible or below a visible block.

1.

a. The following three-dimensional figure is built on a tabletop. If slices parallel to the tabletop are taken of this figure, then what would each slice look like?

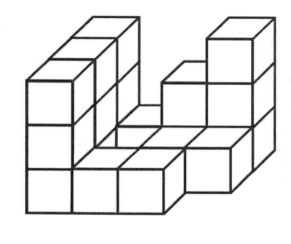

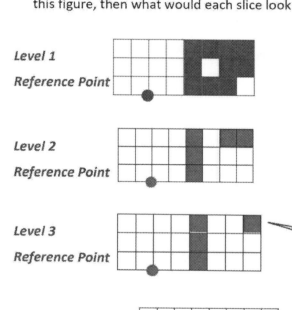

Each reference point shows the cubes that exist in each layer of the figure.

b. Given the level slices in the figure, how many cubes are in the figure?

Level 1: There are 10 cubes between Level 0 and Level 1.

Level 2: There are 5 cubes between Level 1 and Level 2.

Level 3: There are 4 cubes between Level 2 and Level 3.

The total number of cubes in the solid is 19.

I know the number of unit cubes can be determined by counting the shaded squares in Levels 1 to 3.

EUREKA MATH

2.

a. The following three-dimensional figure is built on a tabletop. If slices parallel to the tabletop are taken of this figure, then what would each slice look like?

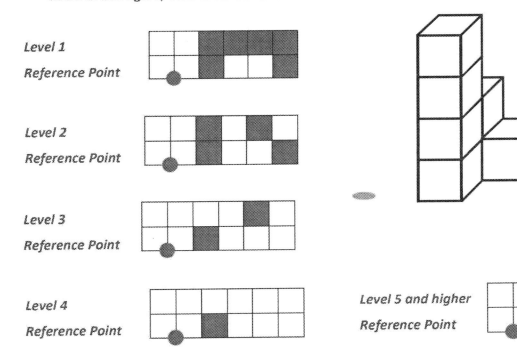

Level 1
Reference Point

Level 2
Reference Point

Level 3
Reference Point

Level 4
Reference Point

Level 5 and higher
Reference Point

b. Given the level slices in the figure, how many cubes are in the figure?

Level 1: There are 6 cubes between Level 0 and Level 1.

Level 2: There are 4 cubes between Level 1 and Level 2.

Level 3: There are 2 cubes between Level 2 and Level 3.

Level 4: There is 1 cube between Level 3 and Level 4.

The total number of cubes in the solid is 13.

> This time I have four levels of cubes to add together.

3. When drawing different reference points, why do we not include Level 0?

Level 0 and Level 1 represent the same cubes: Level 0 represents the bottom of these cubes, and Level 1 represents the top of the same cubes. If we showed both Level 0 and Level 1, we would count the same cubes twice.

> When I create the reference point drawings, I am showing the top of each cube.

G7-M6-Lesson 20: Real-World Area Problems

1. A farmer has four pieces of unfenced land as shown below in the scale drawing where the dimensions of one side are given. The farmer trades all of the land and $5,000 for 3 acres of similar land that is fenced. If one acre is equal to $43,560 \text{ ft}^2$, how much per square foot for the extra land did the farmer pay rounded to the nearest cent?

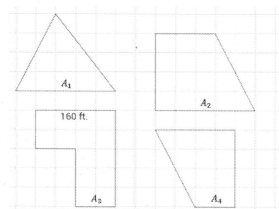

$A_1 = \dfrac{1}{2}(5 \text{ units} \times 4 \text{ units})$

$A_1 = 10 \text{ square units}$

$A_2 = (3 \text{ units} \times 4 \text{ units}) + \dfrac{1}{2}(2 \text{ units} \times 4 \text{ units})$

$A_2 = 12 \text{ square units} + 4 \text{ square units}$

$A_2 = 16 \text{ square units}$

$A_3 = (4 \text{ units} \times 5 \text{ units}) - (2 \text{ units} \times 3 \text{ units})$

$A_3 = 20 \text{ square units} - 6 \text{ square units}$

$A_3 = 14 \text{ square units}$

> I use composition and decomposition to calculate the areas of the different plots of land.

$A_4 = \dfrac{1}{2}(2 \text{ units} \times 4 \text{ units}) + (4 \text{ units} \times 2 \text{ units})$

$A_4 = 4 \text{ square units} + 8 \text{ square units}$

$A_4 = 12 \text{ square units}$

The sum of the farmer's four pieces of land:

$A = 10 \text{ square units} + 16 \text{ square units} + 14 \text{ square units} + 12 \text{ square units}$
$A = 52 \text{ square units}$

The sum of the farmer's four pieces of land in square feet:

4 units are 160 feet in length so 1 unit is 40 feet in length. Since each unit is square, each unit is 40 feet in length by 40 feet in width, or $1,600 \text{ ft}^2$.

The total area of the farmer's pieces of land is $83,200 \text{ ft}^2$ because $52 \times 1,600 = 83,200$.

EUREKA MATH

The sum of the farmer's four pieces of land in acres:

$$83,200 \div 43,560 \approx 1.91$$

The farmer's four pieces of land total about 1.91 acres.

> I can use the square feet to determine the number of acres the farmer owns. I use this information to determine the number of extra acres he purchases.

Extra land purchased with $5,000:

$$3 \text{ acres} - 1.91 \text{ acres} = 1.09 \text{ acres}$$

Extra land in square feet:

$$(1.09 \text{ acres})\left(\frac{43,560 \text{ ft}^2}{1 \text{ acre}}\right) = 47,480.4 \text{ ft}^2$$

> I need to determine the amount of extra square feet before I can determine the cost per square foot.

Price per square foot for extra land:

$$\frac{\$5,000}{47,480.4 \text{ ft}^2} \approx \frac{\$0.11}{\text{ft}^2}$$

The farmer paid about $0.11 *per square foot for the extra land.*

© 2015 Great Minds eureka-math.org
G7-M6-HWH-1.3.0-10.2015

2. A stop sign is an octagon with eight equal sides and eight equal angles. The dimensions of the octagon are given below. One side of the octagon is to be painted red. If Derek has enough paint to cover 150 ft^2, can he paint 50 stop signs? Explain your answer.

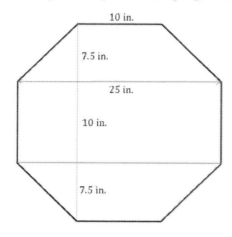

> I decompose the octagon into three quadrilaterals I am more familiar with.

Area of top trapezoid:

$$A = \frac{1}{2}(10 \text{ in.} + 25 \text{ in.})(7.5 \text{ in.})$$
$$A = 131.25 \text{ in}^2$$

Area of middle rectangle:

$$A = 25 \text{ in.} \times 10 \text{ in.}$$
$$A = 250 \text{ in}^2$$

Area of bottom trapezoid:

$$A = \frac{1}{2}(10 \text{ in.} + 25 \text{ in.})(7.5 \text{ in.})$$
$$A = 131.25 \text{ in}^2$$

Total area of a stop sign in square inches:

$$A = 131.25 \text{ in}^2 + 250 \text{ in}^2 + 131.25 \text{ in}^2$$
$$A = 512.5 \text{ in}^2$$

> I need to convert square inches to square feet to determine if Derek has enough paint for 50 stop signs.

Total area of a stop sign in square feet:

$$512.5 \text{ in}^2 \left(\frac{1 \text{ ft}^2}{144 \text{ in}^2}\right) \approx 3.56 \text{ ft}^2$$

Total area of 50 stop signs:

$$(3.56 \text{ ft}^2)(50) = 178 \text{ ft}^2$$

Derek does not have enough paint for 50 stop signs because the total area of the stop signs is approximately 178 ft^2, which is more than 150 ft^2.

EUREKA MATH

3. A custom home builder is building a new kitchen. The diagram below is of a new kitchen countertop. Approximately how many square feet of counter space is there?

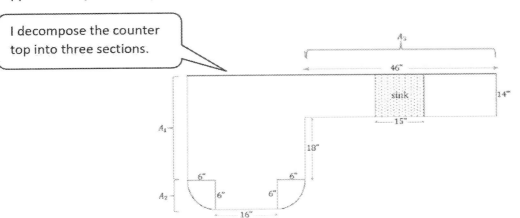

I decompose the counter top into three sections.

The width of the first section is 16 in. plus the radius (6 in.) of both quarter circles.

$A_1 = (16 \text{ in.} + 12 \text{ in.})(14 \text{ in.} + 18 \text{ in.})$
$A_1 = (28 \text{ in.})(32 \text{ in.})$
$A_1 = 896 \text{ in}^2$

$A_2 = (16 \text{ in.} \times 6 \text{ in.}) + \frac{1}{4}\pi(6 \text{ in.})^2 + \frac{1}{4}\pi(6 \text{ in.})^2$
$A_2 \approx 96 \text{ in}^2 + 28.26 \text{ in}^2 + 28.26 \text{ in}^2$
$A_2 \approx 152.52 \text{ in}^2$

The second section has a rectangle and two quarter circles. I remember the area formula for a quarter circle is $A = \frac{1}{4}\pi r^2$ and I can use 3.14 as an approximate value for π.

I subtract the area of the sink from the area of the third section because the countertop does not cover the sink.

$A_3 = (46 \text{ in.} \times 14 \text{ in.}) - (15 \text{ in.} \times 14 \text{ in.})$
$A_3 = 644 \text{ in}^2 - 210 \text{ in}^2$
$A_3 = 434 \text{ in}^2$

Total area of counter space in square inches:

$$A \approx 896 \text{ in}^2 + 152.52 \text{ in}^2 + 434 \text{ in}^2$$
$$A \approx 1,482.52 \text{ in}^2$$

Total area of counter space in square feet:

$$1,482.52 \text{ in}^2 \left(\frac{1 \text{ ft}^2}{144 \text{ in}^2} \right) \approx 10.3 \text{ ft}^2$$

To answer the question, I need to convert in^2 to ft^2. I know 12 in. are in 1 ft., which means 144 in^2 are in 1 ft^2.

There is approximately 10.3 ft^2 of counter space.

G7-M6-Lesson 21: Mathematical Area Problems

1. In class, we generalized that $(a + b)^2 = a^2 + 2ab + b^2$. Use these results to evaluate the following expressions by writing $51 = 50 + 1$ and so on.

   a. Evaluate 51^2.

   > I can decompose 51 to the expression $50 + 1$. Therefore, 50 represents a in the general equation, and 1 represents b in the general equation.

   $$51^2 = (50 + 1)^2$$
   $$= 50^2 + 2(50 \cdot 1) + 1^2$$
   $$= 2,500 + 100 + 1$$
   $$= 2,601$$

   b. Evaluate 201^2.

   $$201^2 = (200 + 1)^2$$
   $$= 200^2 + 2(200 \cdot 1) + 1^2$$
   $$= 40,000 + 400 + 1$$
   $$= 40,401$$

   > I refer back to the general equation and substitute 200 for a and 1 for b. After substitution, I follow order of operations to simplify the expression.

   c. We can also generalize $(a - b) = a^2 - 2ab + b^2$. Use these results to evaluate the following expression by writing $99 = 100 - 1$, etc.

   Evaluate 99^2.

   $$99^2 = (100 - 1)^2$$
   $$= 100^2 - 2(100 \cdot 1) + 1^2$$
   $$= 10,000 - 200 + 1$$
   $$= 9,801$$

   > I recognize that I can decompose 99 into a subtraction expression. Therefore, I need to use the general rule for $(a - b)^2$ instead of $(a + b)^2$.

2. Use your knowledge that $a^2 - b^2 = (a - b)(a + b)$ to explain why:

   a. $40^2 - 10^2 = (30)(50)$.

   $$40^2 - 10^2 = (40 - 10)(40 + 10) = (30)(50)$$

   b. $87^2 - 45^2 = (42)(132)$.

   $$87^2 - 45^2 = (87 - 45)(87 + 45) = (42)(132)$$

   > I can use the general equation to prove that the given number sentence is true. The first term, 40, represents a, and the second term, 10, represents b.

EUREKA
MATH™

3. Create a model for the product. Use the area model to write an equivalent expression that represents the area.

$(x + 2)(x + 3)$

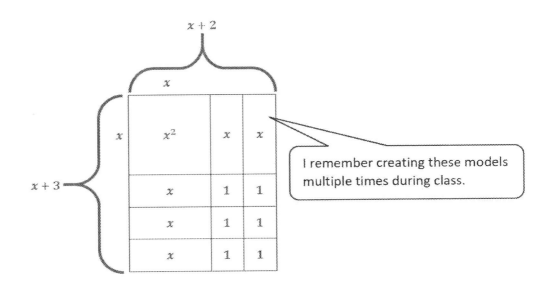

I remember creating these models multiple times during class.

$x^2 + 2x + 3x + 6$

4. Use the distributive property to multiply the following expressions.

a. $(3 + 9)(4 + 8)$

$$(3 + 9)(4 + 8) = (3 + 9) \cdot 4 + (3 + 9) \cdot 8$$
$$= 3(4) + 9(4) + 3(8) + 9(8)$$
$$= 12 + 36 + 24 + 72$$
$$= 144$$

I multiply each value in the first set of parentheses by each of the values in the second set of parentheses and then simplify.

b. $(h - 5)(h + 5)$

$$(h - 5)(h + 5) = (h - 5) \cdot h + (h - 5) \cdot 5$$
$$= h(h) - 5(h) + h(5) - 5(5)$$
$$= h^2 - 5h + 5h - 25$$
$$= h^2 - 25$$

I know $-5h$ and $5h$ are opposites, so their sum is 0. Therefore, there are only two terms in the product.

There is a variable present in this expression, which means that I collect like terms.

G7-M6-Lesson 22: Area Problems with Circular Regions

1. A circle with center O has an area of 117 in^2. Find the area of the unshaded region.

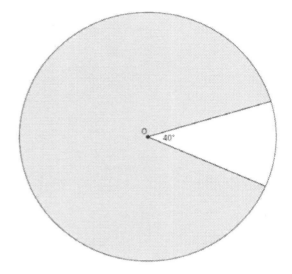

I know the entire circle represents $360°$, which means $40°$ represents $\frac{40}{360}$, or $\frac{1}{9}$, of the circle. Therefore, the area of the unshaded region is $\frac{1}{9}$ of the area of the entire circle.

$$A = \frac{1}{9}\left(117 \text{ in}^2\right) = 13 \text{ in}^2$$

The area of the unshaded region is 13 in^2.

2. The following region is bounded by the arcs of two quarter circles, each with a radius of 7 cm, and by line segments 10 cm in length. The region on the right shows a rectangle with dimensions 7 cm by 10 cm. Show that both shaded regions have equal areas.

Figure 1

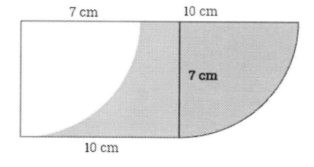

7 cm   10 cm

7 cm

10 cm

Figure 2

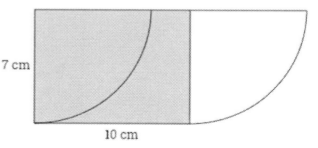

7 cm

10 cm

EUREKA
MATH

For Figure 1, I subtract the area of the quarter circle from the area of the rectangle and then add the area of the extra quarter circle.

The shaded region in Figure 2 is a rectangle, which means I find the product of the length and width to calculate the area.

$A = \left(10 \text{ cm} \times 7 \text{ cm} - \frac{1}{4}\pi(7 \text{ cm})^2\right) + \frac{1}{4}\pi(7 \text{ cm})^2$

$A = 70 \text{ cm}^2 - \frac{49\pi}{4} \text{ cm}^2 + \frac{49\pi}{4} \text{ cm}^2$

$A = 70 \text{ cm}^2$

$A = 10 \text{ cm} \times 7 \text{ cm}$

$A = 70 \text{ cm}^2$

3. The diameters of four half circles are sides of a square with a side length of 6 cm.

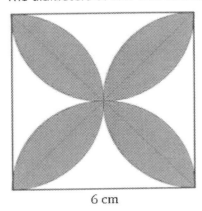

6 cm

Figure 1

Figure 2 isolates one quarter of Figure 1.

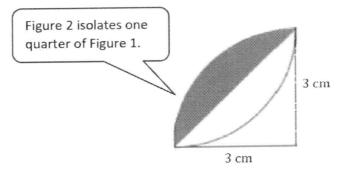

3 cm

3 cm

Figure 2
(Not drawn to scale)

a. Find the exact area of the shaded region.

Area of the shaded region in Figure 2:

$$\frac{1}{4}\pi(3 \text{ cm})^2 - \frac{1}{2}(3 \text{ cm} \times 3 \text{ cm})$$

$$\frac{9}{4}\pi \text{ cm}^2 - 4.5 \text{ cm}^2$$

To calculate the shaded region in Figure 2, I calculate the area of a quarter circle and subtract the area of a right triangle.

Total shaded area:

$$8\left(\frac{9}{4}\pi \text{ cm}^2 - 4.5 \text{ cm}^2\right)$$

$$18\pi \text{ cm}^2 - 36 \text{ cm}^2$$

There are 8 identical shaded regions, so I multiply the area by 8. To calculate the exact area, I leave π in the answer.

The exact area of the shaded region is $18\pi \text{ cm}^2 - 36 \text{ cm}^2$.

b. Find the approximate area using $\pi \approx \frac{22}{7}$.

> To calculate the approximate area, I replace π in my expression from part (a) with $\frac{22}{7}$.

$$18\left(\frac{22}{7}\right) \text{ cm}^2 - 36 \text{ cm}^2$$

$$56\frac{4}{7} \text{ cm}^2 - 36 \text{ cm}^2$$

$$20\frac{4}{7} \text{ cm}^2$$

The approximate area of the shaded region is $20\frac{4}{7}$ cm².

4. A square with a side length 8 inches is shown below, along with a quarter circle (with a side of the square as its radius) and two half circles (with diameters that are sides of the square). Write and explain a numerical expression that represents the exact area of the shaded region in the figure.

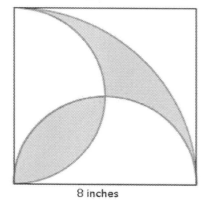

8 inches

Figure 1

> Even though the shaded regions in both figures have the same area, it is easier to calculate the area of the shaded region in Figure 2.

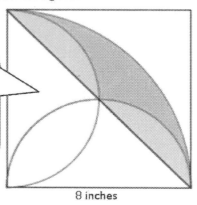

8 inches

Figure 2

> I recognize a quarter circle and a right triangle.

$$\frac{1}{4}\pi(8 \text{ in.})^2 - \left(\frac{1}{2} \cdot 8 \text{ in.} \cdot 8 \text{ in.}\right)$$

$$16\pi \text{ in}^2 - 32 \text{ in}^2$$

The shaded area in each figure has the same area. This area can be found by subtracting the area of a right triangle with leg lengths of 8 in. from the area of the quarter circle with a radius of 8 in.

EUREKA
MATH

5. Four circles have centers on segment YZ. The diameters of the circles are in the ratio $5:2:2:1$. If the area of the largest circle is 100 ft², find the area inside the largest circle but outside the smaller circles.

The ratio of the areas of the four circles is $25:4:4:1$.

Let x represent the area of one of the medium circles in ft²:

> I can use the ratio of the areas and the given area to determine the area of the medium circles.

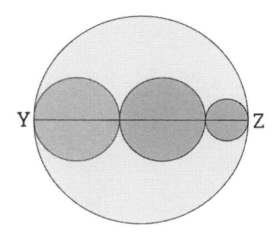

$$\frac{4}{25} = \frac{x}{100}$$

$$(100)\left(\frac{4}{25}\right) = (100)\left(\frac{x}{100}\right)$$

$$16 = x$$

Let y represent the area of the smaller circle in ft²:

$$\frac{1}{25} = \frac{y}{100}$$

$$(100)\left(\frac{1}{25}\right) = (100)\left(\frac{y}{100}\right)$$

$$4 = y$$

> Once I know the area of the three smaller circles, I can subtract these areas from the given area of the largest circle.

Area inside the largest circle but outside the smaller three circles:

$$A = 100 \text{ ft}^2 - 16 \text{ ft}^2 - 16 \text{ ft}^2 - 4 \text{ ft}^2$$

$$A = 64 \text{ ft}^2$$

The area inside the largest circle but outside the three smaller circles is 64 ft².

G7-M6-Lesson 23: Surface Area

To calculate the surface area of a figure, I find the area of each face and then calculate the sum of these areas.

Even though the top and bottom of the figure look different, they cover the same area.

Determine the surface area of the figures.

1.

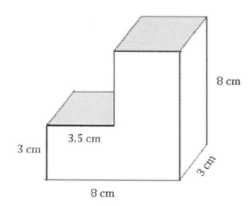

Area of the top and bottom: $2(8 \text{ cm} \times 3 \text{ cm}) = 48 \text{ cm}^2$

Area of left and right sides: $2(3 \text{ cm} \times 8 \text{ cm}) = 48 \text{ cm}^2$

Area of front and back:

$2(8 \text{ cm} \times 3 \text{ cm}) + 2(4.5 \text{ cm} \times 5 \text{ cm}) = 93 \text{ cm}^2$

I decompose the front and back faces into two rectangles in order to calculate the area.

Total surface area: $48 \text{ cm}^2 + 48 \text{ cm}^2 + 93 \text{ cm}^2 = 189 \text{ cm}^2$

2.

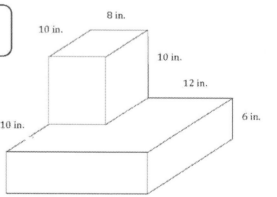

The bottom of the top prism is not part of the surface area.

Surface area of top prism:

Area of top: $10 \text{ in.} \times 8 \text{ in.} = 80 \text{ in}^2$

Area of front and back sides: $2(8 \text{ in.} \times 10 \text{ in.}) = 160 \text{ in}^2$

Area of left and right sides: $2(10 \text{ in.} \times 10 \text{ in.}) = 200 \text{ in}^2$

Surface area of bottom prism:

Area of top: $(20 \text{ in.} \times 20 \text{ in.}) - 80 \text{ in}^2 = 320 \text{ in}^2$

Area of bottom: $20 \text{ in.} \times 20 \text{ in.} = 400 \text{ in}^2$

Area of front and back sides: $2(6 \text{ in.} \times 20 \text{ in.}) = 240 \text{ in}^2$

Area of left and right sides: $2(6 \text{ in.} \times 20 \text{ in.}) = 240 \text{ in}^2$

I subtract 80 in^2 from the area of the top of the bottom prism because this is the area that the top and bottom prisms overlap.

Total surface area: $80 \text{ in}^2 + 160 \text{ in}^2 + 200 \text{ in}^2 + 320 \text{ in}^2 + 400 \text{ in}^2 + 240 \text{ in}^2 + 240 \text{ in}^2 = 1,640 \text{ in}^2$

EUREKA MATH™

3.

> I know that the prism has a rectangular base and four triangular faces. I remember that the area formula for a triangle is $A = \frac{1}{2}bh$.

Area of front and back: $2\left(\frac{1}{2}(10 \text{ ft.} \times 14 \text{ ft.})\right) = 140 \text{ ft}^2$

Area of left and right: $2\left(\frac{1}{2}(18 \text{ ft.} \times 12 \text{ ft.})\right) = 216 \text{ ft}^2$

Area of the base: $10 \text{ ft.} \times 18 \text{ ft.} = 180 \text{ ft}^2$

Total surface area: $140 \text{ ft}^2 + 216 \text{ ft}^2 + 180 \text{ ft}^2 = 536 \text{ ft}^2$

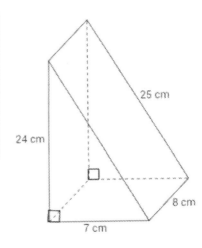

4.

Area of the front and back:

$$2\left(\frac{1}{2}(7 \text{ cm} \times 24 \text{ cm})\right) = 168 \text{ cm}^2$$

Area of bottom:

$$7 \text{ cm} \times 8 \text{ cm} = 56 \text{ cm}^2$$

Area that can be seen from left side:

$$24 \text{ cm} \times 8 \text{ cm} = 192 \text{ cm}^2$$

Area that can be seen from the right side:

$$25 \text{ cm} \times 8 \text{ cm} = 200 \text{ cm}^2$$

> I know the triangular prism has two triangular bases and three rectangular faces. I need to find the area of each of these five faces in order to calculate the surface area.

Total surface area: $168 \text{ cm}^2 + 56 \text{ cm}^2 + 192 \text{ cm}^2 + 200 \text{ cm}^2 = 616 \text{ cm}^2$

G7-M6-Lesson 24: Surface Area

Determine the surface area of each figure.

1.

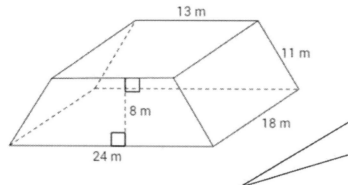

> I know that trapezoidal prisms have two bases that are trapezoids. The area formula for a trapezoid is $A = \frac{1}{2}(b_1 + b_2)h$, where b_1 and b_2 represent the lengths of the two bases.

Area of front and back: $2\left(\frac{1}{2}(13\text{ m} + 24\text{ m})8\text{ m}\right) = 296\text{ m}^2$

Area of top: $13\text{ m} \times 18\text{ m} = 234\text{ m}^2$

Area of left and right sides: $2(11\text{ m} \times 18\text{ m}) = 396\text{ m}^2$

> The other four faces are all rectangles.

Area of bottom: $24\text{ m} \times 18\text{ m} = 432\text{ m}^2$

Total surface area: $296\text{ m}^2 + 234\text{ m}^2 + 396\text{ m}^2 + 432\text{ m}^2 = 1{,}358\text{ m}^2$

EUREKA MATH

2. Determine the surface area after two square holes with a side length of 3 m are cut through the solid figure composed of two rectangular prisms.

Surface area of the top prism before the hole is cut:

Area of top: $5 \text{ m} \times 6 \text{ m} = 30 \text{ m}^2$

Area of front and back: $2(5 \text{ m} \times 6 \text{ m}) = 60 \text{ m}^2$

Area of sides: $2(6 \text{ m} \times 6 \text{ m}) = 72 \text{ m}^2$

> I first find the surface area of both prisms before the holes are cut.

Surface area of the bottom prism before the hole is cut:

Area of top: $12 \text{ m} \times 12 \text{ m} - 30 \text{ m}^2 = 114 \text{ m}^2$

Area of bottom: $12 \text{ m} \times 12 \text{ m} = 144 \text{ m}^2$

Area of front and back: $2(12 \text{ m} \times 4 \text{ m}) = 96 \text{ m}^2$

Area of sides: $2(12 \text{ m} \times 4 \text{ m}) = 96 \text{ m}^2$

> Each of the four faces inside each hole are rectangles. The width of all eight rectangles is 3 m. The length of the rectangles in the top hole is 5 m. The length of the rectangles in the bottom hole is the same as the height of the bottom prism, or 4 m.

Surface area of holes: $4(3 \text{ m} \times 5 \text{ m}) + 4(3 \text{ m} \times 4 \text{ m}) = 108 \text{ m}^2$

> I add all the areas together, but I also have to subtract the places where holes are cut. Each hole is a 3 m by 3 m square, which means the area cut is 9 m². There are four places this area is cut out of the original prism, which means I subtract an area of 36 m² from the total surface area.

Total surface area:

$30 \text{ m}^2 + 60 \text{ m}^2 + 72 \text{ m}^2 + 114 \text{ m}^2 + 144 \text{ m}^2 + 96 \text{ m}^2 + 96 \text{ m}^2 + 108 \text{ m}^2 - 36 \text{ m}^2 = 684 \text{ m}^2$

3. The base of a right prism is shown below. Determine the surface area if the height of the prism is 6 cm. Explain how you determined the surface area.

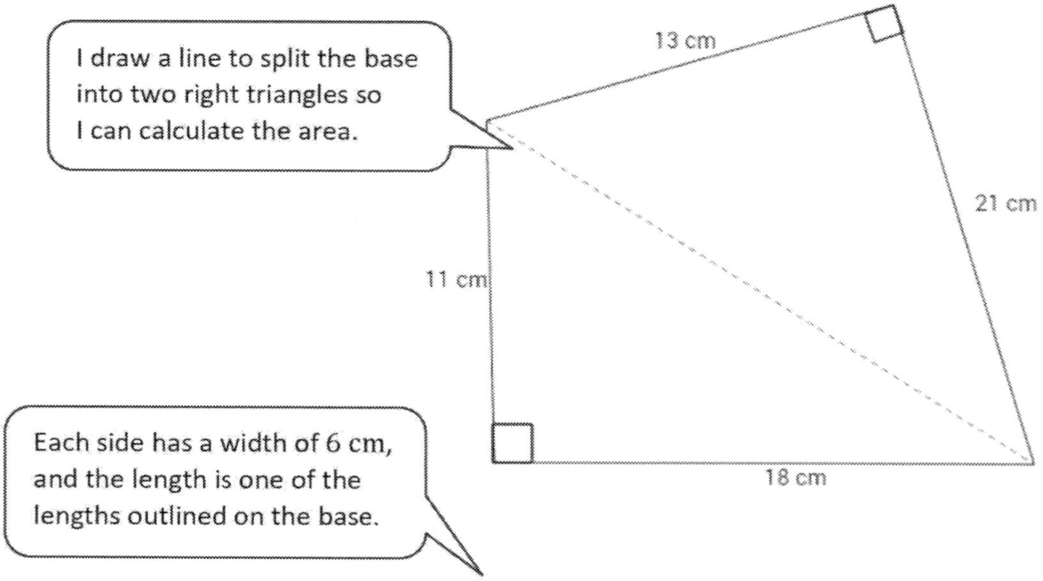

> I draw a line to split the base into two right triangles so I can calculate the area.

13 cm

21 cm

11 cm

18 cm

> Each side has a width of 6 cm, and the length is one of the lengths outlined on the base.

Area of sides: $(11 \text{ cm} \times 6 \text{ cm}) + (18 \text{ cm} \times 6 \text{ cm}) + (21 \text{ cm} \times 6 \text{ cm}) + (13 \text{ cm} \times 6 \text{ cm}) = 378 \text{ cm}^2$

Area of bases: $2\left(\frac{1}{2}(11 \text{ cm} \times 18 \text{ cm})\right) + 2\left(\frac{1}{2}(21 \text{ cm} \times 13 \text{ cm})\right) = 471 \text{ cm}^2$

Total surface area: $471 \text{ cm}^2 + 378 \text{ cm}^2 = 849 \text{ cm}^2$

G7-M6-Lesson 25: Volume of Right Prisms

1. Two right prism containers each hold 37.5 gallons of water. The height of the first container is 12 inches. The height of the second container is 10 inches. If the area of the base of the first container is 5 ft², find the area of the base of the second container. Explain your reasoning.

Let B represent the area of the base in the second container.

$$12 \times 5 = 10 \times B$$
$$60 = 10B$$
$$\left(\frac{1}{10}\right)(60) = \left(\frac{1}{10}\right)(10B)$$
$$6 = B$$

> I know the two containers have the same volume. Therefore, the product of the area of the base and the height of each container must be equal.

The area of the base of the second container is 6 ft^2.

> There are three different dimensions in a right rectangular prism: length, width, and height.

2. Two containers are shaped like right rectangular prisms. Each of the larger container's dimensions are 30% more than the smaller container's dimensions. If the smaller container holds 15 gallons when full, how many gallons does the larger container hold? Explain your reasoning.

> Each dimension of the larger container is 1.3 times larger than those of the smaller container because 100% + 30% is 130%.

The volume of the larger container is 1.3^3, *or* 2.197, *times larger than the volume of the smaller container.*

$$15 \text{ gallons} \times 2.197 = 32.955 \text{ gallons}$$

> The volume of the larger container is 2.197 times bigger than the volume of the smaller container.

The volume of the larger container is 32.955 *gallons.*

3. An aquarium in the shape of a right rectangular prism has a base area of 40 in² and height of 13 in. Currently, the aquarium is only partially filled, and the height of the water is 8 in. A few decorations are added to the bottom of the aquarium, which makes the water rise to the top, completely submerging the decorations but without causing overflow. Find the volume of the decorations.

The height of the water increased 5 in. because the height increased from 8 in. to 13 in.

$$40 \text{ in}^2 \times 5 \text{ in.} = 200 \text{ in}^3$$

The volume of the decorations is 200 in³.

> The volume of the decorations will be the same as the change in the volume of the water. I can calculate the change in the volume by multiplying the change in height by the area of the base.

4. A rectangular swimming pool is 20 feet wide and 40 feet long. The pool is 4 feet deep at one end, and 15 feet deep at the other.

   a. Sketch the swimming pool as a right prism.

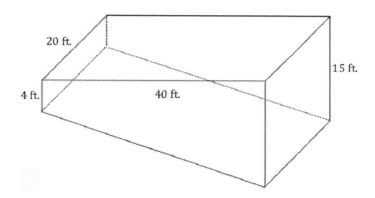

   b. What kind of prism is the swimming pool?

   The swimming pool is a right trapezoidal prism.

   > There are two trapezoidal bases in the swimming pool.

EUREKA
MATH™

c. What is the volume of the swimming pool in cubic feet?

> The area of the trapezoidal base is half the sum of the lengths times the height.

$$V = \left(\frac{1}{2}(4 \text{ ft.} + 15 \text{ ft.})(40 \text{ ft.})\right)(20 \text{ ft.})$$

$$V = \left(\frac{1}{2}(19 \text{ ft.})(40 \text{ ft.})\right)(20 \text{ ft.})$$

$$V = (380 \text{ ft}^2)(20 \text{ ft.})$$

$$V = 7,600 \text{ ft}^3$$

The volume of the swimming pool is $7,600 \text{ ft}^3$.

d. How many gallons will the swimming pool hold if each cubic feet of water is about 7.5 gallons?

$$(7,600 \text{ ft}^3)\left(\frac{7.5 \text{ gallons}}{1 \text{ ft}^3}\right) = 57,000 \text{ gallons}$$

The swimming pool will hold about $57,000$ gallons of water.

EUREKA MATH™
© 2015 Great Minds eureka-math.org
G7-M6-HWH-1.3.0-10.2015

G7-M6-Lesson 26: Volume of Composite Three-Dimensional Objects

1. Find the volume of the three-dimensional object composed of right rectangular prisms.

    Volume of top and bottom prisms:

    $2(14 \text{ in.} \times 14 \text{ in.} \times 4 \text{ in.}) = 1{,}568 \text{ in}^3$

    Volume of middle prism:

    $5 \text{ in.} \times 5 \text{ in.} \times 10 \text{ in.} = 250 \text{ in}^3$

    Total volume:

    $1{,}568 \text{ in}^3 + 250 \text{ in}^3 = 1{,}818 \text{ in}^3$

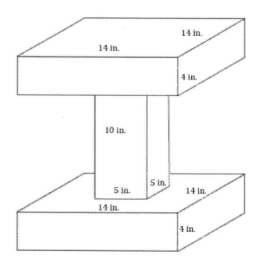

> Similar to surface area, I can find the volume of each part of the object and then calculate the total volume by finding the sum of all the partial volumes.

© 2015 Great Minds eureka-math.org
G7-M6-HWH-1.3.0-10.2015

EUREKA MATH™

2. Two students are finding the volume of a prism with a rhombus base but are provided different
    information regarding the prism. One student receives Figure 1 while the other receives Figure 2.

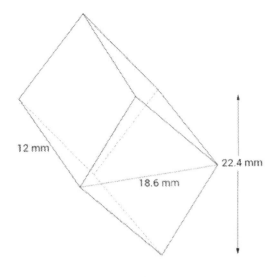

Figure 1

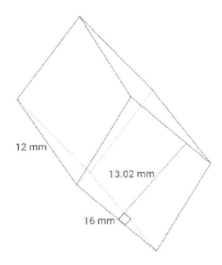

Figure 2

Find the volume in each case; show that the volumes are equal.

> In Figure 1, I split the base into two triangles in order to find the area of the base, and then I multiply by the height of the prism.

Volume of Figure 1: $2\left(\frac{1}{2}(18.6 \text{ mm} \times 11.2 \text{ mm})\right) \times 12 \text{ mm} = 2,499.84 \text{ mm}^3$

Volume of Figure 2: $16 \text{ mm} \times 13.02 \text{ mm} \times 12 \text{ mm} = 2,499.84 \text{ mm}^3$

> In Figure 2, I can use the information provided to find the area of the base and then multiply by the height of the prism.

EUREKA
MATH™

© 2015 Great Minds eureka-math.org
G7-M6-HWH-1.3.0-10.2015

3. A plastic die cube for a game has an edge length of 2.5 cm. Throughout the cube, there are 15 cubic cutouts, each with an edge length of 3 mm. What is the volume of the cube?

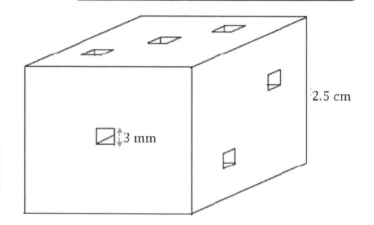

> I know all sides of a cube are equal length.

Volume of large cube:

$$(2.5 \text{ cm})^3 = 15.625 \text{ cm}^3$$

Volume of cutout cubes:

$$15(3 \text{ mm})^3 = 405 \text{ mm}^3$$

> I notice that the units for the two different volumes don't match. I convert mm^3 to cm^3 by dividing by 1,000.

2.5 cm

3 mm

Total volume of the die: $15.625 \text{ cm}^3 - 0.405 \text{ cm}^3 = 15.22 \text{ cm}^3$

> I find the total volume by subtracting the volume of the cutouts from the volume of the large cube.

4. A right rectangular prism has each of its dimensions (length, width, and height) increased by 20%. By what percent is its volume increased?

> When I increase each dimension by 20%, the new dimensions will be 100% + 20%, or 120%, of the original dimension.

$$V' = 1.2l \cdot 1.2w \cdot 1.2h$$
$$V' = 1.728lwh$$

The larger volume is 172.8% of the smaller volume, which means the volume increased by 72.8%.

> The smaller volume represents 100%, so the increase is the difference between the two percentages.

Lesson 26:   Volume of Composite Three-Dimensional Objects

© 2015 Great Minds eureka-math.org
G7-M6-HWH-1.3.0-10.2015

EUREKA
MATH

G7-M6-Lesson 27: Real-World Volume Problems

1. Olivia has a leak in her new roof, so she puts a container in the shape of a right rectangular prism under the leak. Rainwater is dripping into the container at an average rate of 14 drops per minute. The container Olivia places under the leak has dimensions of 6 cm × 4 cm × 9 cm. Assuming each rain drop is roughly 1 cm^3, approximately how long does Olivia have before the container overflows?

Volume of the container:

$$6 \text{ cm} \times 4 \text{ cm} \times 9 \text{ cm} = 216 \text{ cm}^3$$

Number of minutes until the container is filled with rainwater:

$$216 \text{ cm}^3 \left(\frac{1 \text{ min.}}{14 \text{ cm}^3}\right) \approx 15.43 \text{ min.}$$

The bucket will overflow in about 15.43 minutes.

> I determine the volume of the container and then use the rate to determine how long Olivia has until the container overflows.

2. A basement flooded and contains 10,000 ft^3 of water that needs to be drained. At 1:00 p.m., a pump is turned on that drains water at the rate of 9 ft^3 per minute. Four hours later, at 5:00 p.m., a second pump is activated that drains water at the rate of 5 ft^3 per minute. At what time will the basement be free of water?

Water drained during the first four hours:

$$\left(\frac{9 \text{ ft}^3}{1 \text{ min.}}\right)(240 \text{ min.}) = 2,160 \text{ ft}^3$$

Volume of water that still needs to be drained:

$$10,000 \text{ ft}^3 - 2,160 \text{ ft}^3 = 7,840 \text{ ft}^3$$

Amount of time needed to drain the remaining water:

> Once I determine how much water is drained when only one pump is working, I can determine how much water is left in the basement.

> When both pumps are working, I know the rate is 14 ft^3 per minute because I add the two rates together.

$$(7,840 \text{ ft}^3)\left(\frac{1 \text{ min.}}{14 \text{ ft}^3}\right) = 560 \text{ min.}$$

It will take $13\frac{1}{3}$ hours to drain the basement, which means the basement will be free of water at 2:20 a.m.

EUREKA MATH

© 2015 Great Minds eureka-math.org
G7-M6-HWH-1.3.0-10.2015

3. A pool contains 12,000 ft³ of water. Pump A can drain the pool in 10 hours, and Pump B can drain the pool in 15 hours. How long will it take both pumps working together to drain the pool?

Rate at which Pump A drains the pool: $\frac{1}{10}$ *pool per hour*

Rate at which Pump B drains the pool: $\frac{1}{15}$ *pool per hour*

> I can determine the rate at which each pump drains the pool in order to determine the rate the water drains when both pumps are working together.

> I remember to find common denominators before adding the fractions.

Together, the pumps drain the pool at $\left(\frac{1}{10}+\frac{1}{15}\right)$ *pool per hour, or* $\frac{1}{6}$ *pool per hour. Therefore, it will take 6 hours to drain the pool when both pumps are working together.*

4. A 1,500-gallon aquarium can be filled with water flowing at a constant rate in 6 hours. When a decorative rock is placed in the aquarium, it can be filled in 5.25 hours. Find the volume of the rock in cubic feet (1 ft³ = 7.48 gal.).

Rate of the water flow into aquarium:

$$\frac{1,500 \text{ gal.}}{6 \text{ hours}} = \frac{250 \text{ gal.}}{1 \text{ hour}}$$

Volume of the rock in gallons:

$$\left(\frac{250 \text{ gal.}}{1 \text{ hour}}\right)(0.75 \text{ hour}) = 187.5 \text{ gal.}$$

> When the rock is placed in the aquarium, I know that it takes 0.75 hours less to fill. I can use the unit rate and time to determine the volume of the rock.

Volume of the rock in cubic feet:

$$(187.5 \text{ gal.})\left(\frac{1 \text{ ft}^3}{7.48 \text{ gal.}}\right) \approx 25.07 \text{ ft}^3$$

The volume of the rock is approximately 25.07 ft^3.

> In order to answer the question, I need to convert the volume of the rock from gallons to cubic feet.

EUREKA
MATH™